ON THE
THRESHOLD

Analysing Canadian and World Issues

ON THE
THRESHOLD

Analysing Canadian and World Issues

Fraser Cartwright
Kim Earle
Kingsley Hurlington

National Library of Canada Cataloguing in Publication

Cartwright, Fraser, 1947-
    On the threshold / Fraser Cartwright, Kim Earle, Kingsley Hurlington.

Includes index.
ISBN 0-7715-8235-8

    1. Human geography. I. Earle, Kim II. Hurlington, Kingsley III. Title.

GF43.C37 2002   304.2   C2002-901183-3

Publisher: Janice Schoening
Project Editor: Alexa Kudar
Project Team: Eileen Brett, Bev Crann, Carol Ann Maclean
Copy Editor: Cathy Zerbst
Photo Research: Karen Taylor
Permissions Editor: Elizabeth Long
Cover and Page Design: Dave Murphy/ArtPlus Limited
Page Layout: Valerie Bateman/ArtPlus Limited
Technical Art: Sue Ledoux/ArtPlus Limited
Maps: Sue Ledoux/ArtPlus Limited

We acknowledge the financial support of the Government of Canada through the Book Publishing Industry Development Program for our publishing activities.

ISBN 0-7715-8235-8
1 2 3 4 5 GG 06 05 04 03 02
Written, Printed, and Bound in Canada

Reviewers and Consultants

The authors and publishers would like to thank the consultants and reviewers for their input — advice, ideas, directions, and suggestions — that helped to shape this learning resource. Their contribution in time, effort, and expertise was invaluable.

Reviewers

Arlene Beckett
Peel District School Board

Michael Bernards
Ottawa-Carleton Catholic School Board

Christine de Souza
York Catholic District School Board

Robert D. Goodbun
Upper Canada District School Board

Joe Maurice
Algoma District School Board

Pamela Kainola Potvin
Rainbow District School Board

Patricia Smith
Ottawa-Carleton Catholic School Board

Dan Somers
Toronto Catholic District School Board

Consultants

Heather Auld
Manager, Atmospheric Science Division
Meteorological Service of Canada, Environment Canada

Henry Hengeveld
Senior Science Advisor on Climate Change
Meteorological Service of Canada, Environment Canada

A. S. Kanya-Forstner
Department of History, York University

Environmental Systems Research, Inc. — ESRI Canada
K-12 Department

Acknowledgments

We live in a fragile world, a world that is challenging our ability to co-exist with it. At a time when human use and domination of the environment has never been greater, the risks to the survival and development of all life forms has never carried more serious consequences. Our actions have enormous impact on present and future generations of all life on earth. Yet this is a changing and evolving story. We have entered this story at a moment in time. As learners, it is our responsibility to understand as many of the issues and challenges confronting this planet as we can. Through awareness and understanding, we can work toward a quality of existence that is rich, sustainable, and enjoyable for the foreseeable future.

Education provides an important role in awareness and understanding. Students today are major stakeholders in their future world. In this regard, we gratefully acknowledge the large number of students in our senior geography classes for their vision of reality, which was instrumental in building this book.

We also extend our thanks to the people and organizations who helped our research, validated our ideas, and reviewed our strategies. We have particularly appreciated the dedication and professionalism of the team at Gage Learning Corporation who allowed us to participate in this important educational project.

Finally, we express our deep thanks to our families and friends for their patience, support, and encouragement. The time we have spent participating in this project has been time away from what is most precious.

Fraser Cartwright
Kim Earle
Kingsley Hurlington

Dedication

To my wife Bonnie, sons Jeffrey and Johnathan, and the thousands of students who have made this possible. *FC*

To my husband Owen for his never-ending patience. *KE*

TABLE OF CONTENTS

CHAPTER 10 *Change and Challenge* **270**

As a citizen of this planet, you share the responsibility for its future care, which is not an easy task. For thousands of years, the relationship between humans and the planet seemed in balance. People extracted from their environments only what they needed for basic survival. While a few small groups of people still enjoy this relationship today, a vast proportion of the world's population has embraced a pattern of continual "development": the spreading of towns and cities (resulting in loss of land for growing food); higher rates of energy consumption (from diminishing oil reserves); increased consumerism in a global marketplace; and the continual chase for wealth.

Much of this development occurs in what is often called the "developed world" — the richer countries that make up only 20 percent of the world population, but consume the vast majority of what the world has to offer. Meanwhile, the poorer "developing world" is also increasing its levels of development. As yet, developing countries do not have the necessary wealth to match the development in richer countries, but this may change.

Just as people are influenced by others, developing countries are influenced by lifestyles in developed countries, via television and movies. It is not uncommon to see satellite dishes in remote regions whose inhabitants live a rural lifestyle. As a result of exposure to the lifestyles portrayed in the media, people in developing countries demand higher levels of housing, industrialization, financial investment, education, and consumerism. As more and more of the world demands such development, increased pressure is put on the world's resources of energy, lumber, food, and water.

What can be done? History has shown that groups of people find it difficult to come together as a world community, and prefer to function as separate nations. However, it is essential that individuals realize a common, shared responsibility for the care of the planet. Global challenges must be met by a global community, working together to find solutions, and this global community must be able to make informed decisions if solutions are to be effective.

Enrolling in school programs such as *Canadian and World Issues* is an important start in learning about global issues. The authors of *On the Threshold* want to provide you with information and skills that will help you think constructively about the issues facing the global community, and those facing Canada as a part of that community. We invite you to respond to the issues and challenges presented in this book, and to make decisions about workable solutions. As joint caretakers of our world, your generation's contribution will be necessary to ensure future development does not cross the threshold of sustainability.

Fraser Cartwright
Kim Earle
Kingsley Hurlington

Tour of the Textbook

Special features throughout this book were designed to increase your understanding of issues, encourage discussion, and spark your interest. Here is a look at the features included and the ways in which you can use them.

Chapter opener

The chapter opener introduces an aspect of the issue (or issues) to be explored. It provides a starter for discussions and a useful reference point for material appearing later in the chapter.

CHAPTER 3

A World of Disparity

Migration: My experience

In 1993, many Moldovian families immigrated to Canada in search of a better life. After the communist rule collapsed, the citizens from many of the countries of the former Soviet Union now had the ability to leave the country permanently, as long as they met the necessary requirements. My father was among the group of anxious people boarding the plane to Canada.

He arrived in Newfoundland as a refugee, with a couple of friends. The three of them started with nothing: no money, no food, no shelter, but lots of hope. My father, who was a computer engineer, along with his two friends, a surgeon and a dentist, made their living delivering pizzas for a few months. A year later, my father began working for a small computer firm as a computer programmer. He kept moving up in his field, and by the time the rest of my family moved to Canada, he worked in

FIGURE 3-1 Lida Mankovski, 17 years old, a student at Middlefield Collegiate Institute, Markham, Ontario

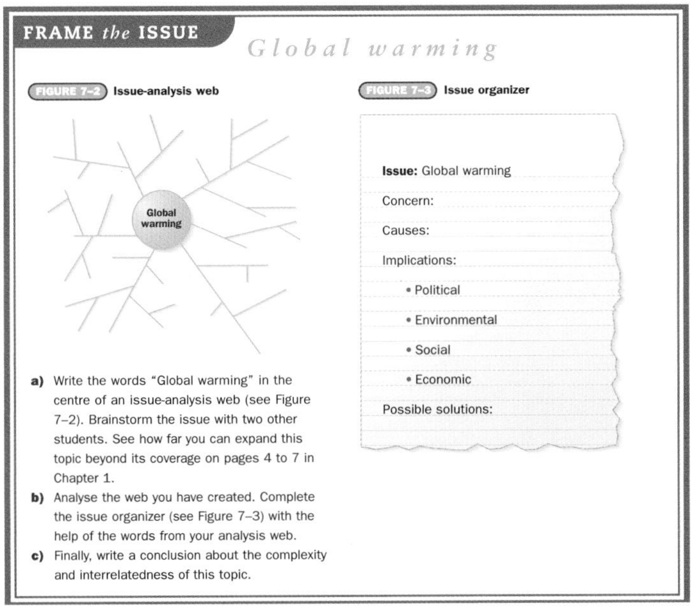

Frame the issue

This step-by-step framework offers a way of approaching and analysing any issue in the textbook. First, you brainstorm the topic; then you organize your thoughts.

FRAME *the* **ISSUE**   *Global warming*

FIGURE 7-2 Issue-analysis web

Global warming

FIGURE 7-3 Issue organizer

Issue: Global warming

Concern:

Causes:

Implications:

• Political

• Environmental

• Social

• Economic

Possible solutions:

a) Write the words "Global warming" in the centre of an issue-analysis web (see Figure 7–2). Brainstorm the issue with two other students. See how far you can expand this topic beyond its coverage on pages 4 to 7 in Chapter 1.

b) Analyse the web you have created. Complete the issue organizer (see Figure 7–3) with the help of the words from your analysis web.

c) Finally, write a conclusion about the complexity and interrelatedness of this topic.

Tech it out

Geotechnology, or geographic information systems (GIS), plays an increasing role in geographic studies. Information and activities illustrate the benefits of applying technological tools to your analysis of an issue.

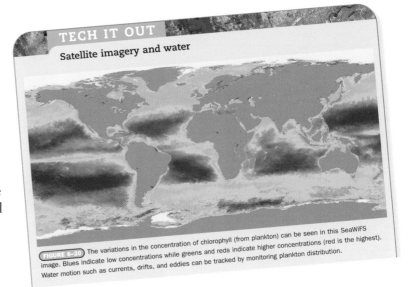

TECH IT OUT
Satellite imagery and water

FIGURE 6–20 The variations in the concentration of chlorophyll (from plankton) can be seen in this SeaWiFS image. Blues indicate low concentrations while greens and reds indicate higher concentrations (red is the highest). Water motion such as currents, drifts, and eddies can be tracked by monitoring plankton distribution.

Issue briefing

The California grey ant

A welcome guest on the peach trees of Californian farms is the California grey ant. Traditionally, this ant would have been destroyed through insecticide spraying, but California Clean (an organization of farmers dedicated to farming using "clean" methods) discovered that the ant is really an asset. They learned that drops of nectar on their peach trees would attract the California grey ant. Following a snack of nectar, the ant turns its attention to a real meal — the peach tree borer — which normally devastates peach trees. This partnership between farmers and the California grey ant is an excellent example of integrated pest management (IPM).

FIGURE 4–10 Peach trees and the California grey ant form a mutually beneficial relationship.

Issue briefing

This feature offers examples and additional information to support topics covered in the chapter.

Global warning

These are brief descriptions of current or potential global trouble spots. You can use this material to increase your understanding of the topic, as a starting point for a discussion or a report.

Global WARNING
TASTE SHIFTS

In China — which contains nearly one-fifth of the world's population — there has been a significant taste shift away from a diet based on rice and fish, to one based on meat and poultry. Due to China's large population, this shift will have an immense impact on world grain levels.

Meat and poultry require up to seven times more grain for animal feed than is necessary when humans consume the grain directly. Diets based on rice and fish require less grain than diets based on meat. A rice diet means that humans eat the grain directly, and less grain is necessary for feeding fish than for feeding pigs, chickens, cattle, and so on. Despite this fact, increasing numbers of people are opting for a meat-and-poultry-based diet. To satisfy China's current taste shift, the country would need to import the equivalent of all the wheat currently exported in the world today.

FIGURE 4–1 Amount of grain needed to sustain a meat-and-poultry-based diet

To produce 1 kg beef takes 7 kg grain

To produce 1 kg pork takes 4 kg grain

To produce 1 kg poultry takes 2.5 kg grain

a) What is meant by a "taste shift"?
b) Can you think of any taste shifts that have taken place in North America during your lifetime?
c) How might taste shifts to meat-and-poultry-based diets add further stresses to the world's capacity to feed itself?
d) What can be done, and by whom, to redirect or curb taste shifts that threaten the planet's sustainability?

Frame of reference

Here you will find definitions and explanations of the key terms and concepts used. They facilitate understanding of related concepts and calculations.

Case in point — The Grand Banks

The fishing grounds off the Grand Banks, just east of the island of Newfoundland, were among the most productive in the world, yielding up to 276 000 tonnes of northern cod. In the 1950s, these fertile fisheries changed forever with the arrival of giant trawlers from other countries. In 1968, catches totalled 725 000 tonnes. The Canadian government was warned by fishery experts about the amount of overfishing close to its shores so, in 1976, it extended Canadian sovereignty out to 370 kilometres. However, this did not stop foreign fleets from fishing inside this limit, claiming the area was international waters.

FIGURE 1-16 Fishing off the Grand Banks

The line demarcating the extent of Canadian sovereignty (as defined by Canada) is illustrated above. How might fish migration add to the difficulties of managing fish stocks?

At a glance — The Grand Banks

- Total area: 93 200 km²
- Terrain: series of raised submarine plateaus
- Nearest land: southeast coast of Newfoundland
- Depth range: 36–185 m
- Fishing hazards: fog, icebergs, transatlantic shipping lanes
- Oil drilling: began in the late 1970s with the Hibernia oil field discovery

Although catches from this fishery declined to 126 000 tonnes by 1978, they did recover, leading experts to believe that these grounds could not be permanently harmed. Even so, Canadian fleets, with the help of new "draggers" (large nets dragged along the ocean floor, disturbing the sediment and driving the fish up into the net), continued to catch large amounts of fish and deplete the fish stocks.

In the 1980s, catches totalled around 226 000 tonnes per year. Experts again warned that these totals exceeded sustainable limits. However, catching fish meant more work and revenue for the fishing industry, so these warnings were ignored.

In 1986, the Canadian government set quotas on how much fish could be caught. In 1992 however, seeing a possible collapse in the fishing industry, they banned all cod fishing. Some 40 000 jobs were lost, ending 400 years of fishing in the East Coast region. Scientific research showed that there were only 1700 tonnes of cod by the end of 1994; the fishery had collapsed.

Who was at fault? Experts blamed a combination of government subsidies and business interests for encouraging improvements in fishing technology. Foreign fishing fleets catching uncontrolled amounts of fish, and lack of scientific monitoring also contributed heavily. Fisheries throughout the world are threatened with similar collapse, as they have not heeded experts' warnings or learned how to avert a disaster like the East Coast fishery collapse.

20. What factors contributed to the fishery collapse in the Grand Banks and what were the consequences?

21. How do you think workers in the fishing industry of Newfoundland and Labrador see the situation, as opposed to the Canadian government or people in other parts of Canada?

22. What lessons in sustainability does the East Coast fishery collapse teach?

Case in point

A real-life case study provides detailed information about a part or region of the world affected by the issue that you are exploring.

At a glance

Each "Case in point" feature includes an "At a glance" section, which offers relevant facts and statistical information about the region profiled.

At a glance — *Brazil*

- Population: 174 468 575
- Birth rate: 18.45 births/1000 population
- Death rate: 9.34 deaths/1000 population
- GDP per capita: purchasing power parity — US$6500
- Labour force: services — 53.2%; industry — 23.7%; agriculture — 23.1%
- Population below poverty line: 17.4%
- Industries: textiles, shoes, chemicals, cement, lumber, iron ore, tin, steel, aircraft, motor vehicles and parts, other machinery and equipment
- Exports: US$55.1 billion — iron ore, soybeans, footwear, coffee
- Imports: US$55.8 billion — machinery and equipment, chemical products, oil, electricity
- Debt — external: US$232 billion

Inside the issue

The culminating activity for each chapter offers an opportunity to apply the content and skills you have learned in the chapter. The format ranges from role-playing and mapping exercises to creative group activities.

INSIDE *the* ISSUE

Conference planning

You and a team of fellow international consultants have been hired by the United Nations to plan a world conference that addresses one of the many social issues facing our global community in the twenty-first century. Your goal is to make a digital presentation to the United Nations Communications Panel (your classmates and teacher).

Your presentation must outline:

- the focus of your conference and your conference title
- the location of the conference
- a brief biography of the keynote speaker

To accomplish this goal, you will need to do the following:

- Complete preliminary research for a minimum of three global social issues such as (but not limited to) equity and racism, disease, urban sprawl, and technological advancements.
- Once your preliminary research is complete, select one social issue that your group considers most pressing to our global community. Gather more information about your selected issue.
- Using the gathered information, analyse the issue in terms of its political, environmental, social, and economic aspects.
- From your analysis and research, develop a focus for the conference. Give the conference a name, and provide a written paragraph explaining why the issue has been selected.
- Research several international conferences online. Examine the ways in which these conferences are (or were) organized and promoted. What do you like and dislike about these conferences? What sorts of individuals are invited to speak at these conferences? Which elements might be applied successfully in your own conference planning?
- Determine the location of the conference and explain how your site selection will contribute to the success of your conference.
- Select a keynote speaker for the conference. A strong keynote speaker will attract people to the conference and will motivate the audience. Look for individuals who are viewed as "global contributors" — Nelson Mandela, Mary Robinson, Mother Teresa, or Kofi Annan. Your speaker should have some connection to the issue your conference will be discussing.
- Include a brief biography of your chosen keynote speaker, outlining her or his contributions and current role in society. For ideas, research biographies of keynote speakers at recent or upcoming conferences.

The United Nations Communications Panel will evaluate your presentations. The panel will use the information to determine which five conferences they will sponsor over the next five years, in their efforts to raise awareness, discussions, and possible solutions to global social issues.

FIGURE 10-30 Nelson Mandela, a much admired keynote speaker, addresses the House of Commons in Ottawa.

Who are they?

This feature introduces many of the prominent organizations and groups involved in the world's most pressing issues. Examples of groups profiled include the United Nations, the World Bank, and the International Organization for Migration.

Who are they?

The International Organization for Migration

The International Organization for Migration (IOM), based in Geneva in Switzerland, is an internationally funded organization committed to helping millions of migrants with information, technical assistance, and humanitarian aid. It also provides cultural information, language training, help with transportation, medical assistance, and assistance with documentation (acquiring visas or passports). Since it started in 1951 as the Intergovernmental Committee for European Migration, it has helped over 11 million migrants.

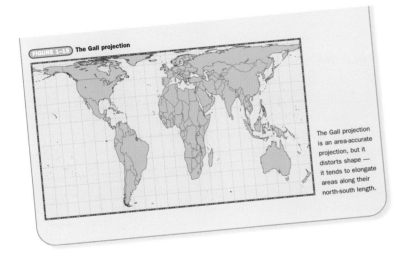

FIGURE 1-15 The Gall projection

The Gall projection is an area-accurate projection, but it distorts shape — it tends to elongate areas along their north-south length.

Gall map projection

World maps in the textbook have been drawn using the Gall map projection, which shows an area-accurate view of the world. This map allows you to see the relative size of a country. It is explained fully on page 21.

Online resource centre

Would you like more information on a topic? An excellent place to start is the *On the Threshold* Web site. This useful extension of the textbook offers updated content, Web links, and additional activities. It's easy to access — just visit www.gagelearning.com/onthethreshold !

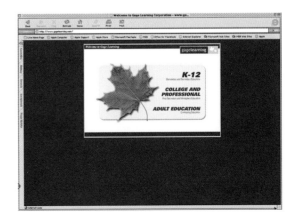

Facing the Issues

It was four days before Anta Gueye knew for certain that her youngest son was dead. Cheik, 16, was one of seven fishermen who had pushed out their small canoe-shaped fishing boat through the waves from the beach in Mbour, a fishing village 80 kilometres south of Dakar on the West African coast.

The men had planned to be at sea for three days — a long time in a boat with no shelter on the unpredictable Atlantic waters. But the fish that were once plentiful nearer to the shore have disappeared, and fishermen have to travel farther afield to find the shoals.

It happened while the crew was asleep. The steel hull of an industrial trawler, one of the many from the developed world that trade in the waters off the West African coast, had cut the small pirogue in half. The men clung to the wreckage, calling out to each other, as the trawler ploughed on toward the horizon.

As the waters settled, the men swam toward each other, knowing their only chance of survival was to stay close together. But there was no sign of Cheik; his crew-mates said he had tied himself to the side of the boat to guard against being tossed overboard during the night. When the trawler hit he had been unable to free himself and was sucked under the water. They never found his body. The next morning the men were rescued by another pirogue fishing the same waters.

Anta Gueye waited on the beach, hoping her missing son had been picked up by another fishing boat. By the fourth day all hope was gone.

For the fishermen of Senegal incidents like these have become a common occurrence. Arona Diagne, who is president of the Senegalese independent fishworkers' association, CNPS, said that more than 300 men have been lost in accidents with trawlers in the waters around Mbour over the last two decades.

With the rapid depletion of fish stocks in Europe and Asia, trawlers from France, Spain, Italy, Japan, Taiwan, and the former Soviet republics have targeted the fertile waters off West Africa to keep pace with their countries' insatiable appetite for fish. Seventy-eight European Union boats are licensed to fish in Senegal in a deal that nets the government in Dakar about US$20 million a year.

a) What issues are raised in this article?

b) Identify the different points of view involved.

c) How might this issue be resolved?

Expectations

- Identify the social, economic, cultural, and political components of geographic issues.
- Demonstrate an understanding of how human-induced changes in the earth's natural systems can diminish their capacity to support human activity.
- Identify current global sustainability issues and environmental threats.

- Evaluate the sustainability of selected trends, related to the consumption of the earth's resources.
- Describe biases that may shape different viewpoints and perspectives on geographic issues.
- Evaluate and communicate perspectives and arguments of various stakeholders involved in a geographic issue.

As global citizens, we share this planet with billions of other people. The choices we make about the ways in which we live our lives affect the world at large. As Canadians living in the world's second-largest country, we are also deeply affected by what happens elsewhere on the global stage.

The issues surrounding the management of earth's physical and human resources are incredibly varied and complex. Examples include overfishing, energy use, global water supply, climate warming, and poverty, all of which are examined in this book. Few of these issues are easy to understand and all are difficult to solve. Yet, present and future generations can contribute to workable solutions by making informed decisions about the effective management of the planet's physical and human resources.

1. Create your own definition of the word "issue." How do you define this word when it is used in the term "world issues"?

2. Identify four issues that you believe face the world's population today.

3. Which of your four issues do you think is the most serious for Canadians today and in the future? Explain your reasons.

4. Choose an issue of particular interest to you. Throughout this course, collect articles related to this issue and create an issue portfolio so that you can analyse them later on.

FIGURE 1-1 Why are Canadians deeply affected by what happens in other regions of the world?

Framing an Issue

Awareness is a vital early stage in addressing an issue — if we are not aware an issue exists, how can we address it? Today, geographers use sophisticated means of measuring and mapping features of the world. As a result, we know more about the issues facing us than we did a few decades ago. For example, scientists can use computer models to map temperature changes in the earth's atmosphere, to predict outcomes for the future (see Figure 1–2).

Characteristics of an issue

Once you are aware that a problem exists, you can begin to analyse it. Issues share some basic characteristics.

Generally, an issue:

- generates concern about how the outcome will affect the well-being of earth's environments and species
- involves interrelated political, environmental, social, and economic aspects
- has complex causes
- has complex solutions

To illustrate these characteristics, consider the following example. Scientists have raised concerns that the atmospheric temperatures of the world are rising faster than predicted. Normally, atmospheric gases keep heat from escaping the earth's atmosphere. **Global warming** occurs when temperatures rise above the natural level, and is thought to be caused by the release of large amounts of carbon and methane into the atmosphere through industrialization, transportation, and the burning of forests.

FIGURE 1–2 **Temperature change between 1975–1985 and 2040–2060**

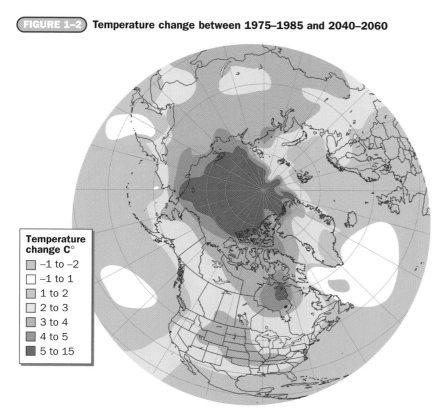

Temperature change C°
- −1 to −2
- −1 to 1
- 1 to 2
- 2 to 3
- 3 to 4
- 4 to 5
- 5 to 15

Computer models like the climate map shown here predict future outcomes. What factors could change such a forecast?

Currently, over 600 studies indicate that average annual temperatures around the world will rise between 1.7°C and 5.5°C before the year 2100. The consequences would include water shortages, loss of cropland, massive spreading of deserts, and gradual melting of icecaps. Widespread migration of people would follow, as they searched for better living conditions.

Global warming has received a great deal of attention worldwide. There is obvious concern over this issue. Such concern drives people to look for solutions.

Implications of an issue

A single issue has interrelated aspects. A good way to examine an issue's complexity is to **brainstorm** the issue, as follows.

Using the webbing technique shown in Figure 1–3, brainstorm the topic of global warming. Write the words "Global warming" in the centre of an issue-analysis web; then surround it with as many words as come to mind when you think of this issue.

FIGURE 1–3 Issue-analysis web

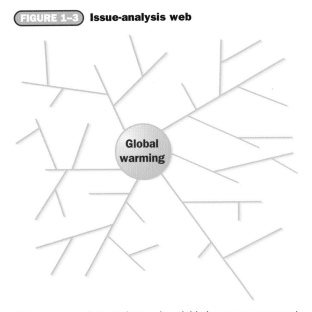

Global warming

When you analyse an issue, it quickly becomes apparent just how complex the issue is.

Because most issues have political, environmental, social, and economic implications, it is helpful to organize the result of brainstorming into these four basic areas. They are outlined below in more detail.

- **Political:** Politics is about power and control. Any organization (for example, a government or a multinational corporation) that designs, administers, and makes judgments about rules or control, has power. When there are global problems, it is necessary to identify who controls the situation. However, when there is no clear controlling power, solutions become more complex.

- **Environmental:** Environmental features are those that impact both the natural environment (for example, a rain forest) and the environment within which people interact with nature (for example, a village or city). Environmental considerations can either be localized (such as a water shortage in a village in India) or they can be global (such as the impact of global warming on the earth's oceans).

- **Social:** Social factors are those having to do with interpersonal relations or the relations among communities, and include cultural factors. "Culture" describes the customs, values, and other forms of human endeavour characteristic of a particular community. Our lifestyles — the way we work, the way we learn, what we eat, where we live, what we do in our free time, the way we dress, the music we listen to, and even the way we relate to our friends and families — are part of our culture and our social systems.

- **Economic:** In discussing economic impact, we should consider an issue's financial costs — the cost of having a problem in the first place and the cost of its remedy — and the financial benefits resulting from proposed solutions.

Framing the issue of global warming

To better understand the complex implications of global warming, let's use a "framework" and group these implications into the four areas described.

- **Political:** A number of questions come to mind. Who has caused the problem? Who is responsible for the solution? Should individual countries be held responsible? Should there be a collective world community response? At present, there are significant international conferences on global warming held every two years. Countries lobby one another to make commitments about reducing the amounts of carbon they release into the atmosphere from industrial activity, or from the clearing and burning of forests to create more foodland. The critical issue at these conferences is how to ensure that countries live up to their commitments.

- **Environmental:** The impact of atmospheric warming will completely change the ecology of the **biosphere**, that is, the environments on earth where living things are found. **Biomes** (ecological communities) will be transformed as the surface conditions influencing their formation change. Climate change will affect soil types and natural vegetation cover. This in turn will affect the survival of the species living within that area. Because of ice sheets melting in Antarctica and Greenland, vast areas of lowland will be flooded, and many coastal cities will be affected.

- **Social:** As environments are modified due to changes in surface conditions, so are the lifestyles of the people who live there. People will migrate from lowland regions and areas of cropland will change, thus affecting the people who depend on them. The collapse of species within **ecozones**

FIGURE 1–4 As global temperatures increase, there will be a gradual melting of icecaps. What effect will this have on major coastal cities? Which large cities are likely to be affected?

(complete ecological units that contain living and non-living resources in an interactive system) may change economic practices for its people. For example, entire fishing communities were wiped out during the 1990s, when the Aral Sea in Uzbekistan and Kazakhstan shrank because excess freshwater was drawn to water local crops. This type of cultural change would multiply under the predicted environmental shifts.

- **Economic:** Global warming will have immeasurable financial consequences. The effect of the changing atmosphere on land features will have an enormous impact on economies. For example, in areas where farming is a strong economic practice, farmers could lose their source of revenue if land became arid or was flooded. On the other hand, if countries attempt to slow global warming, it would take huge financial resources to switch from the traditional burning of fossil fuels to using cleaner forms of energy.

Issue briefing

Bias

In researching issues like overfishing and fast population growth, it is important to ensure that the sources of information are reliable, accurate, and balanced. Everyone has a point of view, which is part of what makes us individuals. However, when we rely on information from another source — be it a person, a magazine article, a television documentary, or a Web site — we must consider the viewpoints or biases being shared. Does the author or source of a piece of information have a stake in the issue being discussed? If so, could this bias the author's position? Bias can cause people to select facts that support their argument or viewpoint, while ignoring others.

We must also distinguish between fact and opinion. A news report stating that one country has loaned money to another is reporting a fact; whereas an article stating that it was wrong for one country to loan money to another is giving an opinion. If the information states opinion rather than fact, is its author qualified to give such an opinion?

a) Revisit the article you summarized in question 6 on this page. Does the article or the source of the article present any possible bias?

b) What strategies might a writer employ to minimize bias in an article or book? How might bias be lessened in a television documentary?

Most issues facing the planet, such as global warming, are controversial. There are various reasons put forward as to how the problem came about, as well as numerous suggestions on how to solve it. This particular issue will be examined in more depth in Chapter 7.

5. Of the implication categories (political, environmental, social, and economic) for global warming, does one concern you more than the others? Why or why not?

6. To what extent does global warming exist today? Locate an article about it in a local newspaper or on the Internet, and summarize its findings.

7. What role do the media play in the growth of concern about issues such as global warming?

Two Current Issues

Two issues that currently concern the global community are land degradation and global poverty. Read about these issues, then apply a framework of issue analysis (that is, "frame the issues") in order to analyse them in an organized manner.

Try to see the ways in which different aspects of an issue are interrelated.

Land degradation

Graphic images of children suffering from extreme hunger and malnutrition prompt the question, "Why do they suffer?" Reasons may range from seasonal droughts to complex economic issues of global food distribution.

Many scientists believe that the breakdown of the earth's foodlands is a major environmental problem that results in catastrophic consequences for thousands of people daily. This breakdown or erosion of the land is called **land degradation** (or **desertification**). There is debate over the terminology used to describe this issue. Some experts believe that the term "land degradation" is more accurate than "desertification," because it emphasizes the fact that the land being degraded is **arable land** (land fit for growing crops).

Land degradation is not to be confused with **drought**, which is a temporary period without rain, and which has always occurred as a result of the natural cycles of climate patterns.

The world's **arid** land (dry land with poor-quality soil, which is loosely called "desert") is increasing. The plant and animal **ecosystems** (systems formed by the interaction of living things) that are able to survive in temperate, wetter places are being destroyed. This drying-out process has a devastating impact on plant productivity, and on human and animal use of the land.

The United Nations Environment Programme (UNEP) estimates that 30 percent of the world's land is dry land, and that one-quarter of this has already been severely damaged — far more than would normally be expected — due to excessively dry conditions.

A variety of reasons for land degradation has been suggested:

- The warming of the world's atmosphere leads to drier conditions in many areas.

- More people are living in and around the margins of dry land, trying to grow food in conditions unsuitable for agriculture, thus further depleting quality of the soil.

- In an attempt to clear land to grow food, people cut down the remaining vegetation and trees, thereby destroying one of the ways in which the soil is naturally conserved and replenished. Trees once covered 40 percent of Ethiopia's land; today, this figure is less than 4 percent.

About 10 million hectares are lost every year to land degradation. According to the United Nations (UN), if this trend continues, up to 200 million more people will soon face hunger (in addition to the 800 million currently suffering) and many ecosystems will be damaged beyond recovery.

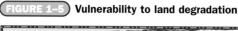 **FIGURE 1–5** **Vulnerability to land degradation**

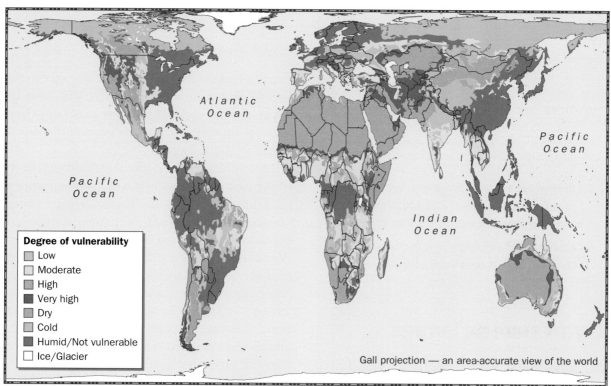

Degree of vulnerability
- ☐ Low
- ☐ Moderate
- ☐ High
- ☐ Very high
- ☐ Dry
- ☐ Cold
- ☐ Humid/Not vulnerable
- ☐ Ice/Glacier

Gall projection — an area-accurate view of the world

Although most of the images of devastation come from Africa, land degradation is global. According to the Worldwatch Institute — a non-profit public policy research organization — Africa contains 32 percent of the world's dry land, while North America contains 12 percent.

FIGURE 1–6 Medical workers from the Red Cross and Doctors Without Borders are working with refugee children in Somalia. Research two international aid organizations that help the millions of refugees who are displaced because of a critical deterioration in their cropland. What sort of assistance do these organizations provide?

Consequences of land degradation

Here are some of the consequences of land degradation:

- *Conflict between groups of people occurs.* Competition for scarce resources of land and water can result in conflict. This conflict breeds further land degradation because, during war, land is destroyed and limited resources are overused. For example, conflicts for control of foodlands in Sudan in Africa have affected food supplies in the country. An estimated 2.4 million Sudanese do not receive an adequate amount of food, according to the Food and Agriculture Organization of the United Nations.

- *Water pollution and flooding results.* Loose topsoil ends up as sediment in river systems, clogging downstream passages and causing rivers to overflow their banks. This results in lower-quality water for drinking, cleaning, cooking, and irrigating land.

Who are they?

The United Nations

The United Nations (UN) was established in 1945 by 51 countries committed to world peace. Today, with 189 member countries and headquarters in New York City, it sustains peace through organizations such as the Security Council and the International Court of Justice (located at The Hague in the Netherlands). The UN organization also includes other well-known bodies such as the United Nations Children's Fund (UNICEF), the World Food Programme (WFP), and the United Nations Environment Programme (UNEP). The UNEP promotes international conferences on topics such as global warming, hazardous waste, and genetically modified foods.

FIGURE 1–7 Terraced hillsides (like this one in the Philippines) help keep the soil moist and create additional cropland. What problems might terracing produce in the long term?

■ ***Environmental refugees*** (those who flee an area for environmental reasons) *become dependent on relief such as food aid and shelter.* According to the New Internationalist organization, there are an estimated 10 million environmental refugees each year, due to land degradation.

■ *The quality of the soil becomes poor.* This threatens the existence of many farming practices. Such farms are no longer sustainable from one year to another, as farmers frequently experience crop failure, sometimes losing their entire annual income. Large commercial farming operations that attempt to maximize yields and profits in dry land areas often practise **monoculture** (planting only one major crop variety) due to the poor soil conditions. However, with only one crop, these farms are more susceptible to pests and disease, and require more fertilizers, pesticides, and irrigation.

Solutions to land degradation

A number of solutions to land degradation have been advocated since the 1977 United Nations conference on desertification. These include:

■ protecting existing potential dry lands

■ using better farming techniques such as regular rotation of crops

■ planting crops that can grow with less water

■ grazing fewer animals on grasslands

■ promoting afforestation programs (planting trees)

■ terracing the landscape (see Figure 1–7)

■ protecting water supplies through conservation and efficient **irrigation** (supplying dry land with water from elsewhere). This guards against **salination** (water becoming salty) that occurs when minerals such as sodium, potassium, magnesium, and calcium are left behind as the water evaporates.

Organizations agree that it is important to involve local people in the decision-making process to protect their lands, because they will be responsible for the continued implementation and maintenance of the solutions, once expert help has been removed.

Who are they?

The New Internationalist

The New Internationalist is a non-government organization (NGO) based in England. Originally sponsored by Oxfam, Christian Aid, and Cadbury-Rowntree, the group produces media materials for many United Nations bodies and other NGOs involved with world development programs. It also publishes magazines around the world on issues of political, environmental, social, and economic concern. One such magazine is the *New Internationalist,* which has an editorial office in Toronto.

Global poverty

One of the world's great challenges is to reduce the massive levels of human poverty that exist around the world. According to the World Bank, it is estimated that 2.8 billion people (about 46 percent of the world's population) live on less than US$2 per day. These people find it difficult to meet life's basic needs, such as health, education, and hope for a better future. They live in regions where nearly 10 percent of children die before their fifth birthday; where there is no opportunity to become involved in decision-making processes that could affect their quality of life; and where they are victims of violence and oppression. To make matters worse, the gap between the rich and the poor is widening. Only 20 years ago, Mozambique — one of the poorest countries in the world — was 50 times poorer than Switzerland. Today, it is 550 times poorer.

Roots of global poverty

How can our technologically advanced world still contain so much poverty? Between the eighteenth century and the middle of the twentieth century, emerging **industrial powers** (countries where large industry plays an important part in the country's economy) profited from the poorer regions of the world through a system of **colonialism**. Colonial powers exploited people and resources in undeveloped regions in Africa, Asia, and Central and South America. Resources were shipped to the industrialized countries to be transformed into manufactured goods. This process helped make countries such as the United Kingdom, France, Belgium, Germany, Italy, Spain, and the Netherlands wealthy.

By the time the poorer countries of the world had gained their independence, the industrialized or **developed countries** of Europe and North America had already secured the means of producing more wealth. The **developing countries** (less industrialized countries) became dependent on international loans. Developing countries remained tied to an economic model in which they supplied developed countries with resources and **cash crops** (crops grown not for local consumption, but for monetary gain) in exchange for currency and a means of paying off growing international debts. Today, the developing countries still owe well over US$2 trillion. For example, in 2000, Tanzania spent nearly five times more money paying its external debt than it spent on the country's entire health-care costs.

Who are they?

The World Bank Group

The World Bank Group, with headquarters in Washington, DC, was originally formed in 1947 to help developing countries improve their economic status by providing them with modest loans and assistance. Today the World Bank, with 177 member countries, lends about US$16 billion each year, and aims to develop sustainable economies and overcome poverty. It also provides funds for research and development, and helps construct infrastructures such as energy installations.

Who makes the decisions? Power is assigned according to the proportion of finance that a country gives the organization. In 2001, the United States provided about 17 percent of the funding for the World Bank, and was therefore allowed that amount of influence. The G7 (the world's seven leading economies: Canada, France, Germany, Italy, Japan, United Kingdom, United States) contribute a total of 45 percent of the funding and therefore carry a significant amount of influence.

FIGURE 1–8 The pesticide factory of US-based multinational Union Carbide in Bhopal, India (shown here) was the site of a poisonous gas leak in 1984. Thousands of local inhabitants died. Research and evaluate the company's response to this tragedy.

Continuing global poverty

There is a worldwide trend of consolidating farm properties into larger units, many of which are owned by multinational corporations that control the flow of resources and food around the world. The process of making the world one big marketplace — a process known as **globalization** — is thought by many to have harmed the poor. Large corporations based in the industrialized world believed that their large-scale investments in creating agribusinesses in poorer countries would "trickle down" through local economies and eventually help the poor. However, some groups representing the poor say that this theory of **trickle-down economics** (where benefits for wealthy corporations and individuals will be passed down through high levels of wages and benefits) is not helping them, because weak laws existing in poor countries allow for environmental and wage exploitation.

The other main factor in continuing global poverty is the high level of population growth in developing countries. Poor families often believe that their wealth lies in their children, who lend a hand in the day-to-day challenge of gathering food and offer hope for the future. However, large families use up scarce resources of food and shelter, continuing the cycle of poverty.

Consequences of global poverty

There are many repercussions when a world is divided by wealth. Below are some problems that stem from global poverty:

- Poor countries are challenged by *huge international debts*. They cannot invest in essential services such as education, and so cannot improve people's everyday conditions. The 2000 National Summit on Africa, held in Washington, DC, reported that countries in Saharan Africa owe financial institutions and Western banks more than US$227 billion. That works out to an average of US$379 for each man, woman, and child living in the region.

- Poor people have *access to only marginal-quality land*, such as land with poor soil or land far up hillsides, which is difficult to farm.

- Poor people who migrate to cities often end up with *bad housing and sanitation.*

- Poor people are often "disenfranchised," meaning that they *lack the political power* to influence their own future and improve their financial situation.

- The children of poor people are more likely to suffer from *serious disease*, due to a lack of sanitation and basic health care. In poor countries, most children who die before they are 5 die from easily preventable medical problems, often from a simple lack of safe drinking water.

- A frequent by-product of poverty is *gender inequality*. According to the United Nations, two-thirds of the world's 840 million illiterate people are female. In poorer families, if it is not feasible for all children to attend school, it is often the girls who are kept at home to help run the household. With only minimal education, women face daunting challenges when seeking higher-paid jobs that would help in the fight against poverty. Chapter 10 discusses how people around the world are working to overcome such gender inequalities.

Solutions to global poverty

Various solutions have been recommended to overcome global poverty:

- A high priority in many countries today is to *make educational opportunities available to the poor*. For example, the Chinese government has set up anti-poverty units, which have spent considerable sums of money increasing basic education and health care. Another example is Uganda's aim to improve job skills by spending money in rural areas. It has set up a national task force to create a poverty-eradication action plan, which aims to develop roads, improve schools, and provide aid for farmers.

- The United Nations aims to *halve the rate of female illiteracy* by 2020, which will enable women to seek employment in fields where math and writing skills are necessary. This will lead to a workforce that includes educated, empowered women.

- More *women in the workforce* also ultimately means more money for families and lower **birth rates** (the number of births per 1000 of the country's population). Families will not feel the need to have many children to help their financial situation.

- The United Nations also hopes to *reduce under-5 mortality* (children dying under the age of 5) from its present high levels to less than 45 per 1000 children by 2015. This could help reduce birth rates in countries that can least afford rapidly growing populations. In sub-Saharan countries, the 2000 level was 151 deaths per 1000 children (compared to 6 per 1000 on average in the world's 30 wealthiest countries).

Frame the issues

In each chapter, you will be asked to "frame" issues by first brainstorming, then applying the organizer. Keep this model in mind as you approach new issues.

FIGURE 1-9 Issue organizer

Issue: Land degradation

Concern:

Causes:

Implications:

   • Political

   • Environmental

   • Social

   • Economic

Possible solutions:

8. To organize your thoughts on the issue of land degradation, or on the issue of global poverty, create and complete an organizer similar to the one in Figure 1–9.

9. Explain how using this organizer helps you understand the issue.

10. To demonstrate that there are often a number of ways in which problems can be solved, provide three possible solutions for land degradation and three for global poverty.

11. Which of the above two issues do you believe will be more difficult to overcome in the years ahead? Explain.

12. In what ways are land degradation and global poverty interrelated?

13. Having completed this activity, how would you now define the term "issue"? Compare this with the definition you gave earlier in this chapter.

Independent States, Shared Resources

Even if we are aware of the pressing issues that confront us, there is no guarantee that we will solve or overcome them. One fact that prevents us from finding solutions to these issues is that, although we hear a lot about globalization in the media, we are not a truly global community.

In reality, the planet comprises some 192 countries or states, each representing thousands of national groups of people, and each with its own culture, needs, and wishes. These distinct cultures have evolved as a result of many factors such as local topography, climate, historical experience, and availability of resources. Most national groups and states act in the best interest of their own people, but even with global organizations such as the United Nations, the world has not found a way in which to act as a complete global community. People tend to think like Japanese, Zimbabweans, Canadians, Chileans, or whatever their nationality — not as global citizens. This way of looking at the world makes it difficult for everyone to join together and find solutions to the world's problems.

The tragedy of the commons

In 1968, Garrett Hardin wrote a classic study called "The Tragedy of the Commons." The study gives us an excellent insight into the challenges facing the planet. Hardin's basic argument is that humans have developed societies within which they act essentially in their own interest, and not for the good of society as a whole.

To explain his term **the tragedy of the commons,** Hardin describes the use of a common pastureland. Each cattle herder or farmer allows his or her livestock to feed from this common land. There is no restriction on how many animals an individual may own and graze on the land.

However, everyone in the community equally shares the cost of grazing. Even if one farmer has five animals, and another just one, the cost for the richer farmer will be the same as that for the poorer farmer. It is therefore in the best interest of all farmers to own as many animals as they can. The downside to this open use of the common ground is that the land will not be able to support the eventual increase in animals. The overused pastureland will collapse into a waste ground and no animals will be able to graze on it. This is "the tragedy of the commons."

Hardin suggests that the solution is to parcel off the common grazing land into equal pieces for each farmer. Any farmer may graze more animals than the piece of land can support, but that will not hurt the other farmers.

For a simulation of the tragedy of the commons, see page 16.

Hardin first applied his theory to population growth. He believed that a "finite world could support only a finite population," and that the population would continue to grow unchecked as people chose to have more children. He maintained that, eventually, this would place stress on the planet's resources and its capacity to feed the growing numbers, and would result in famine. This theory, and the opposition to it, is further discussed in Chapter 2.

The intervention of modern technology has postponed this predicted environmental collapse. The **Green Revolution** (science's contribution to increasing food yields through biotechnology applications) has increased crop yields and food supplies. However, how long can science continue to increase the output of current croplands? Further demands on land, assisted by means such as larger amounts of fertilizer, will most likely not produce the continued increases necessary.

So far, only China has attempted to implement restrictions on population growth — a response in line with Hardin's theory. By attempting to restrict Chinese families to one child each, China is trying to limit the future demands on its resources.

There are many situations worldwide that illustrate the overexploitation of a common area. For example, there has been little control or regulation regarding fishing in the oceans. Fishing fleets from around the world have overfished the oceans, bringing valuable food stocks to near extinction in some areas. Similarly, in some areas there is little control over airspace — factories freely discharge chemicals into the air, and everyone must bear the cost of a dirty atmosphere.

FIGURE 1–10 Both of these examples show harvesting of a resource. In what ways are they similar? In what ways are they different?

14. What is the basic argument on which Garrett Hardin's theory is based?

15. Explain why the term "the tragedy of the commons" is appropriate for Hardin's theory about the shared use of space.

16. What is the solution to the tragedy of the commons, according to Hardin?

17. Identify one example of shared space from your local and one from the global community. Create a set of five rules that may be written to help protect each of these spaces for everyone.

The tragedy of the commons — A simulation

A simulation can help you to understand and apply what you have learned about the tragedy of the commons. Refer to Figure 1–11, which shows two villages (Taranda in the southwest and Bwandu in the northeast) at opposite ends of a grassland area bordered on the east and west by foothills and mountains. To the north is wetland and swamp. The southern area is arid wasteland. On the far side of the western mountains are rich valleys of uncleared, fertile rain forests.

Twenty families live in Taranda and practise livestock herding in order to survive. They own 35 cows, and many chickens and goats. One of the families is named Bakara. The husband and wife have four children, all between the ages of 8 and 16. The children do daily chores such as collecting firewood, tending a small vegetable garden, collecting water from a nearby well, and looking after the cattle.

In the village of Bwandu, there are only ten families with a very similar lifestyle to those in Taranda. The Bwandu inhabitants have 15 cows, many chickens, and a few goats. The farmers from both villages use the common grasslands to graze their livestock.

In Figure 1–11, the common grassland area is represented by 75 squares. Each of the 55 basic squares represents 1 food unit, that is, each provides enough grass to supply 1 cow for 1 year. The 20 squares adjacent to the Crimson River have a value of 1.5 food units. These squares represent more fertile land, the result of rich sediment deposited by occasional flooding of the river.

The foothills of the Rustic Mountains have thick tree growth in the shallow soil of higher ground. This land is described as "marginal" land. If the trees were cleared for grasses to grow, the value would be less, due to the poor quality of the soil. The food unit value here is potentially 0.5 units per square.

FIGURE 1–11 Bwandu and Taranda

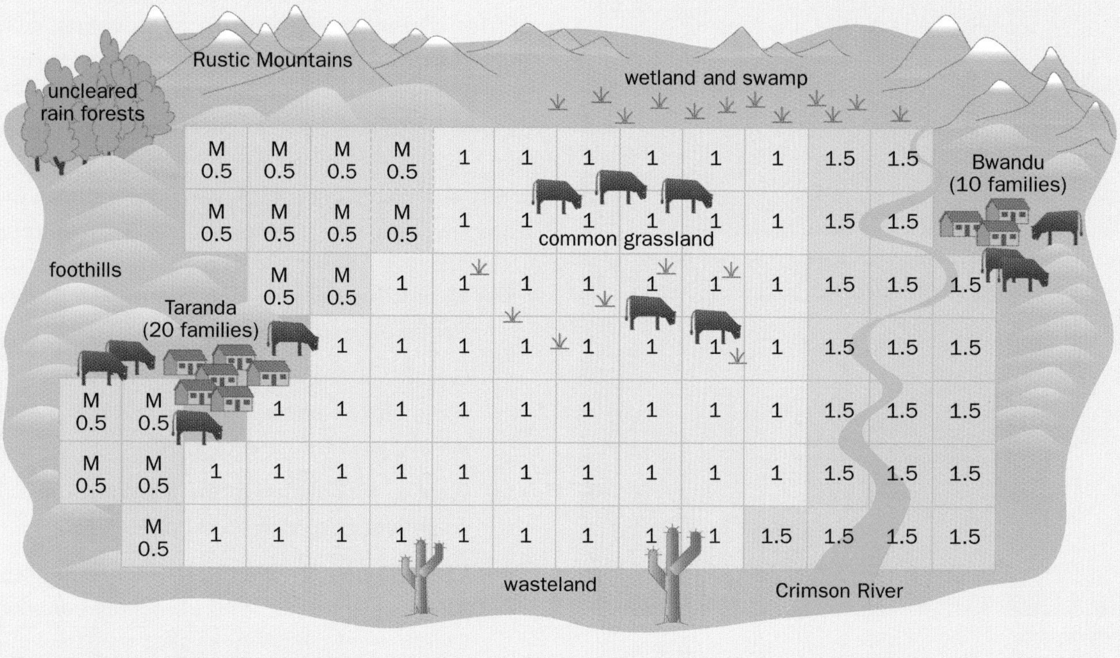

This map shows the grazing land for Bwandu and Taranda. All of the land may be used by both villages.

Run the following simulation to see what happens to these families and their ability to graze their cattle, over a number of years.

Year 1: Each cow requires 1 food unit per year to survive. Total the number of food units available by counting the squares within the common grassland. (55 squares at 1 unit + 20 squares at 1.5 units = 85 food units) Total the number of cows in each village. Calculate the amount of food available for each cow using the following calculation:

$$\frac{\text{available food units}}{\text{total number of cows}}$$

STATUS CHECK:

a) How do you think the farmers of Taranda and Bwandu feel about the food supply for their cows at this point?

Year 2: During this year, through successful breeding practices, 12 families in Taranda gain an extra cow each. This includes the Bakaras, who now have two cows. The farmers of Bwandu gain seven extra cows. Calculate the amount of food available to each cow using the calculation shown above.

STATUS CHECK:

b) How would you describe the quality of the grass in the common grassland area?

c) How do you think the farmers of Taranda and Bwandu feel about the cows' food supply now?

d) How do you think the Bakara family feels about the food supply for its cows?

e) If the Bakaras could get another cow in Year 3, how do you think they would respond?

Year 3: Again, this is a prosperous year for both villages. There are 18 new cows in Taranda, and 12 in Bwandu. The Bakara family was lucky enough to get another cow. Calculate the amount of food available to each cow.

STATUS CHECK:

f) How would you describe the quality of the grass in the common grassland area?

g) How do you think the farmers of Taranda and Bwandu feel about the cows' food supply now?

h) How do you think the Bakara family feels about the cows' food supply?

Year 4: The farmers of Taranda have noticed that the quality of the grass is not as good as it has been in past years. They decide to clear the trees on the lower slopes of the Rustic Mountains. This adds a further 15 squares to the grazing land. However, these squares generate just 0.5 food units each, as it is marginal-quality land.

STATUS CHECK:

i) During this time, the Bakaras are discussing whether to breed more cows. What do you think they decide?

Year 5: It is good that additional grazing land was obtained. The Taranda villagers bred 20 new cows, and the villagers in Bwandu got 14 new cows. Calculate the amount of food available now, for each cow.

STATUS CHECK:

j) How would you describe the quality of the grass in the common grassland area?

k) How do you think the farmers of Taranda and Bwandu feel about the cows' food supply at this point?

l) How do you imagine the Bakara family feels now about the food supply for their cows?

Year 6: Because the tree cover has been cleared away from the slopes of the foothills in order to gain more grazing land, there have been mudslides and a loss of soil. This makes the quality of the grass that grows here worth only 0.25 food units in Year 6.

STATUS CHECK:

m) Can the farmers of these two villages continue to graze their animals in this area at all?

n) How do you think the Bakara family feels about this? What should they do?

o) What are the options facing the farmers from these two villages?

p) How does this simulation demonstrate Hardin's "tragedy of the commons"?

The Club of Rome model

The Club of Rome is a non-profit, non-government think-tank that brings together scientists, economists, businesspeople, international civil servants, heads of state, and former heads of state, from around the world. Its members believe that each human being can contribute to the improvement of our global society. This group has produced a model that links human population growth with the amount of industrial development, pollution, and depletion of resources. See Figure 1–12.

With continued growth in population and the associated growth of industry in the developing world, there will be significant consequences. The demands of a growing global population could result in a collapse of food supply, as will be discussed in Chapter 4. The **gross domestic product (GDP)**, or value of all goods and services produced and consumed domestically, is a measure of levels of industrialization. According to the World Bank, the gross domestic product of the world grew from US$4 trillion in 1950, to US$44 trillion in 2000. Through rapid industrialization in places like China and India, there will likely be a decline in the quality of the environment, which will have a dramatic impact on a number of factors such as life expectancy, industrial output, and natural resources.

Science has never been as focussed on the global environment as it is currently. However, it is still very difficult to monitor and predict the point at which thresholds of sustainability will be reached or exceeded. In the meantime, the signs of environmental stress are all around us.

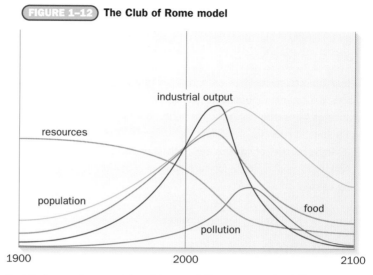

FIGURE 1-12 The Club of Rome model

Explain how a downward trend in any of these categories influences the trend lines of the other categories.

Sustainability: a parable

How to catch a monkey:

a) Hollow out a coconut.

b) Carve a hole in the top and fill the nut with rice. The hole should be just large enough to allow a monkey to put an extended hand inside but not big enough for it to withdraw a whole fistful of rice.

c) Find a likely location and wedge the nut firmly between two large boulders so the top half is clearly visible.

d) Fasten the nut with a chain to a stake in the ground.

e) If the monkey refuses to let go of its handful of rice, it is both trapped and unable to eat the rice.

f) If the monkey relaxes its grip and takes less, it will be both free and fed.

Can our species relax its grip and take only what we need? What can we learn from this parable regarding sustainability?

Sustainability

Sustainability refers to the earth's ability to support our needs and those of every other species on earth. If we keep consuming products at current rates, continue growing in population, and expect the economy to grow every year without replacing what we have taken from the earth, our planet will be reduced to the condition of Hardin's "commons."

The evidence is everywhere:

- Global fish stocks in the open oceans have never been as low as they are today. We have seen the devastating impact of the loss of cod stocks off the East Coast region of Canada.

- **Aquifers** (underground sources of freshwater) are emptying at a frightening pace. According to the Worldwatch Institute, the massive Ogallala Aquifer of the American midwest is emptying at about 1 metre per year (from an estimated depth of 60 metres). It is being depleted at a rate of 20 times that of natural replenishment.

- Forests are being cut down faster than they can be replaced, many by poor migrant people searching for a way to create a cropland for their families. The World Resources Institute estimates that one-quarter of the old-growth forest has been destroyed in the past 40 years.

The New Internationalist organization believes that as we work to become one worldwide trading place — the process of globalization — the world turns into both a global market and a factory. Environmentalist Wayne Ellwood believes that "no corner of the earth is safe from the depredations of industrialization, the dead-zone of consumerism, or the accumulation of human-made garbage and toxic waste."

Lester Brown of the Worldwatch Institute describes the term **threshold** as "the resource limits beyond which supply cannot be sustained." A sustainable society, in Lester Brown's view, satisfies its needs without diminishing the next generation's prospects. He believes that only fundamental changes in our attitude toward population growth

FIGURE 1–13 This satellite image of an area near the border between Brazil and Bolivia (South America) shows several fires burning — the red dots. Heavy deforestation can be seen as light green patches in the dark green of the rain forest.

and our use of energy will enable us to develop and improve the quality of life of the majority of the world's population. In the developed world, efforts to continually raise our quality of life are a major threat to the sustainability of the world's resources.

Economic improvements have been experienced only by what is regarded as the developed part of the world. When countries such as China and India (with a combined 35 percent of the world's population) achieve higher economic standards, there will be enormous demand for consumer goods and for the resources to make them.

18. Using the term "threshold," describe what makes a planet sustainable.

19. What evidence exists to suggest that ours is not a sustainable planet?

Cartography

Maps are the geographer's communication tool. Just like a book, they tell a story, and contain the details required for the story to make sense. A map is a flat representation of the three-dimensional surface of the earth. By their two-dimensional nature, however, maps cannot give true representations of their three-dimensional subject matter.

Map projections

The most accurate way to represent the earth is with a globe. Although it is a fairly accurate representation of the earth, it does have some practical limitations.

The first obvious limitation is shape. People cannot pack a globe into their pockets for a hiking trip — it is simply not realistic. The second limitation is size. A globe that shows a lot of detail — for example, a road system of a city — would have to be extremely large to serve as a navigational tool. Clearly, for convenience, it is necessary to have a flat, two-dimensional representation of the earth.

Transferring details from a globe to a sheet of paper is called making a map projection. Mapmakers (cartographers) are aware of the fact that there is no accurate way

to transfer all the information from a three-dimensional earth to a two-dimensional map. There are four basic characteristics that cartographers try to preserve on a map:

- *Shape:* The shape of an area is directly related to the shape in the real world.
- *Area:* An area's size is proportional to its actual size in the real world.
- *Direction:* The lines of constant direction (for example, north) remain constant anywhere on the map.
- *Distance:* Distances measured on the map are accurate.

There is no projection of the earth that effectively preserves all of these characteristics. To make a map that is true in its representation of shape, cartographers are forced to distort the accuracy of each of the other characteristics. Each type of map projection is designed to focus on a single characteristic.

The Mercator projection

In North America, the most common map projection is the Mercator projection, created to provide an effective

FIGURE 1–14 **The Mercator projection**

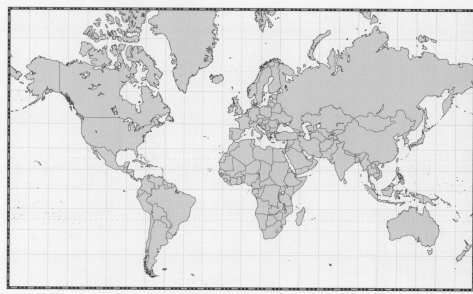

The most popular projection of the world in North America — the Mercator projection — distorts area size.

projection for navigation by sea. This meant that lines of constant direction (called "rhumb lines" or "loxodromes") needed to be straight. The success of the Mercator projection for navigation led to its general popularity.

The Mercator projection distorts the size and shape of areas. A quick comparison of the areas of Greenland, China, Australia, and the continent of South America would lead one to conclude that Greenland is the largest. In reality, Greenland is about one-fifth the size of China, a quarter the size of Australia, and merely one-eighth the size of South America!

Alternative projections

There is no shortage of map projections; there are literally thousands of them, and each one has its advantages and limitations. One alternative is the Gall Orthographic projection that, unlike the Mercator projection, is area-accurate: it allows areas of the world to be seen accurately in terms of relative size. Maps, like other forms of communication, are subject to bias. Given their visual nature, they can create powerful mental pictures of what the world is actually like. For example, the Mercator projection's distortion of shape, size, and distance perpetuates a very "Eurocentric" (showing a European bias) view of the world. It is for this reason that, wherever possible, this textbook uses the Gall projection throughout for its world maps, in an attempt to generate an appreciation of a different view of the world.

a) Looking at Figure 1–14, compare the northern hemisphere with the southern hemisphere of the globe. Which area looks larger? Which area is larger in reality? Verify by looking at Figure 1–15.

b) It has been said that maps are political in nature. Do you agree with this viewpoint? Why would someone say that the Mercator projection presents a Eurocentric view of the world? Discuss this with your classmates and write a short, reflective response.

c) Research two other map projections. What are their advantages? What are their limitations?

FIGURE 1–15 The Gall projection

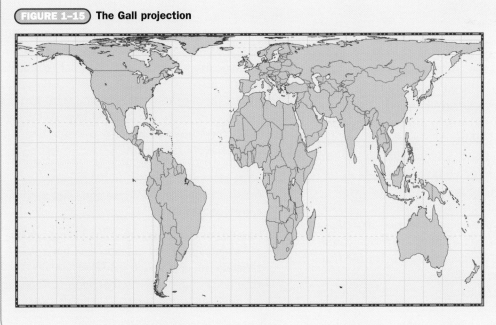

The Gall projection is an area-accurate projection, but it distorts shape — it tends to elongate areas along their north-south length.

Case in point — The Grand Banks

The fishing grounds off the Grand Banks, just east of the island of Newfoundland, were among the most productive in the world, yielding up to 276 000 tonnes of northern cod. In the 1950s, these fertile fisheries changed forever with the arrival of giant trawlers from other countries. In 1968, catches totalled 725 000 tonnes. The Canadian government was warned by fishery experts about the amount of overfishing close to its shores so, in 1976, it extended Canadian sovereignty out to 370 kilometres. However, this did not stop foreign fleets from fishing inside this limit, claiming the area was international waters.

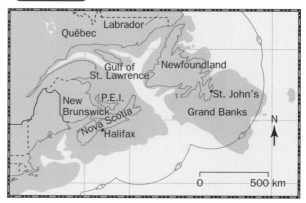

FIGURE 1–16 Fishing off the Grand Banks

The line demarcating the extent of Canadian sovereignty (as defined by Canada) is illustrated above. How might fish migration add to the difficulties of managing fish stocks?

At a glance — *The Grand Banks*

- Total area: 93 200 km²
- Terrain: series of raised submarine plateaus
- Nearest land: southeast coast of Newfoundland
- Depth range: 36–185 m
- Fishing hazards: fog, icebergs, transatlantic shipping lanes
- Oil drilling: began in the late 1970s with the Hibernia oil field discovery

Although catches from this fishery declined to 126 000 tonnes by 1978, they did recover, leading experts to believe that these grounds could not be permanently harmed. Even so, Canadian fleets, with the help of new "draggers" (large nets dragged along the ocean floor, disturbing the sediment and driving the fish up into the net), continued to catch large amounts of fish and deplete the fish stocks.

In the 1980s, catches totalled around 226 000 tonnes per year. Experts again warned that these totals exceeded sustainable limits. However, catching fish meant more work and revenue for the fishing industry, so these warnings were ignored.

In 1986, the Canadian government set quotas on how much fish could be caught. In 1992 however, seeing a possible collapse in the fishing indus-try, they banned all cod fishing. Some 40 000 jobs were lost, ending 400 years of fishing in the East Coast region. Scientific research showed that there were only 1700 tonnes of cod by the end of 1994; the fishery had collapsed.

Who was at fault? Experts blamed a combination of government subsidies and business interests for encouraging improvements in fishing technology. Foreign fishing fleets catching uncontrolled amounts of fish, and lack of scientific monitoring also contributed heavily. Fisheries throughout the world are threatened with similar collapse, as they have not heeded experts' warnings or learned how to avert a disaster like the East Coast fishery collapse.

20. What factors contributed to the fishery collapse in the Grand Banks and what were the consequences?

21. How do you think workers in the fishing industry of Newfoundland and Labrador see the situation, as opposed to the Canadian government or people in other parts of Canada?

22. What lessons in sustainability does the East Coast fishery collapse teach?

The North Sea — Area under threat

Western European countries with a rich maritime tradition surround the North Sea. It contains a variety of aquatic species, such as plants, fish, whales, shellfish, seals, and otters, and attracts a large variety of seabirds.

For hundreds of years, Western European fishing fleets have been able to reap the benefits of the abundant fishing grounds in the shallow continental-shelf areas of the North Sea. However, since the early 1990s, the fishing industry has noted a sharp drop in the amount of fish being caught in this area. Scientists have said that the amount of fishing done here exceeded the threshold levels (natural replacement) of the species. The situation is similar to that of the Canadian Grand Banks.

Cod fishing in the North Sea is particularly hard hit. Whereas the United Kingdom's fishing trawlers regularly caught 275 000 tonnes in the 1980s, they caught only 45 000 tonnes of cod in the year 2000. As well, haddock and whiting are too overfished to replenish themselves.

Industrial fishing

One threat in the North Sea is the increased amount — over half of the North Sea's total fishing tonnage — of industrial fishing, where huge numbers of fish are processed into oil and fish meal. This has encouraged a style of fishing (similar to that using sea-floor draggers) that is non-selective about the species caught. Critics blame this non-selectivity for the collapse of the once-healthy mackerel and herring fish stocks. Because supertrawlers catch both large and small fish indiscriminately, industrial fishing deprives other fish, marine mammals, and birds of the small fish that make up their food supply.

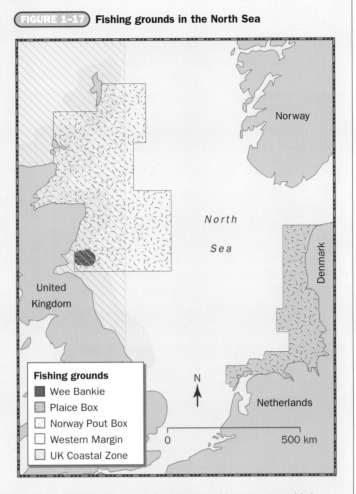

FIGURE 1–17 Fishing grounds in the North Sea

Fishing grounds
- Wee Bankie
- Plaice Box
- Norway Pout Box
- Western Margin
- UK Coastal Zone

The Wee Bankie: This area has large and important seabird colonies.

The Plaice Box: This is a nursery area for cod and plaice.

The Norway Pout Box: Here, large fish stocks of young haddock and whiting are threatened by industrial fishing for Norway Pout, a type of catfish.

The Western Margin: This is a very sensitive area for seabirds that feed off fish populations.

The United Kingdom Coastal Zone: These coastal areas are the habitat nurseries for young herring, cod, and haddock.

As northern fisheries collapse, fleets of European and North American fishing trawlers will turn their attention to the southern oceans. A net from one of these ships is said to be capable of wrapping together 12 jumbo jets. As you read in the introductory story of this chapter, fishing trawlers from the European Union (EU) are already fishing, with disastrous consequences, in areas close to Senegal in Africa.

Food shortages

The World Wildlife Fund (WWF), a non-government organization dedicated to nature conservation, believes that worldwide fishing harvests far more fish than fisheries can sustain. Experts are predicting that, within a few years, human populations will be short of fish for consumption by 18 million tonnes every year. Greenpeace, an environmental group, believes that worldwide consumption levels could fall from the 1990 level of 10.2 kilograms per person to between 5.1 and 7.6 kilograms by 2050. This will affect more than 1 billion people who rely on fish as their main source of protein. Most of these people live in developing countries.

Join the North Sea task force

In groups of six students, you will be assigned one of six roles. You are representatives who are joining a task force to discuss the problem of depleted fish stocks in the North Sea. Your objective is to develop a six-point action plan to improve the situation or solve the issue.

a) Review the information about the North Sea fishery in this chapter. Study the role that has been assigned to you and make notes on the position you will take, and possible statements you will make.
b) Join representatives with the same role from the other groups in your class. Share your ideas and decide on the best possible stance and objectives for your role.
c) Rejoin your task force group and begin the first session. Representatives should introduce themselves individually and state briefly what they hope to achieve from this meeting.
d) Begin an open discussion, once the introductions have been made.
e) Take a "time-out" and return for a meeting with delegates who have the same role in other groups. You may wish to share experiences and report on the progress made toward the action plan.
f) Return to your task force group and continue until you have an action plan that is agreed upon and signed by all representatives.
g) Share your action plan with the other groups.

FIGURE 1–18 Fishing communities on the North Sea will suffer if the issue of depleted fish stocks is not resolved.

Role 1: Fisheries Minister — United Kingdom

You are concerned about the depletion of stocks and are worried about the loss of employment for the United Kingdom's fishers, and the decline in taxable revenues for the government.

You believe that all the Western European countries should accept liability for this problem.

Role 2: Board member of Fish Unlimited, an environmental activist group

You are devastated about the loss of the diverse marine habitat in the North Sea.

You have been presenting evidence for a long time regarding this issue and nobody seems to listen.

You blame all the Western European fishing fleets and their governments.

Role 3: President of the Union of Fishworkers of Europe

Your major concern is the threat to the livelihood of your members, who are the fishing industry workers in all the Western European countries.

Role 4: Canadian delegate to the World Fisheries Organization

You have seen the threats to fisheries on a global scale. You know the risks to fisheries and have been invited to give your opinions about what should be done.

Role 5: Mayor of Peterhead — a Scottish fishing community

Your community will be economically devastated by any move to shut down the North Sea fishery. About 80 percent of your town's economy is based on this fishing industry.

Role 6: Norwegian Minister for Fishing

You believe that the United Kingdom must bear the costs of repairing the fishery's collapse, because most of the environmentally damaged areas are around the east and northeast coasts of the United Kingdom. You do not hold Norway and other European partners responsible.

Follow-up

- Identify four interrelated aspects of the issue of depleted fish stocks in the North Sea (one for each of the following areas: political, environmental, social, and economic).
- Demonstrate an understanding of the following terms by relating them to the case study of the North Sea fishery: sustainability; threshold; the tragedy of the commons
- What similarities and differences are there between the threat to the North Sea fishery and the collapse of the East Coast fishery in Canada?

2

Population Growth

Facing the Future is a non-government organization concerned with educating people about global issues. This group believes that, "ultimately, our own numbers, and the lifestyles many of us choose to live, drive all the critical issues we confront. Left unchecked, the combination of population growth and consumption — along with increasing inequity between rich and poor individuals and nations — will ultimately threaten not only the well-being, but even the lives of a majority of people on this planet."

FIGURE 2–1 **Global population change, 2001**

Time unit	Births	Deaths	Natural change*
Year	131 571 719	55 001 289	76 570 430
Month	10 964 310	4 583 441	6 380 869
Day	360 470	150 688	209 782
Hour	15 020	6 279	8 741
Minute	250	105	145
Second	4.2	1.7	2.5

*Natural change is defined as the difference between the number of births and the number of deaths.

Expectations

- Identify the political, environmental, social, and economic components of global demographic issues.
- Describe selected world demographic trends and explain the factors influencing them.
- Draw conclusions or make judgments or predictions on the basis of reasoned analysis.

- Explain how economic and cultural considerations influence a country's population policies.
- Predict global demographic changes for the future and assess their economic, environmental, and social impacts.

As you read this, you share the planet with over 6 billion (that is, 6 000 000 000) people. During the next hour, the population will increase by 8741 people. By this time tomorrow, an additional 209 782 people will exist — the equivalent of a town the size of Oshawa, Ontario.

Population growth has been compared to a train that slowly pulls out of a station and begins to accelerate. How fast is the train moving right now? Close and open your eyes. During that time, the world's population increased by two people.

Work out some of your own examples of how quickly the population is expanding. Use the data in Figure 2–1.

FIGURE 2–2 How is the issue of population growth related to the topic of sustainability (introduced in Chapter 1)?

World population

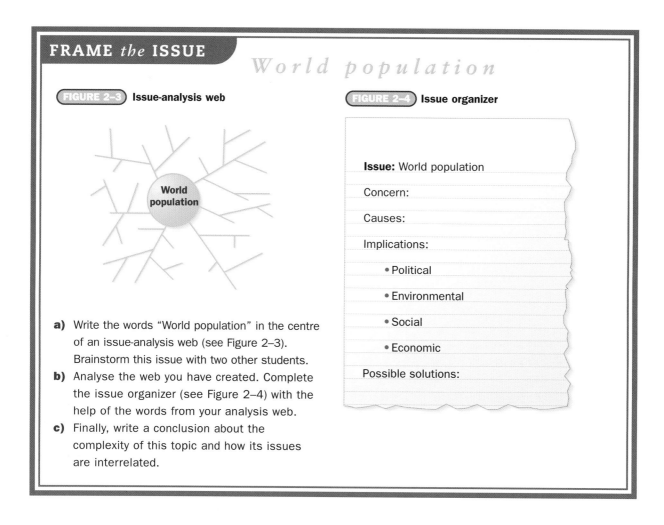

FIGURE 2–3 Issue-analysis web

FIGURE 2–4 Issue organizer

Issue: World population

Concern:

Causes:

Implications:

  • Political

  • Environmental

  • Social

  • Economic

Possible solutions:

a) Write the words "World population" in the centre of an issue-analysis web (see Figure 2–3). Brainstorm this issue with two other students.

b) Analyse the web you have created. Complete the issue organizer (see Figure 2–4) with the help of the words from your analysis web.

c) Finally, write a conclusion about the complexity of this topic and how its issues are interrelated.

Global Population Figures and Predictions

The United Nations (UN) has been making predictions about world population growth since 1990. At that time, they suggested that the population would reach about 9.8 billion by the year 2050. They later revised their estimate to about 8.9 billion, because **fertility rates** (the number of births per 1000 women of childbearing age) throughout the world had fallen faster than anticipated. This may be connected to higher death rates in Africa, where diseases such as HIV/AIDS have taken a significant toll: the average life expectancy in Africa has fallen from 58 to 49 years.

FIGURE 2–5 World population growth

Year	Population (billions)	Year	Population (billions)
1000	0.30	1970	3.70
1250	0.31	1980	4.44
1500	0.50	1990	5.27
1750	0.79	2000	6.06
1800	0.98	2010	6.79
1850	1.26	2020	7.50
1900	1.65	2030	8.11
1950	2.52	2040	8.58
1960	3.02	2050	8.91

FIGURE 2–6 United Nations alternate predictions

Year	Low growth (billions)	High growth (billions)
2000	6.0	6.1
2005	6.3	6.5
2010	6.6	7.0
2015	6.9	7.4
2020	7.1	7.9
2025	7.3	8.4
2030	7.4	8.8
2035	7.5	9.3
2040	7.5	9.8
2045	7.4	10.2
2050	7.3	10.7

FIGURE 2–7 United Nations prediction — World population growth in billions

Year	Billions
1804	1
1927	2
1960	3
1974	4
1987	5
1999	6
2013	7
2028	8
2054	9

The data in Figure 2–5 illustrates the pattern of population growth from year 1000 to 2000, as well as United Nations predictions until 2050.

There is much speculation about how fast the population will continue to grow. The United Nations has produced different scenarios. Figure 2–6 shows two United Nations predictions, one set for low growth and another for high growth.

1. Using the data in Figure 2–5, draw a line graph that shows the United Nations data and predictions for average growth in world population from the years 1000 to 2050. Remember to use an appropriate horizontal scale to show all of the time periods. How would you describe the pattern of growth?

2. Using the data in Figure 2–6, add two more lines to your graph. The line for the high-growth prediction data should be red, and that for the low-growth prediction data should be green. Describe the rate of growth for both the low-growth and high-growth predictions.

3. Figure 2–7 shows the number of years it takes to add a billion people to the population. Calculate the number of years *between* each of the dates on the chart. What does this calculation reveal?

4. Sometimes population predictions are incorrect. What do you think may cause predictions to be too high or too low?

Growth rate deceleration

In the past, the United Nations predictions about population growth have indicated that the numbers continue to grow rapidly. However, as both the low-growth and high-growth predictions show, the rate of world population growth is currently slowing down. The low-growth model suggests that this population will peak at around 7.5 billion in 2040, and will then begin a slow decline, as families will not produce enough children to replace themselves. The high-growth model suggests that, although the rate of growth will decelerate, population numbers will continue to climb to a staggering 10.7 billion.

Has the population growth decelerated to a sustainable rate? Will there be enough resources to meet the needs of the global population? The United Nations has, after all, lowered its predictions for the years ahead, estimating that the world population took 12 years to grow from 5 to 6 billion, but will take a further 14 years to reach 7 billion, and 15 to reach 8 billion. Are we no longer at risk? Not according to Mark O'Connor, a writer on global population trends. He has used the following example of a car running off the road:

A fast-moving car runs off the road toward a big wall. Immediately, the driver steps on the brake. It takes time to slow down, and whether or not the car will hit the wall depends on its speed of deceleration. O'Connor views global population growth in the same way. In 1999 he said, "Now at last it seems the drivers have woken up, have seen their own peril, and are braking. But both the distance travelled and the present very high speed are deadly problems."

According to O'Connor, the rate of population growth is slowing down, but the pace of growth is too fast to prevent the negative consequences of an overpopulated planet. To help understand this view, it is necessary to examine the term **exponential growth**.

Exponential growth

A population grows *exponentially* when its increase is proportional to its base amount. For example, consider a yeast cell that doubles regularly every 10 minutes. After 10 minutes there are 2 cells; after another 10 minutes there are 4 cells; after another 10 minutes there are 8, and so on.

To assess how fast a country's population is growing, **demographers** (scientists who study the statistical data of a population) examine the country's **population-doubling time**. Some countries are doubling their populations in a relatively short time period. For example, Madagascar — an island off the southeast coast of Africa — has an annual growth rate of 3 percent. If this rate is maintained, it will double its population every 24 years. (See the **Rule of 70** in "Frame of reference.") In 2000, Madagascar had a population of 15 506 000. By 2024, it will be 31 012 000 and by 2048, it will be 62 024 000. In less than 50 years, it will have grown by 300 percent! This rapid rate of population growth will place an added strain on Madagascar's current problems of chronic malnutrition and lack of funds for health and education.

Demographers know that the impact of exponential growth is not being felt equally around the world. The demographer Donald Bogue has stated that rapid population growth is found in places that can least afford it, such as areas with low levels of personal income and economic growth. In the questions that follow, this statement will be examined.

FIGURE 2–8 A busy market in Madagascar.

5. Define the term "exponential growth."

6. How is the concept of exponential growth linked to the world's current population increase?

7. How does Mark O'Connor's view support the idea of exponential growth?

8. a) In 2000, Nigeria had a population of 123 337 000. Its annual growth rate is 2.61 percent, according to the 2001 CIA World Factbook. Use the Rule of 70 to calculate the period of time it will take to double its population.

   b) How many years will it take Nigeria to reach a population of 1 billion?

9. Refer to the World Fact File database at www.gagelearning.com/onthethreshold. To see the impact of exponential growth, construct, with a partner, two **choropleth maps** (shaded maps). The first map should show the population-doubling time for each country. The second map should indicate the **gross national product (GNP) per capita** (per person), that is, the total value of all goods and services produced by a country's economy — including those produced abroad — divided by the number of people living in that country, for each country. Note that this is a different calculation to that for gross domestic product (GDP), introduced in Chapter 1.

   a) For population doubling, design a legend with the categories given in Figure 2–9. On a world map, shade each country with the appropriate colour.

FIGURE 2–9 Population-doubling time

Relative change	Doubling time	Colour
2% or more	35 years	Dark red
1.5–1.99%	46–35 years	Medium red
1.0%–1.49%	70–46 years	Pink
Less than 1%	More than 70 years	Orange
Population declining		Yellow

b) For the gross national product per capita map, design a legend with the categories given in Figure 2–10. On a world map, shade each country with the appropriate colour.

FIGURE 2–10 Gross national product per capita

GNP per capita (US$)	Colour code
Less than $1000	Dark green
$1000–$2999	Medium green
$3000–$9999	Light green
Over $10 000	Yellow

c) Analyse the two maps you have created. Write a summary describing the rate of natural change and the relative wealth for each continental region.

d) Is there a relationship between how fast a country doubles its population and its level of wealth?

Effects of different growth rates

Although the world's population is constantly growing, it is not doing so at the same rate in every continent. How will these different growth rates affect the actual numbers of people in these continental regions? Figure 2–11 shows how the population in different regions has grown in 50-year periods from 1850 to the present, and how it is predicted to grow until 2050.

FIGURE 2–11 Population growth for world regions (in millions)

Region	Year				
	1850	1900	1950	2000	2050
Africa	111	133	221	800	1766
Asia	809	947	1402	3684	5268
Europe	276	408	547	727	628
South and Central America	38	74	167	517	809
North America	26	82	172	306	392
Oceania	2	6	13	31	46
Total	1262	1650	2522	6065	8909

10. For each 50-year period, calculate what percentage of the world's population is contained in each region. For example, at the start of the 1900 to 1950 period, 947 ÷ 1576 × 100 = 60 percent of the world's population was living in Asia. Write your answers in a chart similar to Figure 2–11.

11. a) Which region shows the largest increase in actual population numbers between 1850 and 2050?
    b) Which region shows the largest percentage of the world's population between 1850 and 2050?
    c) Which region shows the most significant decline in percentage of the world's population between 1850 and 2050?

12. In which region is the population growing the fastest? For each continental area, calculate the percentage of change in growth between 1950 and 2000, and between 2000 and 2050. For example, the population in Africa grew by 800 − 221 = 579 million between 1950 and 2000. This is a growth of 579 ÷ 221 × 100 = 262 percent.

13. Based on your calculations, write a paragraph summarizing the trends in the distribution of the world's population. Use specific continental examples as support. Conclude your paragraph by explaining whether or not you think these distribution patterns will continue or will change in the future.

Population Impacts

Statistics show that populations are growing disproportionately in different regions of the world. For example, it is predicted that Asia and Africa will contribute most of the population growth between 2000 and 2050; Asia will add a further 1.5 billion, and Africa will more than double its population. During the same period, the population of Europe will decrease by nearly 100 million.

Overpopulation of the world and the fact that developing countries (those that have yet to industrialize to the extent of Europe and North America) generally have high rates of population growth are two situations of concern. Developing countries are moving toward high levels of **consumerism** (increased consumption of goods and services) and this will have an enormous impact on the globe's ability to sustain growth. By 2050, the ratio between developed and developing countries is expected to rise from 1:4 to 1:7.

An **optimum** (ideal) **population** of the world would be one that could thrive without harming the earth's resources while sustaining a standard of living that would satisfy everyone on the planet.

Paul Ehrlich, a biologist, believes that the optimum population depends on the quality of life we choose, and on the impact this has on the planet's resources. He envisions a world where minimum lifestyle needs are met for everyone, even though there may be an uneven distribution of wealth. His world would have a population small enough to preserve biodiversity and wilderness, but also large and dispersed enough to preserve cultural differences and accommodate vibrant cities.

While some experts seek optimum population estimates, others disagree that population growth is a pressing issue at all. Consider the following arguments of some of the key voices on population growth.

Malthusian theory

Thomas Robert Malthus (1766–1843) is known primarily for the concerns he raised about a rising global population in his 1798 publication, "Essay on the Principle of Population." Malthus believed that the human population would increase faster than its food supply. This belief reflected his concerns about the declining living conditions of nineteenth-century England.

However, Malthus believed that once the population exceeded its food supply, "negative checks" such as war, famine, and disease would develop to balance population growth. He did not advocate birth control, but felt that "preventative" strategies such as later marriages could be used to lower fertility levels. He was, however,

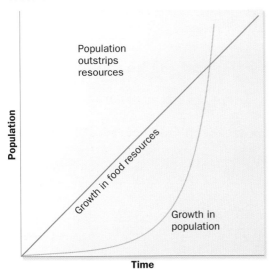

FIGURE 2–12 Growth of population and food resources over time

This graph illustrates Malthus' theory that population increases exponentially (that is, 1, 2, 4, 8, 16, 32 ...) while the food supply grows arithmetically (that is, 2, 4, 6, 8, 10 ...).

pessimistic that people would exercise "moral restraint," and thus projected that the world's population would double every 25 years. If Malthus' calculations had been correct, today's population would be 243 billion (950 million doubling every 25 years).

Despite the inaccuracy of Malthus' predictions, his theories raised the question of how the earth can sustain the world's growing population. Neo-Malthusians have carried forward his beliefs on population growth and food supply, but many of them differ from Malthus, in that they consider birth control to be an acceptable method of reducing population growth.

Current debate on population growth

The most famous debate regarding the impact of global population growth took place between two professors — Paul Ehrlich, a "doomsayer" biologist, and Julian Simon (1932–1998), an optimistic economist. These two men held opposing views on the costs and benefits of population growth. Read the following to understand why Ehrlich's and Simon's viewpoints were so different, and what they predicted for the future.

Paul Ehrlich

Paul Ehrlich has been one of the most vocal forecasters of rapid population growth causing mass famine and economic catastrophe. In 1968, he published *The Population Bomb*, in which he predicted that millions of people would starve to death during the 1970s and 1980s. This did not occur because food production increased faster than population growth.

Currently, Ehrlich focusses on some of the impacts that overpopulation, overconsumption, and damaging technologies may have on the environment: global warming, acid rain, depletion of the ozone layer, starvation, chronic malnutrition, war, crime, and disease.

According to Ehrlich, population size and environmental problems are not linked to developing nations only. For example, he cites the United States — with the third-largest population in the world, a high level of per-capita consumption, and polluting technologies — as proof that population problems occur in developed as well as developing countries.

Is technology the answer? Science has helped to increase food supplies through technological advances, but this has not guaranteed equitable food distribution, and has destroyed soil through extensive use of fertilizers and pesticides.

Ehrlich believes that it is wrong to assume that technology and economics will solve population-growth problems. He suggests that humans are subject to the environment's **carrying capacity** (the maximum number of individuals that a habitat can support), and that the optimum global population will be determined by levels of energy consumption — especially the burning of fossil fuels, on which we currently depend. Rich, industrialized countries today consume 70 percent of all energy. If the world's population grows to 10 billion, it is predicted that the energy consumption of developed countries will jump to almost 90 percent. This is a worrisome situation for Ehrlich, as he calculates that we are already 2 billion people beyond the population numbers for ideal energy consumption levels.

He argues that, even if some populations are reduced through increased literacy, more effective health care, and birth control programs, persuading developed regions (such as North America) to decrease their affluence is much harder. Ehrlich believes that humanity will continue to pay the price for exceeding the earth's carrying capacity unless we realize that there are too many people consuming too much.

FIGURE 2–13 How will the earth sustain itself as the global economy continues to grow, and heavily populated countries increase their economic development?

Julian Simon

In contrast to the views of Paul Ehrlich and other neo-Malthusians, Julian Simon argued that their "dire predictions" would not occur, and that they had been "wrong on food, on energy, on resources, on the environment, on everything." The average life expectancy had lengthened dramatically and, along with other major resources, food production had increased on a per capita basis since World War II. Simon believed that natural resources have provided humanity with infinite materials from which to create or obtain products that could then become renewable resources. For example, coal, oil, and uranium were not "resources" for humans at all until the human intellect saw them as being potentially useful and figured out ways to use them.

Simon argued that people would find ways to conserve resources (for example, firewood) or develop substitutes (for example, solar power) using technology. Where "fixed" resources such as soil existed, people would clear forested regions, irrigate (water) deserts, and drain wetlands, in order to increase available land for food production. Thus, Simon did not view humans as a liability to the planet, but rather, as a valuable asset.

Ehrlich has criticized this reliance on technology, since he believes that it will postpone problems instead of solving them. Followers of Simon might argue, however, that India's ability to feed itself, despite a major population increase from 500 million people in 1966 to 1 billion today supports Simon's belief that anything is possible with the aid of technology.

14. If Malthus and Ehrlich could meet today, what viewpoints would they share?

15. How have Ehrlich's theories expanded beyond those of Malthus?

16. What was Simon's basic argument against Ehrlich's theory?

17. Do you think that, with a global population of 6 billion and counting, we are in danger; or does the high population increase the chance of there being more people able to develop new technological and scientific strategies? Considering the viewpoints you have read, write a one-page response, developing your own viewpoint on the issue of overpopulation.

Global impact — Overpopulation

Despite the overall deceleration of the global population, and successes such as increased levels of food production, many areas still face overpopulation challenges. For example, according to the Food and Agriculture Organization of the United Nations (FAO), there are presently 1 to 2 billion malnourished people in the world, mostly in developing countries.

Twelve million people die each year because of starvation or diseases associated with malnutrition. More problems associated with overpopulation are outlined in the statistics and information below, compiled by the Food and Agriculture Organization of the United Nations:

- *Food surpluses will diminish*, as countries like the United States strive to meet their growing domestic needs. China, with an expected increase of 500 million people by 2050, will need an extra 200 to 400 million tonnes of food each year. Per capita, world grain production has declined for the past 15 years.

- *The world is facing cropland shortages* and more land is needed. Present areas of 1.6 billion hectares must expand to 4 billion hectares by 2050 to meet predicted needs. World croplands amount to 0.27 hectares per capita. (In China, it is only 0.08 hectares each.)

- *Freshwater supplies are dangerously low worldwide*. Some regions are already in crisis due to a lack of freshwater. Eighty percent of all freshwater is used for food production. The World Health Organization (WHO) — affiliated with the United Nations and which aims to help solve world health problems — believes that 940 million people currently lack access to safe freshwater.

- If forests are cut down for more land space at a rate of 17 million hectares per year, *we will run out of forests in less than 50 years.*

- Levels of industrial production are growing rapidly as the developing world joins the consumer-driven global economy, which impacts factors such as *the amount of carbon emissions* that are pumped into the atmosphere.

- *Poverty and housing shortages are increasing*. In Calcutta in India, 70 percent of the population lives in poverty and the homeless population totals 600 000.

- *Political tensions are rising* as national groups fight for control and influence over what they believe to be their territory.

- *One out of every eight species on the planet is threatened with extinction*, which may have a chain reaction that threatens fragile ecosystems.

Who are they?

The Food and Agriculture Organization of the United Nations

The Food and Agriculture Organization of the United Nations (FAO) was founded in 1945 and is one of the United Nations' largest specialized agencies, with 180 member countries. The FAO aims to reduce hunger and poverty through programs that improve agricultural productivity and develop rural areas. The FAO strives to achieve "food security," which it defines as "the access of all people at all times to the food they need for an active and healthy life."

Number crunching

Demographers use state-of-the-art technology when determining population statistics. One of the key components is computerized statistical analysis. This usually requires specialized software packages, but many simple packages (such as Microsoft Excel and ArcView) can be used to help visualize statistical information.

Simple demographic calculations

One of the important goals of statistical calculations is to standardize the numbers that are being examined. Standardizing numbers allows direct comparisons between one set of data and another. For example, if you received a mark of 12 out of 15 on one test, and 23 out of 32 on another, how can you determine which is the better mark? You need to standardize both marks so that they are based on the same amount. By finding the percent mark (that is, based on 100) for each test, it can be stated that the first test mark of $12 \div 15 \times 100 = 80$ percent was considerably higher than the second test mark of $23 \div 32 \times 100 = 72$ percent.

The concept of standardization is very important for studying population — most countries do not have the same number of people in them. Percentages are a popular way of making comparisons; another technique that is commonly used for comparing populations is the "per thousand" calculation. Just as percent refers to 100, per thousand refers to 1000. Many demographic statistics, such as birth rates, literacy rates, and fertility rates, are routinely reported per 1000 people.

The following example shows a calculation to determine the number of children born in Indonesia per 1000 people. The population of Indonesia was approximately 224 784 210 at the turn of the millennium and 5 080 123 babies were born. To determine the birth rate, the following simple formula is used:

$$\frac{\text{number of babies born}}{\text{total population of country}} \times 1000$$

Thus it can be stated that, in Indonesia in the year 2000, the birth rate was:

$$\frac{5\ 080\ 123}{224\ 784\ 210} \times 1000 = 22.6 \text{ per 1000}$$

You can also perform these types of percent and per 1000 calculations using spreadsheet software. Computers perform these types of calculations quickly and accurately, and can present the data in a visually appealing manner.

Mapping demographics in ESRI's ArcView

Using ArcView, you can create a map that shows the various demographic characteristics of a population. For example, if you want to create a map showing population doubling time, you can use ArcView and demographic data (available on the Web site) to create this effectively.

What you need

- ESRI's ArcView 3.x
- The World Data File from www.gagelearning.com/onthethreshold. You may download the file yourself or your teacher will tell you where the data is located. (The data must be downloaded to your server to allow access.)

What you do

- Launch the ArcView program and choose to start with a blank project.
- Select the project window and create a new View by double-clicking on the View button.
- Click on the Add Theme button to add the world demographic theme wcountry.shp to the view. (A theme is a map layer.) This theme will be located somewhere on your computer; check with your teacher.
- Turn the wcountry.shp theme on by clicking on the check box next to the theme name.

Examine the countries on the map — they are all the same colour. You need to turn this basic map into a choropleth (thematic) map using the demographic data contained in the table associated with this file. The data is on a World Demographic Data file. To better understand the data, you should examine this table.

- Click once on the wcountry.shp theme name in order to make it active. (Once selected, it will have a small highlight box around it, and will appear raised.)

- Open the table by clicking on the Open Theme Table button on the toolbar.

You should see a spreadsheet-type table appear. This table contains the name of every country in the world and lots of demographic data for each country. The field you need is called DoubleTime — the doubling time column in the table. The values in this field were calculated using the Growth Rate information and the Rule of 70 (see page 30). You will use the doubling-time data to create your choropleth map.

- Close the table.

You can now create a choropleth map showing the population-doubling time.

- Having closed the table, you are now back in View 1 and your map is visible. Double-click on the wcountry.shp theme name. This brings up the Legend Editor.
- In the Legend Editor, change the Legend Type to Graduated Color.
- In the Classification Field, choose DoubleTime from the drop-down menu. This will change the values in your legend and create five classes of doubling-time values in years for each country.
- Adjust the values of each class: click on Values and type in the ranges for the classifications shown in the table below. Note: There is no way to indicate greater than 70 years, so you will set the largest class to show the largest value available.
- Adjust the Labels (the Labels are what will actually show in the legend for your map) but leave the Color Ramp as it is.

Colour	Values	Labels
Pink	Minus 100–1	Less than 0
Light red	0–34	0–34
Medium red	35–44	35–44
Dark red	45–70	45–70
Darkest red	71–2333 (or highest value)	More than 71

- Click Apply in the Legend Editor and close it.

You should now have a choropleth map on the screen that shows the population-doubling time for each country in the world. You can annotate this map by adding several textboxes, each connected to a region, called a Callout Textbox, as follows.

- The Callout Textbox is accessible through the Text icon which is in the Toolbar's drop-down menu.
  Hold down the Text icon and select the Callout Text Tool.
- With your cursor, drag a line from the region that you are describing to the location where you wish the text box to appear.
- A Text Properties dialogue box will open for you. This is where you can enter the relevant information. Create three text boxes that describe various population trends and projections for three world regions of your choice.

You are now ready to print your map. To do this you need to create a layout document.

- Go to the View Menu and choose Layout. From the Template Manager, choose Landscape and click on OK. This automatically generates a map with a legend, a title, a north arrow, and a scale bar.

There are some changes that need to be made.

- With the Pointer tool, double-click on the title. In the Text Properties box, change the title to World Population-Doubling Time. Click OK.
- Use the Pointer tool again to double-click on the Scale Bar. This brings up the Scale Bar Properties box. Change the Units to read Kilometres. Click OK.
- From the File menu, choose Print. (Make sure your printer is set up to print Landscape!)

Note: For any additional help with ArcView commands, use the online help built into the ArcView software.

Congratulations! Your map is now complete.

  a) Is it possible to use a spreadsheet package to calculate standardized statistics? Prove it by replicating some of the calculations in this chapter, using a spreadsheet.
  b) Discuss the pros and cons of using computers to assist in the calculation of statistics.
  c) Research how a major organization such as Statistics Canada (StatsCan) uses computers to assist in a major project, such as the census.

Visit www.gagelearning.com/onthethreshold for a tutorial on using spreadsheet software to create "population pyramids," introduced in this chapter.

Global impact — Declining populations

Overpopulation is not a concern in every region. In many industrialized, developed countries, fertility rates are well below **replacement levels** (where fewer people are being born than are dying or emigrating). In these areas (illustrated in Figure 2–14), populations face a decline, which will bring about different challenges in areas such as their economies and social welfare programs.

Effects of fertility rates

The term **total fertility rate (TFR)** refers to the average number of children each woman will have in her lifetime. It is estimated that a total fertility rate of 2.1 or less can mean zero population growth after two generations. The 2000 United Nations Population Report states that the total fertility rate for the world is 2.9, that is, 2.9 children born for every woman of childbearing age. In developed countries, the total fertility rate is 1.4. In developing countries (which make up 70 percent of the world's population), the total fertility rate is 3.3.

In developed countries, fertility rates fell from 1.7 in the early 1990s, to 1.4 in 2000. The United Nations predicts that even in developing countries, the rate will fall from 3.3 in 2000, to 2.0 in 2020, then to 1.6 in 2050. In the least developed countries, fertility rates will drop to below 2.0 by 2035. This trend has become known as **depopulation**.

FIGURE 2–14 Total fertility rates in 2000

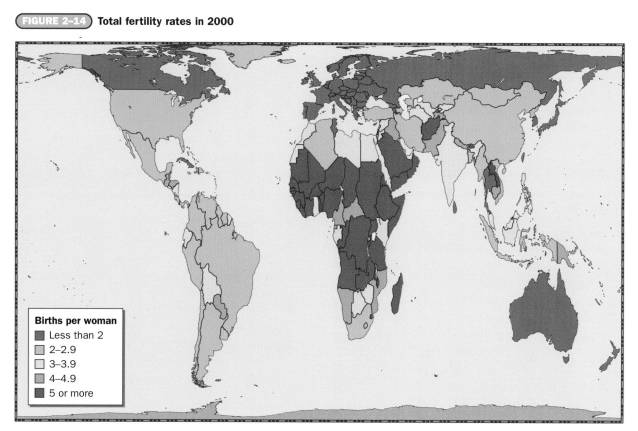

Births per woman
- Less than 2
- 2–2.9
- 3–3.9
- 4–4.9
- 5 or more

Even small changes in fertility rates can have a large impact. For example, India is destined to be the most populated country this century. However, if India's women had an average birth rate just 0.5 below the replacement levels of 2.0, its population would be no higher in 100 years than it is now. On the other hand, if India's women have 2.5 babies each, the population in 100 years would be 3 billion. How would you summarize the pattern of total fertility rates shown on this map?

Between 2040 and 2050, the world's population could actually start to decline. The median age of the world's population would rise from 25 in 1995 to 42 in 2050, impacting on fertility rates in both developed and developing countries. The ratio of children to people over 65 would be 1:3 in developing countries, and 1:8 in developed countries.

Every month, 1 million people in the world turn 60 years of age. The United Nations predicts that over the next 25 years, the percentage of the population over 65 will increase by 87 percent in Kuwait, 136 percent in Ghana, 121 percent in China, and 150 percent in Chile. This "age quake" illustrates the global trend toward aging populations that will continue to affect overall birth rates and contribute to depopulation.

It is important for demographers to consider how many working people a country has to support the youngest and oldest (non-working) members of society. To this end, demographers examine the **dependency load**, which is the proportion of people under 15 and over 65 relative to the working population between 15 and 65 (the population upon which the youngest and oldest individuals are dependent).

Effects of declining populations

- It is difficult for countries to maintain national pension plans when there are fewer people paying into them and more people withdrawing from them. There are three ways to improve the situation: *lower benefits; increased taxes; or restrictions on the number of people who qualify*. In China, it is estimated that one young person supports four elderly people. This situation will likely worsen as birth rates continue to fall and the population continues to age. Canadian corporations and governments also have concerns about the aging population and its effect on the workforce. A 2001 report by the Toronto-Dominion Bank suggests that Canada may have to consider raising the retirement age to 67, due to concern about a "drain" on

pension plans and a decline in the country's economic performance, as experienced workers retire. The Federal Human Resources Department estimates that by 2020, Canada will face a shortage of almost 1 million skilled workers.

- Many young people will migrate in search of job opportunities, as domestic and regional markets shrink, and this will threaten traditions of looking after the elderly in extended families. *Families may have to seek more private health-care and nursing-home facilities* to look after older members of the family, in societies where the intervention of "strangers" in the lives of family members is usually frowned upon.

- As the population ages, demographers and governments worry about *rising health-care costs*. Statistics Canada estimates that the country's dependency load will double from approximately 20 percent in 2001, to almost 40 percent by 2031. Greater economic and social support will then rest on proportionally fewer people.

FIGURE 2–15 What impact will an aging population have on younger generations? According to David Foot's book, *Boom, Bust and Echo*, published in 2000, Canada's aging population will increase spending from CDN$129 billion in 1996 to CDN$226 billion in 2016. However, the items they buy will change from school supplies and child care to golfing products, health and beauty aids, and recreational property.

FIGURE 2-16 Populations over 100 million, 2000–2050

Country	Population (millions) 2001	Population (millions) 2050
India	1 029	1 529
China	1 273	1 478
USA	278	349
Pakistan	144	346
Indonesia	228	312
Nigeria	126	244
Brazil	174	244
Bangladesh	131	213
Ethiopia	65	170
Democratic Republic of the Congo (DROC)	53	160

FIGURE 2-17 Declining populations: Highest rates, 2001

Rank	Country	Decline rate (% per year)
1	Bulgaria	1.14
2	Dominica	0.98
3	Latvia	0.81
4	Ukraine	0.78
5	Georgia	0.59
6	Estonia	0.55
7	Trinidad and Tobago	0.51
8	Russia	0.35
9	Hungary	0.32
10	Lithuania/Yugoslavia	0.27

18. Refer to the data in Figure 2–16, showing the ten most populated countries.
    a) What sort of regional pattern do you see?
    b) Calculate the anticipated percentage increase for these countries between 2000 and 2050. Which countries are expected to grow fastest?

19. Define the term "depopulation."

20. Refer to Figure 2–17. Which global region is experiencing the most depopulation? Why do you think this is so?

Reasons for differing population trends

Why do these diverse situations of overpopulation and depopulation occur? These changes in population are a product of two factors:

- natural increases or decreases: the birth rate and **death rate**, that is, the number of births and deaths for every 1000 people in a country
- migration factors: the number of people who move into the country and the number of people who leave

Will declining fertility rates halt the growth of the world's population? Refer to Figure 2–18, which shows both the expected population increase and the actual amount. Notice that, although the rates of growth are expected to decelerate, actual population numbers continue to grow. This is referred to as **population momentum** and occurs particularly in regions where there is a disproportionately high number of young women in the childbearing age range.

Demographers predict that even if, on average, couples begin having two children each — the **replacement fertility rate** — the world's population will continue to grow for some time before stabilizing. This population momentum adds to concerns about the sustainability of the earth's resources.

FIGURE 2-18 Population change and percentage growth rate

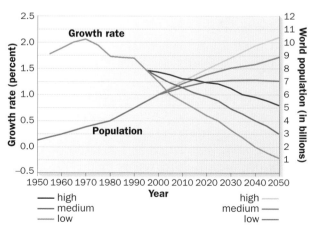

Issue briefing

Changing demographics

Japan

Some parts of Asia, once faced with spiralling population growth, now face the challenges of an aging population. Population control policies, longer life expectancies, economic development, and alterations to the social fabric have resulted in declining fertility rates. This situation is known as "demographic aging."

In Japan — a highly developed nation — an estimated 25 percent of the population is over 65, almost double the percentage of other Asian countries. The fertility rate has declined from 4.5 to 1.4, mostly due to women joining the workforce (now about 40 percent); many families delay having children, or opt to have fewer or no children. In addition, from 1970 to 2000, marriage rates for women aged 25 to 29 fell from 82 to 52 percent. The population is aging. Assisted by one of the longest lifespans in the world today, the median age of the population will rise from 41 to 49 by 2020. (The life expectancy for women is 84 — the highest in the world.)

Declining population has produced a scarce labour supply, which tends to push up wages, providing women with more incentive to join (or remain) in the workforce. The gross domestic product (GDP) has dropped because of higher labour costs. As an incentive to alleviate this situation, a leading toy company — the Bandai Corporation — has offered its workers US$10 000 with every baby they choose to have after their second child.

This demographic situation presents policymakers with unique economic and social challenges, as a significant portion of the population grows older.

Canada

Do fewer babies and people living longer sound familiar? Canada, like other countries, is also experiencing "depopulation." In 2001, Canada's total fertility rate was 1.6 percent. As the birth rate declines and the death rate increases, Canada's growth rate will approach zero by 2035! Why is this happening?

Major factors contributing to declining birth rates are: an increase of women in the workforce; widespread access to health care, contraception, and education; and the fact that women are delaying having children and are waiting longer intervals between having each child. Another important factor is rising death rates, as over one-third of Canada's population begins to age. This aging or "greying" population will more than double from 4 million today to 9 million by 2031. This cohort (group) is often referred to as the "baby boomers" (those born between 1947 and 1966, when post-World War II economic growth afforded larger families of four to six children per couple).

Why worry about this "greying" population? Some anxieties of governments and policymakers include: increasing costs to health care and public pensions; fewer people to assist the elderly; economic decline as a greater number of people retire; and proportionally fewer people to provide growing economic and social support. However,

FIGURE 2-19 How do baby boomers, like these birdwatchers, affect Canada's economic and social environments?

the aging population may also lead to an increase of jobs: in health care for the elderly; in manufacturing products such as health aids; and in services such as funeral homes. There may also be changes to health care and pension policies, and increased immigration.

Another important group to mention is you! Your age cohort — the "echo generation" (born between 1980 and 1995) — is the second-largest demographic group in Canada. You total over 4 million, which is why your group is targeted by retailers, advertisers, and the Internet.

21. Imagine that Country A, with a population of 27 000 000, has 524 000 births and 355 000 deaths within one year. Using the definitions in the "Frame of reference," calculate the crude birth and death rates for that year.

22. Find the absolute population change of Country A by calculating the difference between the number of deaths and the number of births, and adding this to the original population figure.

23. If there are 8 348 000 women between the ages of 15 and 44 in Country A, calculate the country's fertility rate.

24. Refer to the data in Figure 2–20. For Country B, calculate the number of births for each age category, using the age-specific fertility rate per 1000 women. For example, there are 175 982 women in the 35 to 39 age group. This group had 229.3 babies for every 1000 women. To calculate the number of babies, multiply 229.3 by 175.982, which gives us 40 352. Complete this calculation for each age group and add up the total number of babies.

25. Calculate Country B's crude birth rate.

FIGURE 2–20 Country B, total population: 6 998 225

Age range	Number of women	% of women	Age-specific fertility/1000
45–49	122 371	8.2	14.2
40–44	142 987	9.6	98.2
35–39	175 982	11.9	229.3
30–34	200 148	13.5	295.7
25–29	229 729	15.5	349.1
20–24	273 433	18.4	327.4
15–19	339 852	22.9	58.5
Totals	1 484 502	100.0	

26. Refer to the definition of total fertility rate in the "Frame of reference." Calculate the total

fertility rate for Country B: multiply the total number of births by 35 (the number of years between 15 and 49) and divide by the total number of women between 15 and 49. What does this total fertility rate mean, on average, for Country B?

27. In Country B, suppose there are 407 729 females in the 10 to 14 age category. How might this larger group of females affect the birth rate of the country in the years ahead?

28. How does this example show why the age structure of a population is so important in determining its future growth?

29. Giving specific evidence, state whether you believe Country B is a developed or developing country.

Demographic Transition

A country's birth rate does not change from a high to a low one overnight, and a country with high growth does not suddenly become one with a declining population. In-between these states, countries undergo what demographers call **demographic transition**. Demographers have developed a model showing the normal chain of events, as countries move from one stage of population growth to another. To understand why this model was created, you can examine two important variables — birth rates and relative wealth (measured in Figure 2–21 by gross domestic product per capita, or per person) — to see whether there is a relationship between them.

30. a) Set up the axes for a scattergraph similar to that in Figure 2–21. Use the same labels and time intervals.
    b) Using the information in Figure 2–22, plot each country according to both its birth rate and gross domestic product per capita.

31. Draw a continuous line that best divides the scattergraph into two equal portions (the "line of best fit"). On this graph, what relationship can you see between a country's wealth and its birth rate?

The demographic transition model (DTM)

As a country becomes wealthier over a period of time, its birth rate usually declines. When countries remain poor, their birth rate usually remains high. The scattergraph you created demonstrates that there is a positive relationship between high birth rate and low wealth, and between low birth rate and high wealth.

Demographers have used the demographic transition model (DTM) to illustrate how developed countries have completed the transition from high birth rates and death rates in pre-industrial times, to slower or negative growth in more recent decades. The demographic transition model sug-

gests that, as time progresses, more countries will attain the demographic characteristics of the later stages of the cycle. Figure 2–23 shows what happens at each of these stages of development. Demographers do not agree on the exact birth and death rates that make up each stage.

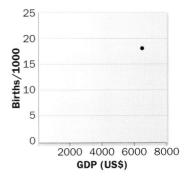

FIGURE 2–21 The information for Brazil has been plotted on this scattergraph, showing a birth rate of 18 per 1000, and a gross domestic product per capita of US$6500.

FIGURE 2–22 Birth rates and gross domestic product per capita

Country	GDP per capita (US$)	Births per 1000
Angola	1 000	47
Belarus	7 500	10
Brazil	6 500	18
Canada	24 800	11
Chad	1 000	48
Chile	10 100	17
Denmark	25 500	12
Djibouti	1 300	41
Egypt	3 600	25
Ethiopia	600	45
France	24 400	12
Germany	23 400	9
Haiti	1 800	32
Iraq	2 500	35
Japan	24 900	10
Kenya	1 500	29
Mexico	9 100	23
Pakistan	2 000	31
Sierra Leone	510	45
Singapore	26 500	13
Switzerland	28 600	10
United States	36 200	14

FIGURE 2-23 Phases of the demographic transition model

	Phase 1: High fluctuating stage	Phase 2: Expanding stage	Phase 3: Late expanding stage	Phase 4: Low growth stage	Phase 5: Declining stage
	• The birth rate is high and stable, while the death rate fluctuates due to incidences of war, famine, and disease. • The population growth is very slow. • The fertility and infant mortality rates are high, but life expectancy is low. • This stage characterizes pre-industrial societies, with most of the population in rural areas.	• The birth rate remains high, but the death rate begins to decline rapidly. • The large natural increase results in a population explosion. • Fertility rates have not adjusted to changes in social norms, such as later marriages and the increase in the number of women in the workforce. • The infant mortality rate begins to decline and life expectancy increases, due to health improvements in areas such as nutrition, clean water, and access to medical treatment. • This stage characterizes developing nations such as Nigeria.	• The birth rate is rapidly declining and the death rate remains low, as life expectancy increases. • The natural increase is declining, but the population still remains high. • The fertility rate begins to decline, due to changes in social norms and/or implementation of population policies. • This stage characterizes developing nations such as China.	• Birth and death rates are low and stable, but the birth rate remains slightly ahead of the death rate. • The population growth is slow and stable. • The fertility rate is low and life expectancy continues to improve. • Economic and social changes occur. Many women enter the workforce or pursue careers, and couples postpone having families while educational goals are sought. • Society is viewed as an "aging" or "greying" society. • This stage characterizes developed nations such as Canada.	• This stage extends the demographic transition model, as low birth rates lead to population declines more frequently in European countries. There is a slowly rising death rate and a stable or slightly declining birth rate. There are also negative natural increase results, meaning that the death rate exceeds the birth rate. • The population is declining. • This stage characterizes countries with present and predicted negative population growth rates such as Russia.

Birth and death rates per 1000 (y-axis: 0, 10, 20, 30, 40, 50)

Birth rate ——
Death rate - - -

Time →

For each phase, name two countries that fit the description. Be prepared to justify your choice.

---

32. Using the birth and death rate data in the World Fact File database, find the stage of development for each country listed on the site. Use the categories shown in Figure 2–24.

33. Using a choropleth technique, create a map that shows the distribution of the demographic stages of development.

34. What conclusions can you draw about the stages of demographic transition that you can see on your completed map?

FIGURE 2-24 Categories for demographic stages of development

Stage	Birth rate	Death rate
1. High fluctuating stage	Over 35	Over 35
2. Expanding stage	Over 35	25–35
3. Late expanding stage	15–35	15–25
4. Low growth stage	10–15	5–15
5. Declining stage	5–10	5–15

Reasons for demographic changes

Why do countries pass through stages of demographic development? This movement is linked to two factors — changes in fertility rates and mortality rates, which are usually both falling.

Reasons for falling fertility rates

- *Legislation* helps determine the number of children within a family.
- *Smaller families are increasingly seen as advantageous* because they are more mobile in a global economy.
- Economic conditions change, creating the *need for two spousal incomes*; women enter the workforce and postpone having families. Also, the perceived value of having an education changes, so many women choose to study further.
- *People have fewer children* because they are more confident that their children will survive beyond the age of 5.
- Improved and affordable *contraceptives* are available.

Reasons for falling mortality rates

- *Lower infant mortality rates* result from improved postnatal care.
- Better health results from *improved sanitation* and *safe water*.
- Improved economies result in *better diets*, which improve health.
- *Improved medicine* prolongs infants' lives (for example, vaccinations against smallpox, cholera, and malaria).

Fertility lag

A pattern that emerges regarding fertility and mortality rates is that, for most countries, the death rate has fallen before the birth rate has begun to fall. On the whole, this has resulted in far more births than deaths and a large, increasing population. However, families eventually do become smaller as lower birth rates decline to the levels of the lower death rates. Why do birth rates take longer to decline than death rates?

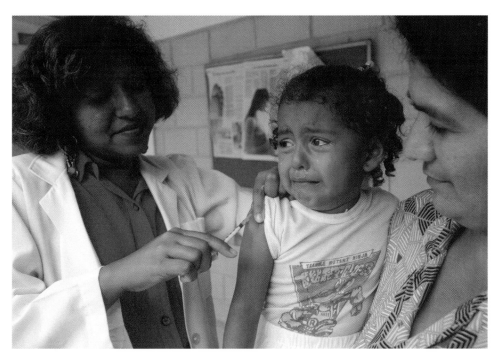

FIGURE 2–25

How does improved health care, such as vaccinations against diseases, lead to falling mortality rates?

Cultural attitudes play a major role in a family's size. In many societies, a great deal of value is placed on having children, as they represent increased levels of help and income in **subsistence economies** (families work the land to feed themselves). Children also represent security because, when parents retire, they expect their children to care for them. In countries that are **patrilineal** (dominated by male influence), families desire a son to look after the family's interests. In areas with high **infant mortality** (children do not survive beyond the first year of life), there is a strong inclination to have many children, so that at least a few of them can be expected to survive.

In some areas, when medical advances and improved living environments produced a decline in death rates in some areas, there was no immediate corresponding fall in birth rates. This is a **fertility lag**. Evidently, attitudes toward things such as family size take time to change.

Population Pyramids

An interesting way to see the pattern of change in a country's population is to use a **population pyramid**. These graphs compare the percentage of males and females in a given population by their age cohorts. Population pyramids allow us to analyse:

- the population percentages and life expectancies of males and females
- the percentage of the population under the age of 15 and over the age of 65, known as the **dependency load potential population**
- the impact of factors that affect the fertility rate, such as population policies
- the number of childbearing women in a population

FIGURE 2–26 Demographic transition model and population pyramids

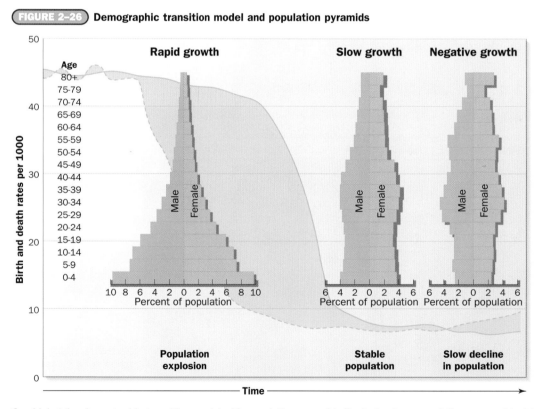

Combining the demographic transition model with population pyramids illustrates how populations are subject to change. An analysis of the combination can guide government policy regarding population control, immigration, and economic development.

Population report

As a demographer, prepare a report examining population composition and trends for Canada and Bangladesh. The 2000 and 2025 population data have been provided for you in Figures 2–27 and 2–28. Include the following in your report:

- population pyramids for 2000, for each country
- the 2025 data added to each of the above pyramids (Instead of drawing a second set of pyramids for 2025, plot the 2025 data on the 2000 pyramids, but do not shade in these new pyramids. This enables you to see the difference between the two years.)

- a description, for each country, of the shapes, types of pyramids, and differences between the 2000 and 2025 pyramids
- a comparison between the demographic changes in Canada and Bangladesh between 2000 and 2025

a) Refer to Figure 2–23. Which stage of the demographic transition model (DTM) do you think each country "matches" in the year 2000? Explain your reasons.

b) Describe how an aging population positively and/or negatively impacts a country.

FIGURE 2–27 Canada, midyear population by age and sex: 2000 and 2025

Age	2000		2025	
	Male	**Female**	**Male**	**Female**
Total	15 477	15 803	18 764	19 400
0–4	946	901	1 003	955
5–9	1 070	1 016	1 036	987
10–14	1 062	1 013	1 050	999
15–19	1 066	1 020	1 057	1 007
20–24	1 052	1 009	1 088	1 044
25–29	1 088	1 059	1 170	1 131
30–34	1 188	1 171	1 311	1 270
35–39	1 397	1 369	1 306	1 275
40–44	1 332	1 319	1 290	1 266
45–49	1 161	1 169	1 235	1 214
50–54	1 034	1 035	1 205	1 204
55–59	782	796	1 220	1 249
60–64	615	645	1 322	1 378
65–69	548	599	1 164	1 269
70–74	459	553	906	1 062
75–79	340	482	674	853
80+	337	647	727	1 237

FIGURE 2–28 Bangladesh, midyear population by age and sex: 2000 and 2025

Age	2000		2025	
	Male	**Female**	**Male**	**Female**
Total	66 322	62 873	90 499	86 997
0–4	7 552	7 116	7 212	6 806
5–9	7 013	6 719	7 482	7 063
10–14	9 490	9 084	7 643	7 239
15–19	8 775	8 263	7 605	7 240
20–24	6 229	6 057	7 346	7 034
25–29	5 460	5 362	6 847	6 580
30–34	4 381	4 335	6 477	6 348
35–39	3 746	3 727	8 897	8 616
40–44	3 305	3 208	8 199	7 750
45–49	2 787	2 528	5 736	5 563
50–54	2 207	1 901	4 884	4 769
55–59	1 731	1 471	3 720	3 673
60–64	1 303	1 141	2 928	2 951
65–69	933	811	2 275	2 296
70–74	652	554	1 586	1 530
75–79	396	314	940	877
80+	362	282	722	662

Case in point — China and the Czech Republic

China and the Czech Republic offer a comparison in terms of demographic trends. Whereas China's large population has been growing rapidly, the population of the Czech Republic has been in decline since the early 1990s. In each case, the probable effects of these trends were viewed as being serious enough for the government to take action.

China

China currently has a population of 1.27 billion, which is approximately 20 percent of the world's population. What happens to the size of China's population over the next 20 years or so will have an impact on the country's political, environmental, social, and economic development.

When the People's Republic of China was formed in 1949, having a large population of workers was regarded as a strength for the infant communist state; families were paid for having a child. By 1953, however, China had a staggering population of 583 million. Still, Chairman Mao regarded more people as more power. The period between 1958 and 1961, known as the Great Leap Forward, emphasized economic success. The communist government worried that factory production could not increase without enough labour, so they continued to encourage population expansion.

By 1964, the population had grown to 695 million, and official policy still encouraged growth. However, farms had begun to be neglected; not enough food was produced, resulting in huge famines. As a result, an estimated 20 million people died. By the 1960s, the birth rate was 42 per 1000 people (compared with Canada's 26.8/1000 in 1960 during the postwar baby boom). A policy of "later, sparser, fewer" was adopted: people were encouraged to marry later, have fewer children, and to space out the years between births. Unfortunately, this policy did little to slow down the population growth. By not paying enough attention to the number of women approaching the fertility age range, Chinese demographers underestimated the impact of the population momentum. In 1979, the world saw China adopt the strongest population control policy ever seen — the "one-child policy." This policy is still in effect today.

The one-child policy

- Any pregnant unmarried women shall be forced to have an abortion. In some provinces, women with one child are to be sterilized.
- After giving birth, a woman who does not practise birth control shall be fined 20 yuan each month.
- Families who obey the policy will receive priority on housing loans, educational opportunities, job promotions, and wage increases.
- Families who disobey the policy will lose housing priority, promotional opportunities, or may get a wage rollback.

FIGURE 2–29 Do you think it is a government's responsibility to regulate family size?

In urban areas, the birth rate has plummeted, but in rural areas (China has a 70 percent rural population), the policy has been less successful. The cultural traditions of having a male heir, and sons to work the farm, remain strong. Families of two or more children are still the norm. The increase in the rural population birth rate still threatens the success of China's population policy.

Some demographers believe that this policy has been a success, and that it has resulted in China having 200 million fewer people today than if the policy had not been in place.

China's population continues to grow, but the rapid aging of the population in urban areas has the government concerned. There are currently nine working people available to support one retired person. In the year 2025, the ratio will be 4:1 and by 2050, it will be only 3:1. In urban areas, 70 percent of families have only one child, compared to 10 percent in rural areas. To counter this trend, Chinese policymakers have said that when two registered (that is, no siblings) singles marry, they may have two children. This is expected to boost the cities' population numbers by an extra 20 to 30 million.

If China maintains this level of population growth, the population will reach 1.4 billion by 2010, and peak at 1.6 billion in 2050. From then on, the population size will do what many neo-Malthusians believed to be impossible — it will start to shrink.

The Czech Republic

After the Second World War, the former country of Czechoslovakia was a communist state under the control of the former Soviet Union. Like most other European countries, at the end of the war Czechoslovakia had a baby boom: the birth rate was in excess of 20 per 1000. However, this lasted only a short time. From 1947 on, fertility rates began to fall slowly, until the late 1960s.

Under communism, many Czechoslovakian families felt uncertain about their future but, during the 1960s, gradual optimism about the possibility of democracy and freedom from the Soviet Union led to slightly increased birth rates. This dream of freedom collapsed in 1968, when the Soviet Union invaded Czechoslovakia and imposed further political and economic controls.

At a glance — China and the Czech Republic

Year: 2000	China	Czech Republic
Population	1 273 111 290	10 264 212
Population growth rate	0.88%	−0.07%
Birth rate/1000	15.95	9.11
Death rate/1000	6.74	10.81
Life expectancy (total)	71.62	74.73
Life expectancy (women)	73.59	78.43
Life expectancy (men)	69.81	71.23
Sex ratio (male:female)	1.06:1	0.95:1
% of population aged 0–14	25.01%	16.09%
% of population aged over 65	7.11%	13.92%

Fertility rates rose slightly, but then levelled off in the 1980s as birth rates and death rates stabilized, resulting in zero population growth. After the democratic revolution and the break from the Soviet Union in 1989, significant economic and social changes took place. For example, young people began to marry later: they chose education and careers ahead of starting families.

On January 1, 1993, the country divided when its two national groups separated and formed two countries — the Czech Republic and Slovakia. By the 1990s, birth rates were falling significantly, because of fewer marriages and higher divorce rates. In 2000, the fertility rate of

FIGURE 2–30 Locals and tourists wander around Prague, Czech Republic. What effects have government policy changes had on the Czech Republic's population growth?

FIGURE 2–31 Population — China and the Czech Republic

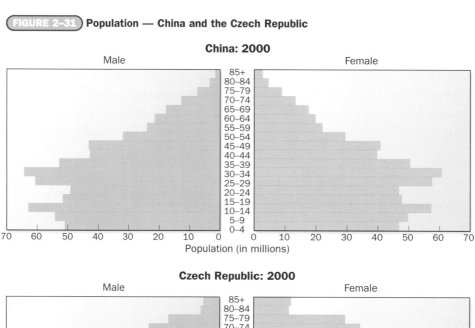

China: 2000

Male / Female

Population (in millions)

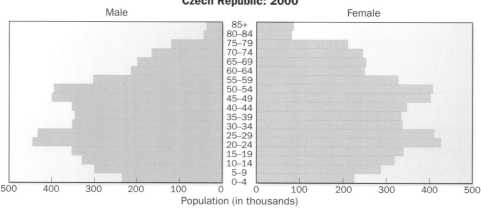

Czech Republic: 2000

Male / Female

Population (in thousands)

1.21 children was among the lowest in the world. The Czech Republic began to experience low fertility levels, a declining total population, a rapidly aging population, and an uneven age structure.

In 1999, these concerns led the Czech government to turn its attention to a policy of social change, which included investigating ways to increase the birth rate and address issues such as high rates of divorce and abortion.

The Czech population and social policy

- A policy of **pronatalism** (a positive attitude toward having larger families) should continue to be encouraged.

- Family allowances will be paid, and will increase with each child, up to the third child.

- Parents should be free to make decisions about how many children they want.

- Parents should not have more children than they can afford, so that they can maintain an adequate standard of living.

- There will be improvements in social conditions (for example, housing, child care) for young couples.

It is estimated that the total fertility rate in the Czech Republic will rise from its current level at around 1.3, to 1.47 by 2010, and that the life expectancy will rise from age 71 to 78.

35. Create a timeline from 1945 until the present. Place notes on the timeline, highlighting significant events that impacted the size of China's and the Czech Republic's populations during this period.

36. a) Refer to the "Case in point" information. Create an organizer in which you compare the population trends for China and the Czech Republic.
    b) Explain how the population trends led to each country's population policy.

37. Write a summary about your predictions for future population growth in each of these two countries.

FIGURE 2–32 China — Predicted population (in thousands), 2025

Age	Total	Male	Female
Total	1 464 027	741 372	722 655
0–4	87 729	45 083	42 646
5–9	90 094	46 388	43 706
10–14	87 734	45 372	42 362
15–19	89 469	46 446	43 023
20–24	95 545	49 743	45 802
25–29	95 149	49 605	45 544
30–34	100 579	52 376	48 203
35–39	116 018	60 362	55 656
40–44	94 851	48 774	46 077
45–49	91 165	46 440	44 725
50–54	111 959	56 866	55 093
55–59	115 417	58 303	57 114
60–64	91 211	45 299	45 912
65–69	67 242	33 027	34 215
70–74	60 781	28 490	32 291
75–79	35 494	15 963	19 531
80–84	18 809	7 828	10 981
85+	14 781	5 007	9 774

FIGURE 2–33 Czech Republic — Predicted population (in thousands), 2025

Age	Total	Male	Female
Total	9 678	4 685	4 993
0–4	354	182	172
5–9	386	198	188
10–14	417	214	203
15–19	440	226	214
20–24	463	237	226
25–29	464	237	227
30–34	592	302	290
35–39	652	331	321
40–44	695	352	343
45–49	865	436	429
50–54	826	414	412
55–59	655	325	330
60–64	620	300	320
65–69	591	275	316
70–74	604	266	338
75–79	507	207	300
80–84	304	112	192
85+	243	71	172

FIGURE 2–34 China — Midyear population estimates and average growth rates: 1950–2050 (population in thousands, rate in percent)

Year	Population	Year	Population	Period	Growth rate
1950	562 580	1996	1 216 388	1950–1960	1.5
1960	650 661	1997	1 227 714	1960–1970	2.3
1970	820 403	1998	1 239 086	1970–1980	1.8
1980	984 736	1999	1 250 464	1980–1990	1.5
1990	1 138 895	2000	1 261 832	1990–2000	1.0
1991	1 153 725	2010	1 359 141	2000–2010	0.7
1992	1 167 160	2020	1 434 458	2010–2020	0.5
1993	1 179 918	2030	1 483 121	2020–2030	0.3
1994	1 192 572	2040	1 491 737	2030–2040	0.1
1995	1 204 791	2050	1 470 469	2040–2050	–0.1

FIGURE 2–35 Czech Republic — Midyear population estimates and average growth rates: 1950–2050 (population in thousands, rate in percent)

Year	Population	Year	Population	Period	Growth rate
1950	8 925	1996	10 313	1950–1960	0.8
1960	9 660	1997	10 301	1960–1970	0.1
1970	9 795	1998	10 291	1970–1980	0.5
1980	10 289	1999	10 281	1980–1990	0.0
1990	10 310	2000	10 272	1990–2000	0.0
1991	10 305	2010	10 157	2000–2010	–0.1
1992	10 316	2020	9 891	2010–2020	–0.3
1993	10 327	2030	9 409	2020–2030	–0.5
1994	10 331	2040	8 745	2030–2040	–0.7
1995	10 325	2050	8 015	2040–2050	–0.9

38. Refer to the population pyramids for China and the Czech Republic, Figure 2–31 on page 50.
   a) Write a summary of these population pyramids, in terms of their overall shape, symmetry, and any anomalies that exist.
   b) How can you tell from each pyramid when changes in population trends (for example, the "one-child policy" in China, or feelings of upcoming freedom in Czechoslovakia during the 1960s) occurred?
   c) Each pyramid has a narrow base. What does this mean for the future growth of the population in these two countries?

39. a) Using the age group prediction for 2025, draw two pyramids similar to those in Figure 2–31 for China and the Czech Republic.

   b) What changes will occur in the pyramid shapes between the years 2000 and 2025? Explain why these changes will take place.

40. Compare the population features in "At a glance" on page 49, and in Figures 2–32 and 2–33. What are the main changes that will occur between the years 2000 and 2025 in China and the Czech Republic?

41. Refer to Figures 2–34 and 2–35, showing midyear population totals for China and the Czech Republic between 1950 and 2050. Draw a line graph for each set of totals. Write a summary about the pattern that emerges.

42. Write a newspaper editorial for a Canadian newspaper, in which you express your opinion about population policies of China and the Czech Republic, and about their future population numbers.

Global population infomercial

The United Nations Population Fund has recently hired you and three other members of an advertising agency. The mandate of the United Nations Population Fund is to help developing countries find ways to help control their population growth. As well as the issue of overpopulation, there are concerns about declining populations.

It is your advertising team's job to create and present a ten-minute infomercial to heighten global awareness of — and suggest possible solutions to — the problems (of a selected country) facing rapid population growth, or significant population decline. It is obviously important that your infomercial be thoroughly researched, carefully planned, and professionally conveyed, so that your audience is engaged and accurately informed.

Your infomercial will need to:

- describe the demographic and economic situation of the country
- explain which stage of the demographic transition model the country is in
- outline the key elements of the selected country's population policy
- evaluate the positive, negative, and interesting aspects of the selected country's population policy
- include relevant visuals (for example, charts, graphs, images) and/or other presentational material
- be presented creatively, either in a "live," video, audio, or digital format

Once your infomercial is complete, the advertising team will need to discuss how an international viewing audience will react to your evaluation of the population policy. In order to prepare, each member of the advertising team should to write a one-page reflection on:

- why they think people may agree or disagree with this population policy
- what they think about the effectiveness/appropriateness of this policy

Share your reflection with fellow team members. Expand this discussion to include the ideas of other advertising teams, once all the infomercials have been presented.

FIGURE 2–36 A crowded street in New Delhi, India in March, 2001. At that time, the country's population passed the 1 billion mark.

A World of Disparity

Migration: My experience

In 1993, many Moldovian families immigrated to Canada in search of a better life. After the communist rule collapsed, the citizens from many of the countries of the former Soviet Union now had the ability to leave the country permanently, as long as they met the necessary requirements. My father was among the group of anxious people boarding the plane to Canada.

He arrived in Newfoundland as a refugee, with a couple of friends. The three of them started with nothing: no money, no food, no shelter, but lots of hope. My father, who was a computer engineer, along with his two friends, a surgeon and a dentist, made their living delivering pizzas for a few months. A year later, my father began working for a small computer firm as a computer programmer. He kept moving up in his field, and by the time the rest of my family moved to Canada, he worked in Ottawa as a software architect.

FIGURE 3–1 Lida Mankovski, 17 years old, a student at Middlefield Collegiate Institute, Markham, Ontario

I came to Canada in grade 7, at 12 years of age, knowing no English. I was in complete culture shock. The Moldovian perception of Canada and the United States is that they are perfect; at least we children got that impression. To live in Canada meant living a completely different lifestyle: Coca-Cola, brightly coloured packages, clean streets, happy people waving and saying hello.

In Moldova, I would never see people of different races as we do in Canada. After I came to Canada and saw how multicultural it truly was, I was in awe. Another big cultural shock was that people changed their clothes every day! At school in Moldova, I remembered people by what they wore, and not their faces, because it would be the same thing over and over, every day.

To immigrate to Canada meant leaving everything behind, including friends and family. However, I can confidently say that despite longing to see their faces again, the move was definitely worth it.

a) Does any aspect of Lida's experience surprise you?

b) Compare Lida's experience with your own, or that of someone you know. What are the similarities and differences?

Expectations

- Analyse the causes and effects of economic disparities around the world.
- Analyse the causes of selected examples of economic disparity in the local or regional community.
- Select and compare statistical indicators of quality of life for a variety of developed and developing countries.
- Identify different methods of grouping countries by level of economic and social development, and evaluate the implications of these categorizations.

- Evaluate factors that may compound problems of hunger and poverty in a selected country.
- Analyse the causes and consequences of recent events involving refugees in Canada (or in another part of the world) and evaluate the effectiveness of the relevant policies for dealing with refugees.

As Canadians, we generally live in a world of relative prosperity and affluence. The United Nations (UN) regularly votes Canada as one of the most livable countries on earth. Many of us take a comfortable lifestyle, good health, an income, and an education for granted. We accept political freedom and involvement, and the power to change our governments, as rights of citizenship. Because we cherish human rights, it is difficult for many of us to appreciate the conditions described in this chapter.

Much of the world is impoverished, deeply in debt, and offers inhabitants few opportunities to improve their situation. Regions and individuals are trapped in circumstances of poor health, little income, deep debt, environmental danger, and dependency on others to survive. To escape such conditions, millions of people move to other parts of the world in search of a better life.

Sometimes we need not look far to see people in trouble. All the so-called "rich" countries of the world have large numbers of people living below what is described as the **poverty line** (the line dividing those able to afford life's basic necessities from those unable to do so). In this chapter, we will examine the **disparity** (differences and inequalities) between the world's richer inhabitants (the "haves") and the poorer countries and their inhabitants (the "have-nots"). The ways in which poverty is being addressed is a significant world issue.

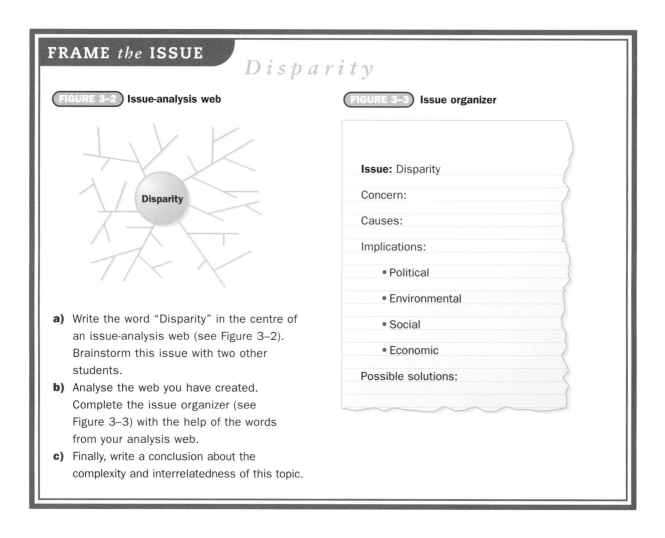
Economic and Social Development

In addition to the demographic stages of transition discussed in Chapter 2, countries usually pass through economic and social stages of development as well. For example, their economies advance, their quality of life is enhanced, and significant improvements occur within the population in areas such as longevity, standards of education, and income levels.

Since the Industrial Revolution, the world has seen a significant transformation, as Europe and the Americas rapidly moved toward economies of industrialized production. These economies brought important social and economic changes to these regions and also other world regions, as vast amounts of resource exploitation and development were needed to fuel them. As the world altered, richer and poorer countries emerged.

Richer countries are often described as "industrialized" or "developed," but what is a developed country, and how do we measure a country's level of development? What aspects are taken into account? Refer to Figure 3–4, which highlights the major dimensions taken into account when assessing levels of development. See how many of them you touched on when you "framed the issue" of disparity.

When we visualize the "developed" parts of the world, we think of things such as:

- industrialization and the manufacturing of products
- high levels of consumerism (patterns of purchasing goods and services)
- advanced networks of **infrastructure** (air, rail, road)
- high participation rates in university and college education
- ownership and control of large amounts of **capital** (money)
- the formation and hosting of **multinational corporations** (corporations or companies based in more than one country)
- centres of global communication
- centres of political power and influence

Countries in economically poorer parts of the world are called "less developed" or "developing."

Both of these terms, especially the latter, imply that such countries are moving toward higher levels of modern production and consumerism, to become more like the developed countries of Europe and North America. These terms also suggest that there are distinct stages through which countries pass as these economic transitions take place.

A number of theories have been proposed as to how and when countries attain higher levels of development. Here are two of these theories, applied to today's disparate world.

Modernization theory

The Stages of Economic Growth: A Non-Communist Manifesto, by W. W. Rostow, describes five stages of economic growth:

Stage 1, the traditional society: This stage is characterized by rural and agricultural economies. During this phase, little change and only low levels of technology are evident.

FIGURE 3–4 The major dimensions of development

Cultural dimensions:
local histories and cultures

Human dimensions:
health (life expectancy, mortality)
education
basic needs
capabilities
freedom
choices

Political dimensions:
democracy
ideology
freedom
institutions (such as property rights)

Development

Economic dimensions:
size of the economy
incomes
purchasing power
job availability
efficiency

Environmental dimensions:
sustainable development
environmental balance
ecological sensitivity

Social dimensions:
inequality
poverty
intergenerational inequity

Gender dimensions:
gender inequalities
– income
– participation (in government, leadership, business, etc.)
– education
– life expectancy

Stage 2, preconditions for takeoff: This stage is apparent when a strong central government encourages **entrepreneurs** (people who start their own businesses) to develop businesses. In this stage, natural resources begin to be exploited.

Stage 3, the takeoff: This stage is characterized by higher rates of capital investment and a proliferation of entrepreneurs, leading to the development of a manufacturing industry. A level is reached where business sustains economic growth at a level of over 10 percent of the national income. This can be achieved through **foreign aid** (money given to a country to help it develop). During "takeoff," people start to save money, thereby creating a class of future spenders.

Stage 4, the drive to maturity: This stage is guided by a strong manufacturing sector. During this phase, there are widespread applications of modern innovation and technology. Urbanization concentrates the workforce in cities, so rural areas decline. Continued high levels of savings create wealth.

FIGURE 3–5 Rostow's theory

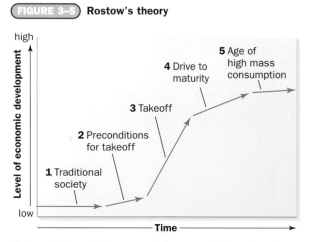

Rostow believed that, as countries passed through each stage of the model, they would draw on the experiences of other countries that developed before them, accelerating the time necessary to move from one stage to another. Do you think it is likely that modern scientific, engineering, and telecommunication innovations will help countries to pass through stages of development faster than they did before, or even leapfrog some of the stages? Why or why not?

Stage 5, the age of high mass consumption: This stage implies a predominantly urban society, and the widespread use of (and interest in) modern technology. There are rapid technological innovations, high levels of productivity, and a high per capita income.

The developing world initially found it difficult to reach Rostow's latter stages. Some countries, such as Brazil and Mexico, borrowed heavily to create the capital necessary to do so, but fell deeply into debt. Their debt repayments caused them economic hardship. They became rich in human resources and ability, but the gradual creation of business wealth did not follow.

Often, the capital for the developing world's business remains in those developed countries that invest in multinational corporations. These multinational businesses are mostly based in the developing world. Any profits they make are returned to the developed countries.

1. In your own words, describe the five stages of Rostow's modernization theory.

2. Why did Brazil and Mexico find it difficult to achieve the higher stages of development?

3. Make a copy of the the chart in Figure 3–6. Using a database such as the online Central Intelligence Agency (CIA) World Factbook, research two more examples for each stage of development. Select countries with the following per capita income (US$):
   Stage 1: less than $1000
   Stage 2: $1000–$2999
   Stage 3: $3000–$5999
   Stage 4: $6000–$12 000
   Stage 5: more than $12 000
   Discuss and decide (with a group, or with the class) the appropriate figures for infant mortality, urban population percentage, and employment in industry. One example of each stage has been provided for you in Figure 3–6; use these examples as a guide to help you select the other two countries.

FIGURE 3-6 Examples for Rostow's modernization theory

	Income per capita (US$)	Infant mortality per 1000 live births	Urban population (percent)	Industry employment (percent)
Stage 1				
Mali	$600	121.44	26	2
Stage 2				
India	$1 600	63.19	28	10.8
Stage 3				
Kazakhstan	$3 200	59.17	56	15.8
Stage 4				
Turkey	$6 200	47.34	66	15
Stage 5				
Germany	$22 700	4.71	86	33.7

Core and periphery theory — Immanuel Wallerstein

Immanuel Wallerstein, an expert on world economy, believes that the system of economic development based on capital has existed since the time period 1450 to 1670. He maintains that, during that period, countries centred in Western Europe formed an economic "core" around which development in the rest of the world — the "periphery" — took place. These Western European countries had strong central governments and bureaucracies, as well as armies to support later economic expansion. Trading developed around the urban areas of London, Paris, and Madrid. Capital was concentrated in very large amounts and would later finance the development of empires.

Wallerstein's "periphery" included Asia, Africa, Eastern Europe, and Latin America. These countries were essentially controlled by other countries. They developed economies to feed materials back to the core. Much of the labour provided by the periphery was forced labour, controlled by representatives of the core countries.

Wallerstein suggests that there were (and still are) four categories into which each region of the world may be placed: *core, semi-periphery, periphery,* and *external.*

Wallerstein currently sees a dynamic change taking place in countries that are rapidly developing and industrializing, in that these countries

FIGURE 3-7 Wallerstein's model

Core
- core countries initially developed in Europe
- strong central governments with military support
- surplus money from periphery returns to the core
- agricultural labourers move to growing cities to work in industry
- international trade works in core's favour

Semi-periphery
- cores are in decline or peripheries grow stronger
- access to international banking is declining
- manufactures goods (electrical or computer hardware/software) that have high value
- exploits the periphery countries

Periphery
- most ownership of industrial output in the hands of core investment
- no central, strong government
- surplus profits return to the core
- raw materials sent back to the core for consumer markets
- inexpensive labour for extracting resources and for agriculture

External
- countries remain outside the world economy
- not controlled by other economic or political powers
- isolated contact with trading countries

often form their own core. A good example of an emerging core is the East Asian market. Here, the growing industrial economies of South Korea, Singapore, Taiwan, and China (especially Hong Kong) have joined Japan to form a core of trade and a centre of banking and investment. To some extent, emerging cores sometimes challenge the status of the traditional European and North American cores. However, they usually remain regional cores.

Generally, Wallerstein's theory supports the notion that the traditional cores will continue to dominate the "periphery" regions of the world — the economies of Latin America being dominated by North America, or African economies being dominated by Europe. Cores may shift in size or even multiply, but their function remains the same.

Wallerstein also sees the development of the present capitalist world economy as detrimental to a large proportion of the world's population.

FIGURE 3-8 Cuba is an example of an external country. Do you think this will change in the near future? Why or why not?

In addition to believing that the world's cores will continue to dominate, he thinks the economic and social disparities between sections of the world economy will increase, rather than provide prosperity for all. This theory suggests that the gap between rich and poor serves the economic needs of the richer countries: rich companies will be able to exploit labour markets where people will work for very low wages. This will sustain the profits of multinational corporations and the wealthier countries in which they are based (the cores). Wallerstein may be correct that the disparities between richer and poorer countries will continue to grow. The Human Development Report, an annual report commissioned by the United Nations Development Programme (UNDP), found that the ratio between the wealth of the top and bottom 20 percent of the world's nations has steadily widened from 30:1 in 1960, to 60:1 in the 1990s.

4. Summarize the main characteristics of Wallerstein's core, semi-periphery, periphery, and external regions.

5. Where was the original core area of development? Why did it occur?

6. According to Wallerstein, what needs of wealthy countries are being served by the underdeveloped countries?

7. The People's Republic of China remained somewhat isolated from the rest of the world throughout the last decade, in terms of trade markets and agreements. In what ways is China trying to re-establish a connection with the important core regions of the world? To answer, research China's relationship with the World Trade Organization (WTO), an international organization which seeks to improve trade by ensuring fair trade competition between countries.

8. Consider both Rostow's and Wallerstein's models of development and describe what you think is each one's strength and weakness.

9. Which model of development is more appropriate for describing today's world? Justify your choice.

A World of Disparity **61**

Case in point — Brazil

The following is an excerpt from a newspaper article, by Robert J. Samuelson, published in May 2001.

Brazil wends its way to the First World

Over the years, we have applied various labels to countries like Brazil: "Third World," "developing," "emerging," and "newly industrialized," to name a few. But even a brief visit here (my first) shows how our vocabulary has been overtaken. What you find is some First World, some Third World and much in between. The economic transformation of the world's poor regions — now dubbed "globalization" — is one of the great stories of our time. But its very messiness defeats easy stereotypes.

The São Paulo metropolis is Brazil's commercial, industrial, and financial centre. It's certainly

FIGURE 3–9 South America

smaller than greater Tokyo (33 million) and New York (20 million), and at almost 18 million [has about the same population as] Bombay.

Though not handsome, the city isn't squalid, and outwardly, much of the population is bustling toward middle-class consumerism. Downtown has the usual office and apartment towers, luxury stores, and restaurants. Cellphones are widespread. At rush hours, there are the familiar traffic jams. Middle-class Brazilians confess (or brag) that they're compulsively borrowing on their credit cards at an astonishing interest rate of 8.5 percent a month. Outside the city centre, some working-class neighbourhoods look like the Bronx: clusters of small homes and apartments mixed with stores, repair shops, and warehouses.

In 2000, Brazil's economy expanded 4.2 percent, feeding optimism that strong growth can continue. I talked with several editors of *Exame*, the country's major business magazine, who cited several reasons for confidence.

The most important is the conquest of **hyperinflation** [the value of money falls at a very fast rate, making costs rise quickly], which, until the mid-1990s, seemed invincible. In 1994, [the

At a glance — Brazil

- Population: 174 468 575
- Birth rate: 18.45 births/1000 population
- Death rate: 9.34 deaths/1000 population
- GDP per capita: purchasing power parity — US$6500
- Labour force: services — 53.2%; industry — 23.7%; agriculture — 23.1%
- Population below poverty line: 17.4%
- Industries: textiles, shoes, chemicals, cement, lumber, iron ore, tin, steel, aircraft, motor vehicles and parts, other machinery and equipment
- Exports: US$55.1 billion — iron ore, soybeans, footwear, coffee
- Imports: US$55.8 billion — machinery and equipment, chemical products, oil, electricity
- Debt — external: US$232 billion

inflation rate] was 2076 percent. Hyperinflation exhausted Brazil's morale and energy. People shopped daily, before prices rose. They moved their earnings instantly into accounts indexed for inflation. The introduction of a new currency (the *real*) in mid-1994 gradually tamed the monster. Last year, inflation was 7 percent.

[Another] reason is Brazil's sheer potential. With about 170 million people, it is the world's fifth-most-populous nation (after China, India, the United States, and Indonesia). As recently as 1985, Brazil's per capita income of US$5500 was almost equal to South Korea's. By 1998, it was half of South Korea's US$13 300. The Latin debt crisis of the 1980s and hyperinflation caused a "lost decade." On paper, there's vast untapped demand for housing, cars, appliances, roads, or almost anything.

Brazil's longstanding ambition is to achieve First World status, writes Lincoln Gordon in his book *Brazil's Second Chance*. Based on São Paulo's prosperity, the dream seems plausible, but as Gordon points out, it's hardly inevitable. Rural poverty is crushing, and cities [have pockets of] slums and *favelas* (squatters' neighbourhoods). Two reporters from *O Estado*, the city's largest paper, gave me a tour of one in São Paulo.

Jammed between a highway and a food warehouse, it's a tangle of unpaved alleys. Perhaps 1000 people live in 200 or so meagre dwellings. The flimsiest are shacks with wooden sides and tin roofs; the sturdier homes are made of cinder blocks. Iraneide, a woman of 30 who is our guide, says that life is much better in the city than the Northeast, from which she migrated a year ago. She is probably right. Most shacks have TVs and stoves. Still, it's desperately poor.

Many of these neighbourhoods exist on the edge of the law. In 1999, greater São Paulo had 9000 murders. Violence breeds security consciousness. Houses and apartments in wealthy neighbourhoods are typically walled and gated, frequently with security guards.

Brazil's prospects depend heavily on foreign investment, which in turn depends heavily on the global economy and political stability. The first is faltering, and an economic crisis in neighbouring

FIGURE 3–10 Describe the physical and social conditions of the *favelas*.

Argentina compounds the uncertainty. Meanwhile, politics remains a question mark. Between the mid-1960s and the mid-1980s, Brazil was ruled by the military. Until the election of Fernando Henrique Cardoso in 1994 — he was re-elected in 1998 — popularly elected presidents had floundered. But Cardoso can't run again in 2002.

"We Brazilians think that we are a country of promise, but that the time of promise is always passing," says Lourival Sant'Anna, a respected journalist. "My parents were part of a generation in the 1950s who felt that they were building the country. But they became completely disillusioned by the military, high inflation and the lost decade."

The larger lesson is that there is no simple path to the First World. Each country takes its own journey, shaped by history, culture, and chance. The consequences are never entirely predictable, which is why all our generalizations usually don't fit the facts on the ground.

© 2001, *Newsweek*. Reprinted with permission.

10. How does São Paulo demonstrate that Brazil is in a mixture of development stages?

11. What are the two significant reasons for optimism about Brazil's future development?

12. Brazil's future prospects are described in this article as depending on foreign investment and political stability. How is Brazil seen to be faring in these areas?

13. How well does Brazil fit either the Rostow or Wallerstein model?

The Rich and the Poor

The gap between the rich and the poor of the world is widening. A country's wealth is evident when you look at its buildings, expressways, airports, and homes, and when economic well-being is spread throughout most of its population. Obviously, there are individuals and corporations that are exceedingly wealthy, but even the "working" classes in these regions show comparative economic well-being.

Some places, such as Beijing, New Delhi, Rio de Janeiro, and Nairobi also have many impressive buildings but in these cities the vast majority of the population does not share in the economic benefits of growth. Instead, most of the wealth belongs to a minority, or consists of capital invested by foreign-owned multinational corporations.

The trend of a widening gap between affluence and poverty (within developing countries, and between developed and developing countries) is unlikely to change. This is due to three factors — capital, power, and knowledge — all of which are controlled or founded in the developed world. The quality of life and level of consumerism continues to improve in the developed world. For example, in the past 50 years, the richest 20 percent of the world's population has doubled its consumption of metals (such as steel) and its use of energy. In contrast, there has been little or no growth in these areas in the poorest 20 percent of the world's population.

The world is still economically dominated by the minority of countries that makes up the developed or industrialized world. Take a look at some of the glaring differences in today's world, as recorded in the 2001 United Nations Human Development Report:

- The 20 percent of the world's population that lives in the highest-income countries commands 86 percent of the world's gross domestic product (GDP), 82 percent of the world's export markets, 68 percent of foreign direct investments, and 74 percent of the world's telephone lines. The 20 percent living in the lowest-income countries commands about 1 percent of each of these sectors.

FIGURE 3-11 Calgary (left) and Paris (right) are wealthy cities in developed countries. How are they typical of other such cities? How do they differ from poorer cities in developing countries?

- In 1998, the percentage share of the worldwide market held by the top ten corporations by sector was: telecommunications — 86 percent; pesticides — 85 percent; and computers — almost 70 percent. These corporations are all based in the richer regions of Europe, North America, and Japan.
- Industrialized countries hold 97 percent of all patents worldwide.
- The income gap between the richest 20 percent and the poorest 20 percent of the world's population (as measured by average national income per head) increased from 30:1 in 1960, to 74:1 in 1997.

14. How would you define the terms "rich" and "poor"?

15. What trends are emerging regarding the relationship between the rich of the world and the remainder?

16. What do you think the implications of these trends will be in the future?

Measuring Levels of Poverty

There are a number of ways to quantify the level of poverty around the world. The most widely accepted measurement is the annual Human Development Report, which was started in 1990. The United Nations Development Programme commissions this report and its goal is to assess, on an annual basis, the "long-term well-being" of the world's population. It looks at development in four different ways, using four different indexes:

- the Human Development Index (HDI)
- the Gender-related Development Index (GDI)
- the Gender Empowerment Measure (GEM)
- the Human Poverty Index (HPI)

Each index measures data that reflects the conditions of people within individual countries and regions.

The two sets of data that are most useful in measuring the disparity in the world's economic wealth are the Human Development Index and the Human Poverty Index. These two indexes form the basis of the Gender-related Development Index (which utilizes similar information, ranging from literacy and life expectancy to gender differences within individual countries).

The Gender Empowerment Measure examines the degree to which women have power in political and economic decision making. Sometimes a country's development ranking drops, when gender is taken into account. For example, Chile ranked thirty-ninth out of 174 countries on the 2000 Human Development Index. However, although it also ranked thirty-ninth on the Gender-related Development Index, it dropped to forty-ninth on the Gender Empowerment Measure. This means that in the year 2000, Chilean women did not have as many political and economic opportunities as women in other countries. Canada ranked third in the world on the 2000 Gender-related Development Index and sixth on the Gender Empowerment Measure.

Human Development Index (HDI)

The Human Development Index measures the "well-being" of people, using three basic criteria:

- longevity: measured by life expectancy at birth, and under-5 mortality rates
- knowledge: measured by educational attainment (using a combination of adult literacy rates and combined elementary, high school, and post-secondary school enrolment)
- basic standard of living: measured in US dollars by the gross domestic product per capita (GDP per capita) and purchasing power parity (described below)

Gross domestic product per capita (GDP per capita) is a measure of the value of the total production and consumption of goods and services taking place within a country in one year, divided by the number of people living in that country. A drawback to this measurement is that it uses the most globally accepted currency — the US dollar. It does not take into account what the local currency can buy, using local costs.

Purchasing power parity (PPP) takes into account the local cost of living when comparing one country with another. The purchasing power parity measures the income of people against the relative cost of something simple, such as a basket of food. To illustrate, *The Economist* magazine publishes a "Big Mac index" each year, showing the relative cost of a McDonald's hamburger in various countries. The 2001 index states that in April the cost of a Big Mac was:

United States		US$2.54
Canada	CDN$3.33	US$2.14
Switzerland	Sfr6.30	US$3.65
China	9.9 yuan	US$1.20

Figure 3–12 shows how the three development indicators that make up the Human Development Index can be used to determine differences between countries. In their Human Development Report, the United Nations ranks countries according to their Human Development Index "scores."

Human Poverty Index (HPI)

Three factors are considered for the Human Development Report's Human Poverty Index:

- longevity: measured by how long you can expect to live, calculated according to one's life expectancy at birth, and how likely individuals are to die at a young age

FIGURE 3–12 Examples from the Human Development Index

Country	HDI ranking	Life expectancy index	Education index	GDP index
Canada	1	0.90	0.99	0.91
Australia	4	0.89	0.99	0.90
Malaysia	61	0.79	0.79	0.73
Sierra Leone (lowest ranking)	174	0.22	0.29	0.25

Figure 3–12 shows the Human Development Index ranking for several countries and their Human Development Index "scores" for individual indicators. The Human Development Index sets a minimum and maximum for each dimension, expressed as a value between 0 and 1. For example, the minimum possible literacy rate is 0 and the maximum is 1; so a country with a literacy rate of 75 percent would be 0.75 on the Human Development Index scale.

- knowledge: measured by the number of literate adults in the country
- standard of living: measured by affordable access to health care and safe water, and by the percentage of malnourished children under age 5 in the country

The three criteria in the Human Development Index and the Human Poverty Index are very similar. However, the Human Development Index focusses more on levels of wealth (assuming that the more money one has, the more one has access to the basic requirements of life), while the Human Poverty Index takes a broader view of access to health care, clean water, and adequate food supply, when considering quality of life.

17. What are the differences between the Human Development Index and the Human Poverty Index, in terms of the factors considered for each?

18. Justify why each of the criteria used in the Human Development Index and Human Poverty Index is a good indicator of a level of development.

19. What other facts besides those collected in the Human Development Index and Human Poverty Index could be used to help determine the longevity, knowledge, and basic standard of living in a country?

20. A significant criticism of the Human Development Index is that it does not measure aspects such as human rights or freedom. How could the United Nations measure these features?

21. How could the Human Development Index, Gender-related Development Index, or Gender Empowerment Measure be used to decrease the disparity in social and economic conditions between the developed and the developing world?

Battling Poverty Worldwide

Since 1945, when the United Nations was formed as a body to promote peace and security, it has been vitally concerned with providing a different kind of security — that of improving the health and well-being of the world's population, especially in areas where fundamental human needs are not being met. Working to reduce poverty is one of its goals. How well has it done?

The Human Development Report indicates that there has been a reduction in the amount of **absolute poverty** (those people unable to acquire life's basic necessities) from 28 percent to 24.5 percent. However, because of population growth, the number of poor in the world has increased. Also, the number of **income-poor** (those who have a low level of financial income in relation to the cost of living) has increased from 1.2 billion to 1.3 billion since 1996.

Countries which have reduced poverty the most are Costa Rica, Trinidad and Tobago, Chile, Cuba, and Singapore — less than 10 percent are poor. These countries have reduced poverty by focussing on improving levels of literacy and ensuring that people receive adequate nutrition and health care. Birth rates have lowered and many women have entered the workforce.

Some countries — the Philippines, China, Kenya, Costa Rica, Peru, and Zimbabwe — have managed to reduce human poverty through health-care initiatives, but have not been successful in reducing income poverty.

Where is poverty most prevalent?

According to the United Nations, in over 80 countries, 34 percent of the population is poor.

- Seven countries have more than 50 percent of the population in a state of poverty: Burkina Faso, Sierra Leone, Niger, Mali, Cambodia, Ethiopia, and Mozambique.
- When the two factors of income poverty and human poverty are combined, the countries of sub-Saharan Africa show levels

of poverty in greater than 40 percent of their populations. The Human Development Report has found that the situation is getting worse in sub-Saharan Africa, where poverty is increasing.

■ The countries of southern Asia also show levels of poverty greater than 40 percent of their populations, when the two factors of income poverty and human poverty are combined. The Human Development Report estimates that, in real numbers, southern Asia alone accounts for more than two-thirds of the poverty in all of the developing world countries.

When there are a large number of income-poor in a country, there are usually a large number of human-poor, and vice versa. However, sometimes a country can have large numbers of income-poor but, because of an emphasis on social programs such as health care and education, can have low numbers of human poor. Such is the case in Peru, where the level of human poverty is at 12 percent, but where income poverty is at a high 49 percent. In Arab countries of the Middle East, income poverty has been reduced to 4 percent of the population, which means that people have more money. However, this has not brought about improvements in education, health care, or life expectancy. As a result, in these same countries, 34 percent of the population is poor.

22. What is the difference between income poverty and human poverty?

23. What may cause countries that are not income-poor to have higher levels of human poverty?

24. Refer to Figure 3–13. How would you summarize the regions that receive high Human Development Index scores, and those that receive low Human Development Index scores?

FIGURE 3–13 Regions classified by the Human Development Index

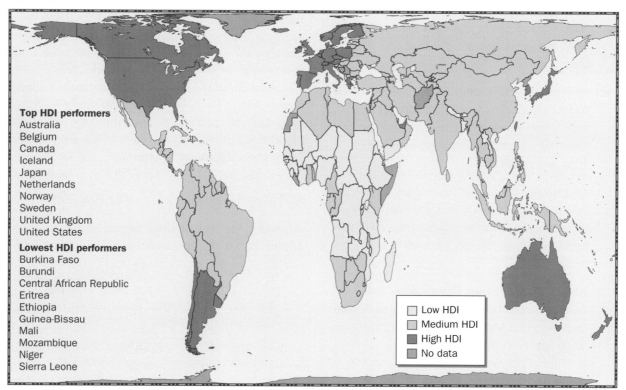

Top HDI performers
Australia
Belgium
Canada
Iceland
Japan
Netherlands
Norway
Sweden
United Kingdom
United States

Lowest HDI performers
Burkina Faso
Burundi
Central African Republic
Eritrea
Ethiopia
Guinea-Bissau
Mali
Mozambique
Niger
Sierra Leone

Low HDI
Medium HDI
High HDI
No data

Case in point — Vietnam

Vietnam has approached the problem of poverty at two levels: seeking first to understand the phenomenon, and then to formulate strategies to overcome it. The focus of the government's socio-economic development strategy since 1986 has been *Doi Moi* — a reform process aimed at transforming the Vietnamese economy to one that is market-based and dynamic. Such economies seek profits, and allow the competition for markets to dictate the success of products and services. This attracts the investment of capital, which leads to eventual economic growth, demonstrated by higher levels of employment and income.

Although Vietnam has reduced income poverty by an estimated 35 percent since launching Doi Moi, poverty remains high, and is concentrated among ethnic minorities living in the northern and central highlands.

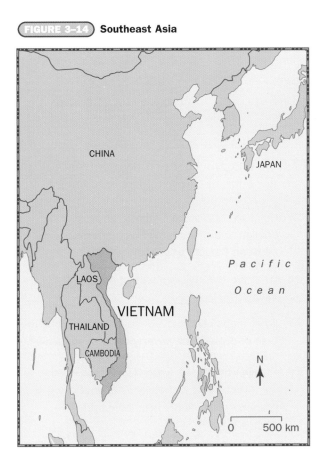

FIGURE 3–14 **Southeast Asia**

Even with a per capita income of US$200, Vietnam has made considerable progress in reducing human poverty. With higher investments in education and health care, the country has achieved an average life expectancy of 66 years, an adult literacy rate of 93 percent, and access to health services for 90 percent of its population. Between 1990 and 1995, it reduced under-5 mortality from 55 per 1000 live births to 46. As measured by the Human Poverty Index (HPI), human poverty in Vietnam is now at a level of 26 percent.

Much of the remaining poverty in the country appears to be linked to five broad, underlying causes:

- isolation — geographic, linguistic, political, and social
- adverse environmental conditions, such as typhoons and floods
- lack of access to productive resources, particularly land and international credit
- unsustainable financial conditions (the country cannot be assured of continued investment capital)
- inadequate participation of the general population in the planning and implementation of development programs

A major aim of Doi Moi has been to create an "enabling" environment based on growth, stability, and equity that ensures that poor people can have more opportunities to create their own prosperity and control their own financial future. Poor families are given land on which to farm; are allowed to grow cash crops such as coffee, tea, and rubber instead of rice; and are offered greater freedom to join co-operatives and trade partnerships.

In rural areas, Vietnam has taken significant steps in land reform. Between 1992 and 1995, the number of borrowers who obtained financial credit from the Vietnam Bank of Agriculture increased almost sevenfold — from 900 000 to 7 million. Also, the development of a rural infrastructure — including improved roads, hospitals, and other

At a glance — *Vietnam and Canada*

	Vietnam	Canada
Population	Population: 79 939 014 Population growth rate: 1.45% Total fertility rate: 2.49 Birth rate: 21.23 births/1000 Death rate: 6.22 deaths/1000	Population: 31 592 805 Population growth rate: 0.99% Total fertility rate: 1.6 Birth rate: 11.21 births/1000 Death rate: 7.47 deaths/1000
Life expectancy	Infant mortality rate: 30.24 deaths/1000 live births Life expectancy at birth: 69.56 years	Infant mortality rate: 5.02 deaths/1000 live births Life expectancy at birth: 79.56 years
Labour force by occupation	Agriculture 67%, industry and services 33%	Services 74%, manufacturing 15%, construction 5%, agriculture 3%, other 3%
Wealth — GDP real growth rate	5.5%	4.3%
Wealth — GDP per capita (PPP)	US$1 950	US$24 800
Example of level of productivity	Electricity production: 22.985 billion kWh	Electricity production: 567.193 billion kWh
External debt	US$13.2 billion	US$1.9 billion
Trade — imports	US$15.2 billion	US$238.2 billion
Trade — exports	US$14.3 billion	US$272.3 billion
Aid	Recipient: US$2.1 billion	Contributor: US$1.3 billion

services — through local initiatives, has been introduced to reduce isolation and the risk of poverty.

An important future challenge is to further develop the enabling environment of growth, stability, and equity, while working to ensure that poor people can participate in that environment by strengthening its economy, incentives, institutions, organizations, families, and human resources. According to the United Nations Human Development Report of 1997, the Vietnamese government aims to eliminate chronic hunger and eradicate income poverty by 2010. It also hopes to ultimately catch up with its more prosperous East Asian neighbours. Although its annual economic growth was an impressive 9 to 10 percent throughout the latter part of the 1990s, this recently levelled off at around 4 to 5 percent (which is still quite good for an emerging, free economy).

25. Refer to "At a glance" above. What, in your opinion, are the most striking differences between Canada and Vietnam?

26. What are the major causes of poverty in Vietnam?

27. What steps can a government take to make the task of overcoming poverty more sustainable?

28. Explain why Doi Moi was effective and whether or not this could be a strategy other developing countries could use to help them overcome poverty.

Canadian Poverty

The United Nations Human Development Index ranks Canada as one of the most livable places on earth. Compared to the rest of the world, Canada scores well in measurements of longevity, educational attainment, and economic well-being. The country has high levels of consumption and is bombarded with advertising, telling its population how to maintain "the good life." Nevertheless, consider the following facts reported by the Canadian Council on Social Development in 2001:

- *About 1.5 million children (one out of five children) in Canada live in poverty*: 548 000 in Ontario and 37.3 percent of children under 12 in Toronto, Canada's largest city.

- Canada ranks tenth among 17 industrialized nations on the United Nations Human Poverty Index. According to the United Nations Children's Fund (UNICEF), Canada has *one of the worst child poverty rates among industrialized nations.*

- *One out of eight school-aged children lives in a family with a very low average income.*

- *Children under the age of 18 — who account for just over one-quarter of the population — make up 39 percent of food bank recipients.*

According to the National Anti-Poverty Organization — a non-government organization (NGO) which represents 250 poverty groups across Canada — one in six Canadians (about 17.5 percent) is poor. Using Statistics Canada (StatsCan) information, this organization suggested that poor people in Canada are usually found in families where the head of the family is under 25. It also indicated that over 60 percent of single youths under 24 live below the poverty line. (Statistics Canada defines the Canadian poverty line or "low income cutoff" as 55 percent; that is, if a Canadian family spends more than 55 percent of its income on basic necessities such as food, shelter, and clothing, then it is income-poor.)

Information gathered by Statistics Canada reveals further insights into poverty in Canada:

- *Poverty is gender-related.* In 2000, Statistics Canada reported that 56 percent of families with children headed by a single mother are poor, with income levels well below the Statistics Canada poverty line.

- *The group most vulnerable to poverty consists of non-elderly, unattached women:* 40.9 percent of non-elderly, unattached women live in poverty, compared to 35 percent for non-elderly, unattached men.

- *Many women enter retirement in a condition of poverty.* In 1999, the average Canadian pension benefit paid to women was CDN$285 per month, compared to CDN$410 for men. On average, Canadian women earn significantly less than men. (In 2000, women earned 80 cents for every dollar earned by men.) The disparity between men's and women's earnings in Canada continues as the earners age. Because pensions are based on earnings, significant differences can be seen.

- *Income is shared unequally.* The richest 20 percent of Canadians earn nearly 45 percent of all income, while the poorest 20 percent earn less than 5 percent of all income.

FIGURE 3–15 Canadian Olympic gold medallist triathlete Simon Whitfield helps out at a Toronto food bank. What role can celebrities play in increasing awareness of issues like poverty?

While it is clear that a portion of people in Canada live in poverty, it is important to note that the actual numbers are debated. Each year, Statistics Canada records how many people are living below the poverty line. This is determined by adding the cost of basic items (such as food, shelter, and clothing) for one family, and then calculating this amount as a percentage of the total income the family receives. The figure is adjusted to reflect the number and age of children in a family, and whether or not a family lives in a large community. This, however, is just one definition of the Canadian poverty line.

Christopher A. Sarlo challenges the Statistics Canada description of poverty lines in his 1996 publication, *Poverty in Canada*. He believes that the cutoff point is twice as high as the cost of basic needs, and maintains that 75 percent of all families labelled "poor in Canada" have greater incomes than they require to satisfy their basic needs. Sarlo therefore suggests that estimates of the number of poor are exaggerated, and that poverty in Canada has been virtually eliminated.

29. Research some specific steps that have been taken to help overcome the disparity between men's and women's earnings in Canada. To what extent have they been effective? What further steps would you suggest?

30. What suggestions would you make to your local politician regarding overcoming poverty in Canada?

31. If you had to determine a poverty line in Canada, how would you define it? Discuss this question with a group of your classmates and report the criteria you agree upon.

International Aid

There are many reasons why people around the world need help. Earthquakes, famine, or war can affect huge numbers of people, causing sudden and serious disruptions in their lives, or threatening their health. On the other hand, some people may live in extreme poverty, trapped in situations where there are no jobs and alternatives are few.

On the suggestion of former Canadian Prime Minister Lester B. Pearson, member countries of the United Nations made a commitment in 1969 to donate 0.7 percent of their gross national product (GNP) as a contribution toward international aid. Only Norway, Sweden, Denmark, and the Netherlands have met this target on a regular basis. The United States, which should be the largest contributor (because it has the largest gross national product), has a 2000 contribution level of 0.15 percent of its gross national product. In the past, Canada had reduced its contributions but, according to the United Nations, has recently recommitted itself to the promised 0.7 percent.

There are misconceptions about what aid is. Almost all aid is a contribution from one country or development organization to another country, in the form of a loan. Like any other credit, it must be paid back over an agreed period of time. Over 40 percent of all aid contributions from countries belonging to the Organization for Economic Co-operation and Development (OECD) is tied to some form of "payback."

There are two channels for giving aid:

- multilateral aid: help using human assistance, goods, food, or medicine, provided through governments or non-government organizations

- bilateral aid: direct help from one government to another

An example of multilateral aid would be the United Nations Development Programme providing money for women's educational development in Afghanistan. An example of bilateral aid would be a grant from the Japanese government for the construction of a hospital in Syria.

There are four main reasons why countries or development organizations provide aid:

- **Economic development:** This is aid to help a recipient country develop an aspect of its economy, such as financing a business opportunity. Often, the recipient country is obliged to import parts or technical assistance from the contributing country, in return for aid.

- **Political influence:** Aid can be provided to create or reinforce the political obligations of a recipient country to a contributing country. For example, by providing millions of dollars worth of food aid, the contributing country may require recipient countries to adhere to the contributing country's foreign policy wishes.

- **Historic obligation:** Some wealthy developed countries keep personal ties with countries that were former colonies. Perhaps there is an obligation to pay back for the time when the receiving country was a target of exploitation. Most likely, their close ties remain because of cultural links such as language, educational exchanges, or military training.

- Belgium, for example, keeps close ties with the Democratic Republic of the Congo.

- **Humanitarian obligation:** This aid is based on feelings of moral responsibility. When people are suffering, there is a moral obligation to send some form of relief. Canada's agreement to take in Kosovar refugees from war-torn Yugoslavia in 1999 was based on these sentiments.

Concerns about foreign aid

Although foreign aid helps distressed people in the short term, or enables them to create a brighter future in the long term, there are some concerns about foreign aid that prompt further research:

- Often, *foreign aid does not reach the poorest people*. Instead, it is channelled through bureaucracies to urban centres, where well-off people live. Israel, Egypt, and Turkey receive far more United States aid than poor countries such as India, or those in Africa. The richest 40 percent of developing countries receive US$2 for every US$1 of aid given to the poorest 40 percent.

- Much *foreign aid is limited in its usefulness* because there is no infrastructure (schools, roads, rail, hospitals, and common services) in place to support improvements in the long term.

- *Foreign aid can inhibit local entrepreneurs*, who find it difficult to compete with low-cost items. For example, local farmers cannot sell their produce while food aid is being provided free of charge.

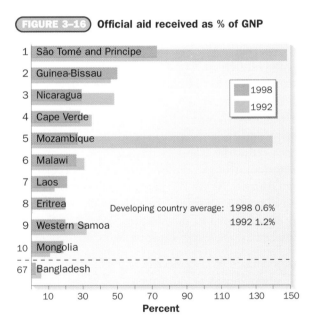

FIGURE 3–16 Official aid received as % of GNP

1 São Tomé and Principe
2 Guinea-Bissau
3 Nicaragua
4 Cape Verde
5 Mozambique
6 Malawi
7 Laos
8 Eritrea
9 Western Samoa
10 Mongolia
67 Bangladesh

1998
1992

Developing country average: 1998 0.6%
1992 1.2%

10 30 50 70 90 110 130 150
Percent

Who are they?

The Organization for Economic Co-operation and Development

The Organization for Economic Co-operation and Development (OECD) has its headquarters in France. It was formed to promote industrial development in developed countries, while helping developing countries improve their status. The group believes in supporting democracies and free markets, and advocates the protection of human rights. It represents the richest countries in the world. In 2001, it had 29 members.

- *Foreign aid may hinder reforms* that would have helped poor people in the long term. For example, a root cause of poverty and chronic hunger in a country may be a lack of access to land for its poor, but land reforms may be delayed or abandoned as long as food is being shipped into the country to feed its poor.

The debt trap — The power of the creditors

Once countries are deeply in debt, they must pay very large amounts of interest on the money they have borrowed. They then have to borrow further to help pay back the interest to international financial institutions (IFIs), such as the World Bank or the International Monetary Fund (IMF). When money is loaned to a country from one of these institutions, this constitutes *multilateral aid*. Once a country is deeply in multilateral debt, its creditor can influence the way in which its economy is run. In the 1970s, the World Bank told Sudan — who owed it money — that it should not grow grain in an attempt to feed itself, but should grow cotton instead, which could be sold on the world market. This money could then be used to pay off some of its debts.

Some people believe that countries deep in debt should be forgiven what they owe, so that they can start to make real improvements. However, according to their own rules, international financial institutions are not allowed to forgive loans; only bilateral aid allows loans to be forgiven. In addition, if a country fails to make payments to an international financial institution, it could lose its credit rating and would find it very difficult to borrow money from anyone again.

According to the World Bank, multilateral debt for low-income countries increased by nearly 600 percent to over US$165 billion, between 1980 and 2000. Low-income countries that are particularly hard hit are those in sub-Saharan Africa — they pay more money to service their debt than they receive in additional financial assistance.

Countries that contribute to the funding of the World Bank and the International Monetary Fund have voting powers on the organization's decisions, based on the amounts of money they provide to the organization. The United States, which is the largest contributor to both the World Bank and the International Monetary Fund, has considerable influence on the policies of these huge financial institutions. It commands 18 percent of the voting power of the World Bank.

Faced with the possible inability of some countries to pay their debts, in 1996 the World Bank and International Monetary Fund proposed a "Heavily Indebted Poor Countries Plan." The plan dictated that, for countries to have their debts reduced to "sustainable limits," they had to adhere to strict social policies for a period of three years. This meant drastic cuts to spending in vital areas such as education and health care. It also meant that for countries to qualify for this help, they had to guarantee 20 to 25 percent of their revenue from exports to pay off the debt. Very few countries could afford to sustain this and, according to many critics, the plan is not working.

32. In groups of four, discuss or debate the effectiveness of international aid versus its drawbacks and limitations.

Who are they?

The International Monetary Fund

The International Monetary Fund (IMF) is an international financial organization. With 183 member countries, its purpose is to promote international financial co-operation. It seeks to develop the economies of all countries, especially those that are developing or are in need of stability. It also provides loans and technical economic assistance. In 2001, it had outstanding loans worth over US$65 billion.

33. Is the percentage of gross national product a fair way to measure the "generosity" of a country? If so, what do you consider an appropriate level of aid as a percentage of gross national product? If not, what other methods could be used?

34. Refer to Figure 3–16 on page 73, which shows the top ten aid receivers.
    a) Which stage of development are these countries in, according to Rostow's model?
    b) Which category would they fall into, according to the Wallerstein model?

35. Many argue that the only way for poorer countries to make real progress is for significant, if not complete, "debt forgiveness" to occur.
    a) List four arguments you would make to the World Bank supporting this idea.

    b) How might the president of the World Bank reply to these arguments? Respond to each of your four proposals.

36. a) Refer to the data in Figure 3–17. Produce a choropleth map showing the location of these indebted countries. Shade the countries according to their total debt as a percentage of their gross national product, using the following scale:

Over 200 percent	Dark red
100–199 percent	Medium red
Less than 100 percent	Light red

    b) Write a conclusion about the distribution of these indebted countries.
    c) Does this data support the ideas of either Rostow or Wallerstein? If so, how? If not, why not?

FIGURE 3–17 Total debt as a percentage of gross national product — Top 50 percentages

Country	Total debt ($US million)	Percentage of GNP	Country	Total debt ($US million)	Percentage of GNP
Angola	12 173	297	Malawi	2 444	137
Bulgaria	9 907	83	Mali	3 202	120
Burundi	1 119	128	Mauritania	2 589	273
Cambodia	2 210	78	Mongolia	739	75
Cameroon	9 829	119	Mozambique	8 208	223
Central African Rep.	921	89	Nicaragua	5 968	336
Comoros	203	103	Niger	1 659	82
Congo	5 119	307	Nigeria	30 315	79
Côte d'Ivoire	14 852	145	Panama	6 689	78
DROC	12 929	208	Papua New Guinea	2 692	77
Ecuador	15 140	82	Samoa	180	102
Equatorial Guinea	306	76	São Tomé and Principe	246	684
Ethiopia	10 352	160	Senegal	3 861	83
Gabon	4 425	91	Sierra Leone	1 243	198
Gambia	477	117	St. Vincent and Grenadines	420	139
Ghana	6 884	92	Sudan	16 843	183
Guinea	3 546	102	Syria	22 435	138
Guinea-Bissau	964	504	Tanzania	7 603	94
Guyana	1 653	249	Thailand	86 172	76
Honduras	5 002	97	Togo	1 448	97
Indonesia	150 875	176	Turkmenistan	2 266	88
Jordan	8 485	147	Vietnam	22 359	82
Laos	2 437	199	Yemen	4 138	105
Macedonia	2 392	97	Zambia	6 865	217
Madagascar	4 394	119	Zimbabwe	4 716	80

Precision farming and the global positioning system (GPS)

Who benefits from technology? Farming is one of the oldest professions, but today, even farming has become a high-tech business. Any farmer — rich or poor — has little control over the conditions necessary for crops to thrive; rich farmers can afford to make use of modern technology.

The use of technology can significantly improve the quality and yield of crops but, despite technological advances, some fundamental difficulties remain. These include the quality of the soil, its delicate chemical balance, and access to water. Modern geotechnologies have been introduced to assist farmers to overcome these challenges. One of these geotechnologies is precision farming.

Precision farming

In industrial nations, both family farms and multinational corporate farms (such as Sunkist Growers Inc.) have begun to see the benefits of using precision-farming techniques.

The concept of precision farming revolves around a technology known as the global positioning system (GPS). This system is based on a set of 24 satellites in orbit around the earth and 5 base stations (the receivers) positioned on the earth. Each satellite is in an extremely precise orbit, and is monitored and maintained by computers at the base stations. The global positioning system is owned by the United States Department of Defence and is used primarily for military purposes. However, the military allows civilians to access the global positioning system network. Today, many people use it for recreation, transportation, navigation, and other purposes.

How the global positioning system works

The global positioning system is based on accurate geometrical calculations called "triangulation": given an object's distance from three known points, it is possible to calculate the object's position.

Measuring the distances from the satellites to earth is done as a function of time — what is measured is the time it takes for a signal to leave the satellite and arrive at the receiver. The signal travels at the speed of light (300 000 kilometres per second). Using this information, the travel time can be determined, which then makes it possible to calculate the distance according to the following formula:

$$\text{distance} = \text{velocity} \times \text{time.}$$

To determine a position on the earth, a small computer called a global positioning system receiver unit is needed. These range in shape and size, but each one has an antenna for receiving information. The global positioning system receiver unit receives the signal from the satellites and triangulates the position. It must receive signals from at least three satellites in order for it to do so, but a fourth satellite is used to improve the accuracy of the calculation. While older systems were somewhat inaccurate (with variations of more than a kilometre), state-of-the-art global positioning system units can triangulate the position of a user to within a metre.

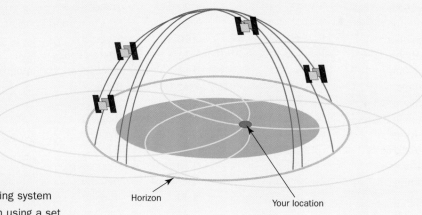

Horizon

Your location

FIGURE 3–18 Global positioning system receiver units calculate position using a set of 24 satellites in orbit around the earth.

Applying the global positioning system to precision farming

Global positioning system data allows farmers to gather information about every square metre of their fields. This information can then be used to make farming decisions. What kind of information are farmers gathering and how are they using it?

Precision farming usually begins with the farmer gathering information about the soil: its type, its nutrient qualities, and its moisture characteristics. This can be done in real time (right away) by special sensors located on a tractor. The information is recorded, along with its location given by the global positioning system. The farmer can then use this information to create a map, based on the soil's characteristics, that shows which seeds should be planted in which part of the field, and how close the seeds should be planted to each other.

In addition, the soil's characteristics can be used to determine how the field should be tilled (or ploughed) — equipment on the tractor can automatically vary the depth of tillage based on the soil type, moisture, or crop.

Next, farmers determine how to protect the crops in the field. A soil map and a crop map can be combined to assess which chemicals (fertilizer, pesticides, and so on) need to be sprayed on the plants to maximize their yield. Again, the entire process is automated, based on global positioning system co-ordinates, as the farmer travels through the field on the tractor.

Finally, when it is time to harvest the crop, the yield of each area of the field can be catalogued. This information can be utilized to determine high-yielding areas of the field and a historical database can be established. This database can then be consulted when making decisions concerning crop planting for subsequent years.

This type of farming allows a farmer to monitor every stage of the crop-growing process and to ensure that every portion of every field is allowed to perform to its full potential. The improvement in crop yield has been significant and provides a competitive advantage for the farms that use it.

Cost of high-tech solutions

The problem with precision farming is the cost. Although the satellites transmit information for free, the cost of

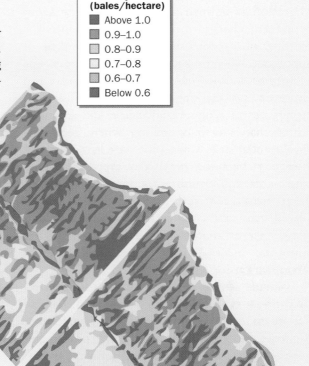

Cotton yield (bales/hectare)
- ■ Above 1.0
- ■ 0.9–1.0
- ■ 0.8–0.9
- □ 0.7–0.8
- ■ 0.6–0.7
- ■ Below 0.6

FIGURE 3–19 The yields of a field have been used to create a map, which may be consulted when making decisions about next year's planting season.

the equipment is high. Setting up and maintaining this technology is very expensive, despite the improvements it may bring about in a farm's performance. Poorer farmers, both in developed and developing countries, cannot afford to implement it.

a) What advantages does precision global positioning system technology provide for those who can afford it?

b) What strategies might be explored to make precision farming technology available to poorer farmers?

c) Using the Internet to assist you, research the cost of implementing precision farming for a small Canadian family farm.

Global Migration

Migration is defined as a permanent or semi-permanent change of residence and involves the crossing of national borders. A great deal of migration, whereby individuals move from one country to another, has taken place globally, as a means of "fast tracking" (trying to keep up with) the process of economic and social development. Rather than stay in a country where economic development is slow and wages are low, migrants move to richer, more highly developed economies where more opportunities for advancement exist. In a typical recent year, up to 1.5 million people moved from one country to another. In today's world, an estimated 150 million people are migrants, according to the International Organization for Migration (IOM).

Canada is one of the world's leading recipients of migrants. About 16 percent of all Canadians are foreign-born. Only four other countries have a higher percentage of foreign-born migrants — Australia, Côte d'Ivoire, Switzerland, and Luxembourg. According to the New Internationalist, approximately 40 percent of Australians — some 18 million people — are migrants or the children of migrants, and are drawn from 150 countries.

There are two basic groups of migrants — those who move voluntarily and those who are forced to do so. **Voluntary migration** includes those who move for better jobs, for family unity, or for study purposes. Migrants include settlers, landed immigrants, temporary workers, guest workers, asylum seekers, students, and undocumented arrivals intending to stay for the short or long term.

We live in a growing global economy where labour is easily transported around the world to the "highest bidder." The International Labour Organization (ILO), formed to protect workers' labour rights throughout the world, believes that modern economic forces will continue to fuel migration. When workers can receive ten times more money for doing the same job in the United States as they did in Mexico, the benefits of migration will prove irresistible.

Migration is helped by technology, since the cost and speed of contact between countries has fallen to a fraction of what it used to be. Migrating 20 years ago meant isolation and loneliness for many. Today, telephones, e-mail, the Internet, and cheaper airline transportation have made migration easier.

Most of this **economic migration** (migration for economic reasons) will naturally be from poor countries to richer ones. For example, the International Labour Organization data shows that, for every American worker who moves to Mexico, six Mexican workers move to the United States. The Organization for Economic Co-operation and Development believes that, by 2020, the developing world's workforce will increase by 40 percent, due to economic development and population increases. That is, 700 million new job seekers will be added to a global workforce of 2.4 billion. This will put tremendous pressure on migration channels to developed countries.

Refugees

Forced migration takes place for many reasons and results in people becoming refugees. **Refugees** are migrants who flee to protect themselves and their families, in order to survive.

Who are they?

The International Organization for Migration

The International Organization for Migration (IOM), based in Geneva in Switzerland, is an internationally funded organization committed to helping millions of migrants with information, technical assistance, and humanitarian aid. It also provides cultural information, language training, help with transportation, medical assistance, and assistance with documentation (acquiring visas or passports). Since it started in 1951 as the Intergovernmental Committee for European Migration, it has helped over 11 million migrants.

Global WARNING

DETERIORATING ENVIRONMENT

In 1998, the New Internationalist suggested that the number of environmental refugees may increase over the next decade, due to:

- land degradation into desert (135 million people threatened)
- rising sea levels in lowland areas (200 million people threatened)
- climate change (50 million people threatened with severe food shortages)
- water shortages (up to 550 million people threatened)

For example, environmental refugees are people forced to move as a result of the deterioration of their environment. The International Organization for Migration estimated that, from 1990 to 2000, some 60 million were forced to migrate because the quality of their land deteriorated. Forced migration can be gradual, as in the case of deforestation or land degradation; or it can be rapid, as in the case of environmental damage through conflict, war, or a natural disaster like a flood. The number of environmental migrants is growing dramatically. Today, about 25 million people annually are classified as environmental migrants.

Another reason for forced migration is fear — fear of conflict, persecution, human rights abuses, or natural disaster. According to the United Nations High Commission for Refugees (UNHCR), a branch of the United Nations formed to help refugees settle safely around the world, there were some 50 million refugees and displaced people worldwide in 2001, compared with 35 million in 1995. The majority of these were women and children. With conflict and environmental degradation widespread in Africa, it is estimated that there are 4 million African refugees in other countries, and probably at least 10 million displaced within their own country.

When poverty — often brought about by environmental problems — becomes life threatening, many people decide they have to move to another country to survive. Sometimes it is difficult to do this; some countries may set limits on the number of new residents it wants. Canada calls its set of limits a "quota system." Such limits have generated many people-for-profit organizations through which people are smuggled across borders for fees, to avoid the often lengthy process of being screened for suitability. Migrant smuggling (human trafficking) is a global business, which generates massive profits for the traffickers, and is often arranged by organized crime syndicates.

Trends in migration

Populations have been migrating for a long time. In the past, reasons varied from forced migration to colonization, whereas more recent reasons are economic benefit or safety.

Who are they?

The International Labour Organization

The International Labour Organization (ILO), an agency of the United Nations (UN), promotes social justice and internationally recognized human and labour rights. The ILO sets international standards of basic labour rights: freedom of association, the right to organize, collective bargaining, equality of opportunity and treatment, and the abolition of forced labour.

During the European colonization of the world in the 1800s and 1900s, millions moved from the developed world to join in the development of other parts of the world. Today, the migrant flow has reversed. Most migrants move from poor, developing countries to the richer countries of Europe, North America, and Oceania (that is, Australia, New Zealand, and other countries in the Pacific Ocean).

According to the International Organization for Migration, current trends in migration include the following:

- *Migration to a larger number of countries* takes place — more countries admit migrants than before.

- *More migration is taking place within countries*, especially in areas where there are regional economic differences. For example, 30 million people migrate within countries each year, and 16 million of these migrate within African countries.

- *Migration to cities* is still very strong, especially in developing world cities; 80 million people have already moved from rural areas to cities. About 1.5 million people migrate to the world's largest cities each year.

- **Two-stepped migration** (movement from poor rural areas into cities, followed by movement to another country) is common practice, especially in poorer countries.

- There is greater **transnationalism**, or allegiance to more than one country, as more people share an international identity.

- In more than 50 countries, *the amount of migration equals 15 percent of the population*. If current trends continue, this percentage will grow.

FIGURE 3-20 **Pattern of migration**

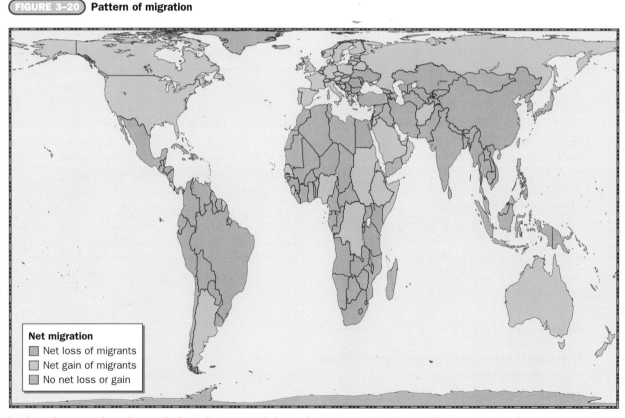

Net migration
- Net loss of migrants
- Net gain of migrants
- No net loss or gain

Look at the countries who are losing migrants, and those that are receiving them. What are some of the impacts felt by those countries?

- *Many migrants tend to be better educated and qualified than the majority of native-born people of the countries to which they migrate.* From the point of view of the country losing the valuable migrant, this is termed **brain drain**. For example, there is an ongoing exodus from Canada to the United States of medical doctors and nurses, computer experts, and those involved in the arts, often after they have received specialized training in Canada.
- *A growing proportion of migrants — 47.5 percent — are women.* Women who have migrated tend to have less traditional roles and participate more fully in the workforce than women who do not migrate.
- *More money is being sent back* from "new homes" to the "old countries," and greater economic links — such as international banks — are being created to handle the transfer of money.
- *More illegal migration* is taking place.
- *Migration is more fast-paced* due to air travel opportunities and rapid means of communication.

What about the geographic trends emerging because of migration? The International Labour Organization believes that we will see more migration from:

- Latin America and South and East Asia, to North America
- Africa, South Asia, the Middle East, Eastern Europe, and Russia, to European countries

Costs and benefits of migration

When educated migrants leave a country, the country loses an investment in its future, particularly if a large amount of money has been invested in its migrants' education. However, this brain drain can also bring reciprocal benefits, that is, "brain-drain gains." The link between two countries through migration often sparks better business opportunities and cultural exchanges, which enhance the process of globalization.

Other benefits to developing countries that experience **out-migration** (migrants leaving the country) include:

- more cultural contacts
- access to new ideas in a global market
- remittances, that is, money received in wages and sent back to the "home" country

Remittances are estimated at over US$250 billion each year, flowing from northern to southern

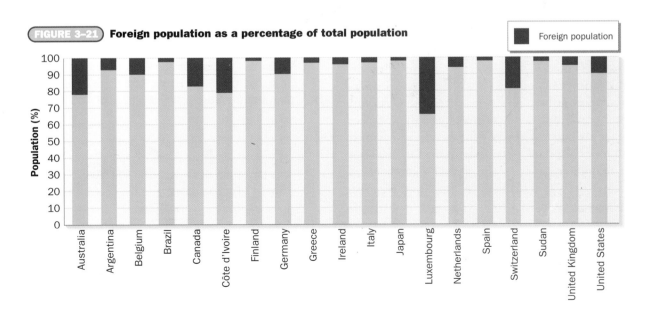

FIGURE 3–21 **Foreign population as a percentage of total population**

Foreign population

Issue briefing

Migration comparison, 2000

How do three countries considered to be attractive destinations for migration purposes compare?

- Canada has three main types of migrant classes:
    family reunification (26 percent)
    independent skilled workers (59 percent)
    refugees (about 13 percent)
    others (2 percent)
    About 210 000 to 235 000 individuals are admitted each year.

- The United States has three main types of migrant classes:
    family reunification (66 percent)
    economic and employment purposes (12 percent)
    refugees (14 percent)
    others (8 percent)
    About 1 million people are admitted each year.
- Australia has three types of migrant classes:
    family members (45 percent)
    skilled migrants (50 percent)
    refugees (5 percent)
    In 2000, Australia accepted 70 000 migrants.

countries. For example, Mexico receives US$2 to $3 billion of these "migradollars" (migration dollars) which form 3 percent of its gross domestic product.

There are misconceptions about accepting increased migrant populations. Some people think that increased immigration results in more competition for existing jobs, and that higher burdens are being placed on social services. The truth is that many economies could not survive without migration. As the average age in developed countries increases, further **in-migration** (migration into the country) will be needed to keep economies running.

In-migration also leads to a larger domestic consumer market and more economic growth. Most European countries and Japan are eager for population growth. They are currently faced with aging populations and declining growth, and need higher tax bases to help pay for their infrastructures and for health care. According to the Organization for Economic Co-operation and Development, an increase of 25 000 immigrants could raise their per capita gross domestic product by more than US$50.

37. How would you define the term "migration"?

38. Explain why migration is important to countries such as Canada and Australia.

39. What are the differences between economic migrants and environmental migrants?

40. What do you consider to be the three most interesting trends regarding migration in today's world? How might these trends impact Canada and its social policy?

41. When people move from one country to another, there are costs and benefits for both countries. Make a list of costs and benefits, for the sender country and for the receiver country.

42. Richer countries colonized most of today's poorer countries during the past two centuries. Do you believe that the rich countries have an obligation to make it easier for people to migrate from developing countries to developed parts of the world? Why or why not?

43. Research a current case involving refugees in Canada or elsewhere. What is the receiving country's policy regarding migrants? How does this policy affect the specific situation you have chosen? For example, does the country in question have a quota system?

44. Research Canada's current immigration policy. Hold a classroom debate to evaluate its effectiveness and relevance in terms of the trends discussed above.

Global migration

FIGURE 3–22 The ten largest groups of refugees, listed by country of origin, 2000

Country of origin	Main countries of refuge	Number of refugees
Afghanistan	Pakistan, Iran	3 567 200
Burundi	Tanzania	567 000
Iraq	Iran	497 400
Sudan	Uganda, DROC, Chad Ethiopia, Kenya, CAR	485 500
Bosnia-Herzegovina	Yugoslavia, Croatia	454 700
Somalia	Kenya, Ethiopia, Yemen, Djibouti	441 600
Angola	Zambia, DROC, Namibia	421 200
Sierra Leone	Guinea, Liberia	401 800
Eritrea	Sudan	377 100
Vietnam	China	369 100

FIGURE 3–23 The most popular countries of resettlement of refugees, 2000

Country of resettlement	Number of refugees
United States	71 500
Canada	13 500
Australia	6 600
Sweden	1 500
Norway	1 500
Finland	760
New Zealand	700
Denmark	460
Japan	140

Your task is to create an annotated global migration map and analyse the trends reflected on it. An annotated map is a useful way of showing information, because it presents data spatially — the information is located in the part of the world to which it refers.

a) Refer to Figure 3–22. On a map of the world, shade each of the countries of refuge in a light green colour.

b) Indicate the total number of refugees within each country.

c) Draw arrows to each of these countries of refuge from the refugees' countries of origin.

d) Refer to Figure 3–23. Shade each of the countries of resettlement in a dark green colour. Annotate the map further by indicating the number of refugees received within each of these countries in 2000.

e) Using the migration information given on the following two pages, draw "flow arrows" to show the movement of migrants throughout the world. Write notes indicating numbers and reasons for migration.

f) On a separate piece of paper, write a conclusion about the overall pattern of migration and direction of flow you see reflected on your map.

g) How does this map compare with the map showing the Human Development Index in Figure 3–13 on page 68? For example, do the regions of out-migration correspond with those countries showing a low Human Development Index rating?

h) Compare your map with the development models of Rostow and Wallerstein. Do areas of in-migration correspond with regions of high consumption, such as Canada, the United States, Europe, and Oceania? Do areas of in-migration correspond with the core areas defined by Wallerstein? Do the areas of out-migration correspond with those that have a highest debt as a percentage of their gross national product (see Figure 3–17, on page 75)? Write a summary describing whether you feel your map supports the theories of Rostow and Wallerstein, and why or why not.

i) It may be argued that significant flows of people from one region of the world to another is evidence of disparity among the world's regions. Does the annotated migration map support this statement? Why or why not?

Migration information from the World Migration Report, 2000

East Asia (China, Hong Kong, Taiwan, Korea, Japan, and so on)

- Migration within this region is strictly controlled. Few immigrant workers can become permanent citizens.
- Japan, Hong Kong, and Taiwan are major destinations for migrant workers.
- Japan contains 1.5 million foreign workers; Taiwan has about 270 000.
- Korea is experiencing a large increase in migration. Approximately 280 000 people move there per year to find work.
- India hosts 100 000 refugees from Tibet and China, and 66 000 from Sri Lanka.
- China has 291 000 refugees from Vietnam on the Chinese mainland.
- Nepal has 96 000 refugees from Bhutan.

Southeast Asia (Malaysia, Singapore, Myanmar, Thailand, and so on)

- Most migration has headed toward East Asia and the Middle East.
- Malaysia (with 1.2 million migrant residents) and Singapore (with foreign workers making up 27 percent of its total workforce) attract large numbers of migrant workers.
- Malaysia has 150 000 Chinese refugees and 45 000 from the Philippines. It received 50 000 during 2000.
- Thailand has over 100 000 refugees who fled Myanmar.
- Conflict in Sri Lanka has caused the displacement of 650 000 of its people.

The Middle East and South Asia (the countries of the Eastern Mediterranean, India, Pakistan, Sri Lanka, and Bangladesh)

- There are a large number of migrant workers in states surrounding the Gulf, mostly from southern Asia (India, Bangladesh, and Pakistan).

- India contains 100 000 Tibetan and 66 000 Sri Lankan refugees.
- Indians living outside India total 15 million.
- In 2001, Pakistan took in 1 million refugees who had fled Afghanistan.
- Israel has received 1 million Jewish settlers in the last ten years.

Sub-Saharan Africa

- There are a large number of forced migrants throughout the countries of central Africa.
- Brain drain is occurring in Nigeria, Senegal, Uganda, Ghana, Zambia, and Zimbabwe, because of migration. People migrate mostly to Europe, North America, and the Middle East.
- Algeria has 165 000 refugees from Western Sahara.
- Some 300 000 Angolan refugees have fled to surrounding countries, mainly to the Democratic Republic of the Congo, and to Zambia.
- Some 95 000 refugees have fled from the Democratic Republic of the Congo to Tanzania, while 25 000 have fled to Zambia.
- Sudan has 400 000 refugees, mostly from Ethiopia, Chad, Eritrea, Uganda, and the Democratic Republic of the Congo.
- There are 338 000 refugees living in Ethiopia, having escaped conflict in Somalia (285 000), Sudan (36 000), and Djibouti (8000).

Eastern Europe, Russia, and the Commonwealth of Independent States

- Russia has received over 2 million returning Russians from newer surrounding independent states.
- Russia has up to 1.5 million unauthorized migrants in the country.

- Russia has over 100 000 refugees from Afghanistan.
- Kazakhstan has 6000 Tajik and 3000 Afghan refugees in the country.
- There is a movement of migrants through Eastern European countries (such as the Czech Republic, Turkey, Romania, and Hungary), on the way to Western European countries, searching for work.

Western and Southern Europe

- The European Union remains a magnet for foreign workers.
- A lot of migrants come to Europe from Morocco, Algeria (mainly to France), Tunisia, and Egypt.
- Europe contains approximately 3 million illegal migrants.
- Germany contains the largest influx of migrants (more than all other European countries combined). Germany contains 5 million registered workers (mostly from Turkey), while France has 2.25 million, and the United Kingdom over 1 million.
- Germany receives most refugees (about 100 000 each year) from Yugoslavia, Turkey, and Iraq.
- The United Kingdom receives 50 000 total refugees each year from Sri Lanka, Yugoslavia, Russia, and Afghanistan.
- Spain receives 8000 migrants each year, mostly from Algeria.

South America

- Argentina attracts most South American migrants (but they also lose significant numbers to the United States).
- Argentina has many Bolivian migrants in the country.
- Over 1.5 million Brazilians live in other countries (mostly the United States, Europe, and Japan).

- Nearly 2 million Colombians live in other countries (mostly the United States and Europe).
- Many Colombians go to Venezuela. An estimated 1 million people live there as illegal migrants.

North and Central America

- The United States receives 1 million people (and an estimated 300 000 illegal migrants) each year. Most come from Mexico (20 percent), China, India, and the Philippines. There are about 8 million Mexican-born migrants in the United States.
- The United States has a total of approximately 5 million illegal migrants living there.
- About US$5.5 billion is sent back to families in Mexico from the United States.
- The United States has over 1 million Cuban migrants.
- Mexico receives many migrant workers from Nicaragua and other Central American countries.
- The Caribbean countries lose many thousands of people each year through migration (mostly to the United States and Canada).
- Canada receives between 200 000 and 250 000 migrants each year, half of them from Asian countries (China, India, the Philippines, and so on). It receives 20 000 to 25 000 refugee claimants each year.
- Canada has one of the quickest processes for naturalization (becoming a citizen) — three years.

Oceania

- Nearly 25 percent of Australians are foreign-born (mostly from the United Kingdom).
- About 25 percent of new migrants to Australia come from Asia. Australia now has approximately 150 national groups living there.

CHAPTER 4

Feeding the Planet

The amount of food available to feed the planet's growing population is a good news/bad news situation. The good news is that we are more efficient at feeding the world's population today than ever before. Within the last four decades, food supplies rose dramatically, due to advances in agricultural science. Although it is not evenly distributed, we currently have enough food, just with the grain we grow, to provide every person on this planet with over 3200 calories of food energy per day. This exceeds the 2600 calories required daily to sustain an individual's normal body weight.

FIGURE 4–1 **Food supply shortfalls**

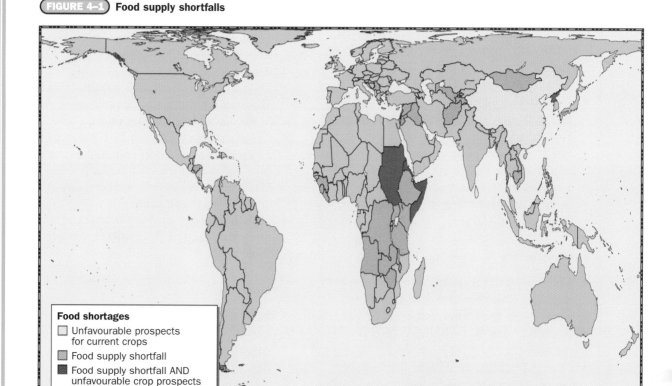

Food shortages
- ☐ Unfavourable prospects for current crops
- ☐ Food supply shortfall
- ■ Food supply shortfall AND unfavourable crop prospects

This map shows areas of the world experiencing food supply shortfalls. Are you surprised by any of the information presented? Why or why not?

- Explain how people perceive resources and sustainable development differently, at different times and in different places.
- Evaluate the effectiveness of methods used by different organizations, governments, and industries to find short- and long-term solutions to hunger and food-supply issues.
- Analyse the impact of past and current trends in agriculture.
- Analyse examples of efforts to increase the productivity in agriculture and its short- and long-term economic, social, and environmental impacts.

- Demonstrate an understanding of remote sensing geotechnology, used in the analysis and synthesis of geographic data.
- Demonstrate an understanding of how economies and environments in some places may be affected by decisions made in other places.
- Explain how local participation in the development process can build sustainable communities.

Scientific research has produced stronger seeds and plants, enabled us to improve the environments within which they grow, and provided them with freshwater through the latest developments in irrigation. In addition, the movement of food around the world has reached record levels, as governments trade their surplus amounts with one another. We are also better prepared to deal with natural disasters that may bring about extreme shortages of food. Giant transporter airplanes, efficient non-government organizations, and advanced storage systems help us to cope with emergencies.

Despite all of this, bad news still exists.

- The Food and Agriculture Organization of the United Nations (FAO) estimates that 15 000 children die each day from diseases related to a weakening of the body, due to lack of food or the right balance of food.
- The United Nations (UN) estimates that approximately 800 million people do not receive adequate food supplies daily.
- The vast improvements we have made in food production are beginning to lose their effectiveness: the chemicals we use on soil are causing a lower return in food production than they did in previous years.
- The amount of available cropland in the world will fall from 0.23 hectares per person in 2001, to 0.13 hectares per person in 2050.
- The cropland we use has suffered in quality because of erosion and soil degradation.

Over the next three decades, we will face an additional 3 billion mouths to feed. How will we produce enough food to sustain everyone nutritionally?

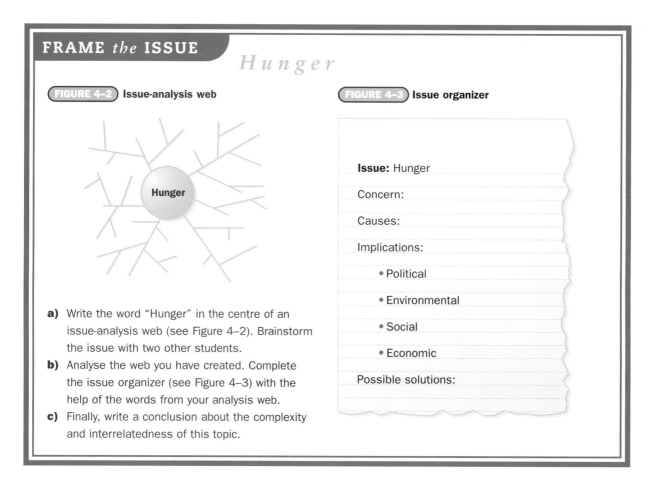

FRAME *the* ISSUE

Hunger

FIGURE 4–2 Issue-analysis web

FIGURE 4–3 Issue organizer

Hunger

Issue: Hunger

Concern:

Causes:

Implications:

• Political

• Environmental

• Social

• Economic

Possible solutions:

a) Write the word "Hunger" in the centre of an issue-analysis web (see Figure 4–2). Brainstorm the issue with two other students.

b) Analyse the web you have created. Complete the issue organizer (see Figure 4–3) with the help of the words from your analysis web.

c) Finally, write a conclusion about the complexity and interrelatedness of this topic.

Chronic Persistent Hunger and Famine

The most pressing food issue in the world today is widespread **chronic persistent hunger (CPH)**, which may be caused by either of the following two conditions:

- Undernutrition: This condition results from not getting enough food to eat. A person who is undernourished — especially a child — becomes too weak to resist common diseases. Many die from common diseases such as measles and diarrhea.

- Malnutrition: This condition results from a poorly balanced diet, where people do not get enough specific nutrients such as proteins, minerals, vitamins, and carbohydrates. Eventually, these deficiencies cause the body to become prone to common diseases such as diarrhea and influenza, and this can result in death. Protein malnutrition can result, especially in children, in an often fatal condition called *kwashiorkor*.

Millions of people — especially children under the age of 5 — suffer from the consequences of chronic persistent hunger. Nine out of ten people who die from a hunger-related disease die from malnutrition or gradual undernutrition. Chronic persistent hunger is a leading cause of death in countries where infant mortality is high. It is a condition that is very difficult to detect, as children with chronic persistent hunger sometimes appear healthy. The Food and Agriculture Organization of the United Nations estimates that more than 13 million children die each year because of chronic persistent hunger.

Another pressing food issue the world faces is **famine**. Although the images of famine that we see on television are dramatic, famine actually accounts for only one-tenth of all hunger-related deaths. Famine is a condition of rapid and severe undernutrition, where food shortages occur because of an inability to grow or collect food. This is often caused by rapid changes in an area's quality of soil, due to lack of rainfall. Famine sufferers often attempt to migrate to areas where help is available, but this is often difficult because they are weak from lack of nourishment.

Both types of starvation — chronic persistent hunger and famine — are tragic. As a global community, we can move emergency food aid into a famine situation quite efficiently, but chronic persistent hunger is a more difficult issue to remedy.

FIGURE 4–4 In the famine-stricken village of Wajid, Somalia, this boy waits with others for aid to arrive. What factors lead to famine? How can other countries help the population cope?

1. Explain what is meant by "good news" and by "bad news" regarding world hunger.

2. Explain why chronic persistent hunger is a more serious problem than famine.

3. How do the media contribute to the myth that famine is the leading cause of hunger-related death? Why might they do this, rather than highlighting chronic persistent hunger?

Issue briefing

Obesity: A malnutritional condition

Nearly one in three children in the developing world is underweight. However, according to the Worldwatch Institute, 55 percent of the population of the United States is overweight and 26 percent is considered obese (a malnutritional condition that can lead to heart disease and diabetes). In Canada, a 1997 National Population Health Survey found that 12 percent of Canadians are considered obese. The number of overweight people in developed nations is quickly on the rise.

According to the Worldwatch Institute, "Both developed and developing nations are paying a high price for malnutrition. The World Bank estimates that ... obesity cost the United States 12 percent of the national health-care budget in the late 1990s — US$118 billion — more than double the US$47 billion attributable to smoking."

In terms of solutions, the Institute suggests that women — as "nutritional gatekeepers" in many communities — be given opportunities for better education and health care.

Another solution, the Worldwatch Institute asserts, would be to launch a campaign similar to those used to discourage smoking, in order to deter consumers from high-fat and high-sodium foods. Taxes could also play a role in deterring people from buying low-nutrient foods.

a) Do you agree with the solutions suggested by the Worldwatch Institute? Which of these solutions do you think would work better?

b) What other steps could be taken to reduce obesity and malnutrition?

Complex Contributors to World Hunger

What is the cause of the hunger that plagues almost 800 million people today? There is no single cause, and until the many contributing factors causing hunger are understood, it will be difficult to find solutions.

Food First (The Institute for Food and Development Policy) defined 12 myths that surround hunger and that illustrate the complexity of this issue. Here are these myths, and Food First's responses to them.

Myth #1	*There is simply not enough food produced in the world to feed everyone.*
Response	There is enough food for everyone to receive about 2 kg a day: about 1 kg grains, beans, and nuts, 0.5 kg fruit and vegetables, and 0.5 kg grass-fed meat, milk, and eggs. Just the amount of grain produced is enough to ensure that each person receives 3500 calories daily.
Myth #2	*Nature is to blame for famine. There is little we can do to prevent large-scale hunger caused by drought or flooding.*
Response	Food is available for those who can afford to buy it, whereas the poor lack land, resources, or money to use as insurance against sudden famine. For example, when there were massive famines in Ethiopia, few suffered in the capital of Addis Ababa.
Myth #3	*There are too many people in the world. It is overpopulated. This results in too many mouths to feed.*
Response	There are heavily populated countries (for example, China) where hunger is not a widespread problem. Even though there are regional problems in these countries, the total production of food has increased enormously.
Myth #4	*Soil erosion, desertification, and the stripping of forests by small-scale farmers to create cropland, are major causes of widespread hunger.*
Response	Multinational corporations growing food for world trade are responsible for more environmental problems than are local farmers. A great deal of commercial farming results in **monocropping** (growing one crop only), most of which is for sale on a world market, rather than being used locally to feed people in poorer countries.
Myth #5	*Scientists will take care of the problem with advances in areas such as biotechnology, plant genetics, and engineering improvements to water supply problems.*
Response	Scientists have increased worldwide yields in foodcrops such as rice and wheat, yet hunger still persists in countries such as Mexico, where some of the scientific advances have taken place.
Myth #6	*Large farms will help. Large-scale production methods and operations will allow us to increase the amount of food available.*
Response	Small-scale farmers farm their land in a more intensive way than commercial farmers, so they reap more per square kilometre.
Myth #7	*The free market can end hunger. Market forces and competition will drive down the cost of food and promote increased production totals.*
Response	Free-market forces do little for the landless poor in the developing world.

International food corporations race to cut expenses faster than their competitors, often at the expense of poor workers and small-scale farmers.

Myth #8 *Free trade is the answer. Allowing countries to trade more freely, without the barriers of tariffs or taxes, will allow more food to move into areas of need.*

Response Allowing more free trade does not help to overcome local poverty and hunger. In Brazil, soybean exports increased dramatically. At the same time, local widespread hunger increased, affecting two-thirds of Brazil's population.

Myth #9 *Those suffering from hunger are too passive to get involved in the fight for better agricultural policies, to become involved in government, or to campaign for better options through political protests.*

Response The poor generally have no political power. Their daily lives are spent on survival. They do not have the resources to attain political support and run for office.

Myth #10 *Developed countries could alleviate a great deal of hunger by using their surplus production to provide more food aid for suffering countries.*

Response Aid shipments from developed nations help in emergency situations. However, they harm local food economies in the long run. It is difficult for farmers to sell their food locally when stockpiles of food aid sit in a warehouse to be given away for nothing.

Myth #11 *Developed nations benefit from the poverty of others. Low wages and poverty drive down the cost of importing goods from the developing world.*

Response If developed countries wish to transform developing countries into more affluent foreign markets to purchase their manufactured goods, they will need to alleviate poverty abroad.

Myth #12 *Open competition for basic resources such as land and water can create large-scale wealth in the hands of a few, thus depriving those people who need it most. Therefore open competition should not be allowed.*

Response Governments can attempt to balance the well-being of the few with that of the many through financial or taxation policies, without curtailing personal freedoms.

4. Although there is currently enough food produced on the planet to feed everyone, many people are starving. After reading the myths and responses, work with a partner to list as many reasons for global hunger as you can.

5. What sorts of steps could governments take to try to ensure that everyone's needs are met — those of large-scale farmers (multinational agribusinesses), small-scale farmers, and the hungry poor?

6. As an individual living in a developed nation, what can you do to help the world's hunger situation? Discuss this question with a partner, then share your feelings with the rest of the class.

7. If you were an executive at a multinational corporation like Nestlé, how would you respond to Food First? Select one of the myths/responses above. From the perspective of a multinational corporate executive, write a response to the myth, and a rebuttal to Food First's response.

Working to Increase Food Supplies — The Options

Despite the fact that there is currently enough food produced on the planet to feed the population, 800 million people are living in hunger and suffer from hunger-related illnesses. Reasons for this are complicated and plentiful, and include politics, economics, and distribution. For example, some people believe that allowing countries to trade more freely, without the barriers of tariffs or taxes, will allow more food to move into areas of need.

Because the world population will continue to grow this century (although at a decelerated rate), the planet will need greater amounts of food in the future. Going forward, an adequate amount of food must exist for any political, economic, or distribution-related solutions to be effective in overcoming global hunger. If current population growth rates continue, sub-Saharan Africa will need 2.5 times more grain than it presently produces, by 2025.

Global WARNING

TASTE SHIFTS

In China — which contains nearly one-fifth of the world's population — there has been a significant taste shift away from a diet based on rice and fish, to one based on meat and poultry. Due to China's large population, this shift will have an immense impact on world grain levels.

Meat and poultry require up to seven times more grain for animal feed than is necessary when humans consume the grain directly. Diets based on rice and fish require less grain than diets based on meat. A rice diet means that humans eat the grain directly, and less grain is necessary for feeding fish than for feeding pigs, chickens, cattle, and so on. Despite this fact, increasing numbers of people are opting for a meat-and-poultry-based diet. To satisfy China's current taste shift, the country would need to import the equivalent of all the wheat currently exported in the world today.

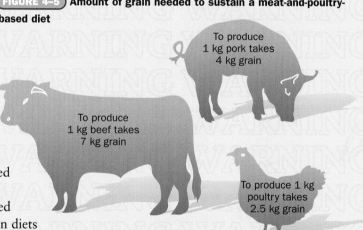

FIGURE 4–5 Amount of grain needed to sustain a meat-and-poultry-based diet

To produce 1 kg pork takes 4 kg grain

To produce 1 kg beef takes 7 kg grain

To produce 1 kg poultry takes 2.5 kg grain

a) What is meant by a "taste shift"?
b) Can you think of any taste shifts that have taken place in North America during your lifetime?
c) How might taste shifts to meat-and-poultry-based diets add further stresses to the world's capacity to feed itself?
d) What can be done, and by whom, to redirect or curb taste shifts that threaten the planet's sustainability?

Creating more cropland

One way to increase food production may be to increase the amount of cropland on which we grow our food. This is not a simple solution. For example, the United States produces its abundant amounts of food on 187 million hectares of arable land (0.7 hectares per person). This arable land produces enough food for 276 million people. The country exports huge quantities of food. But if the United States population grows at 1.0 percent — as it is expected to do — the population will double in 72 years. Meanwhile, **urbanization** (the expansion of cities and towns) and **erosion** (the wearing away of soil by wind or water) will reduce the amount of cropland in the United States to 117 million hectares by 2060. With a population of 520 million, this will mean only 0.2 hectares per person.

In total, there are about 1.4 billion hectares of cropland currently on the planet — about 0.23 hectares per person. Population predictions suggest that this amount of land would equal only 0.13 hectares per person by 2050. To have enough cropland to satisfy the predicted population in 2050, it is estimated that we will need 3.3 billion hectares of cropland by then.

Currently, throughout the world, it is estimated that we are using less than half the land that could be cultivated as cropland. Expansion of farmland could account for a 25 percent

FIGURE 4–6 According to the Worldwatch Institute, we have lost over 25 billion tonnes of topsoil worldwide, due to erosion. It takes 500 years for nature to produce 3 centimetres of topsoil, and 25 centimetres of topsoil is necessary to grow a crop. Thus, we are losing topsoil at 20 to 30 times its production rate.

FIGURE 4–7 Predicted land needs

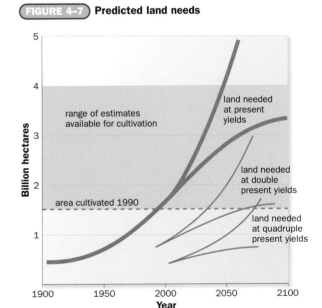

The heavy lines in this graph show the estimated land required to maintain present per capita food production at present yields (if world population grows as predicted). The lighter lines show land needs if crop yields are doubled and quadrupled.

increase in food supply over the next 50 years, but it is becoming difficult to expand farmland further. Take a look at why this is so:

- Potential lands are much less productive, as the best quality land has already been used.
- Much of the available land is located in environmentally sensitive areas, such as in forests that would need clearing, or on desert margins (the edges of deserts) that are drying out and cannot yield much.
- Much of the expansion would be made in hilly areas, which would result in increased amounts of soil erosion.
- Increased costs in time, amount of labour needed, and additives used on the poorer soils would make the land less profitable.

Using more fertilizer

Another way to make existing cropland more productive may be to increase the use of chemical additives. However, this solution is problematic.

Large users of fertilizers, such as the United States, Canada, and the European Union, are witnessing diminished returns on fertilizer usage. Farmers cannot expect to keep pouring larger amounts of chemicals onto soil and expect the same increase in yields as before. Fertilizer usage has levelled off even in countries such as China where, previously, usage had increased from 8 million tonnes in 1980 to 37 million tonnes in 1997.

Also, most fertilizers are petroleum-based. Their costs have risen along with world oil prices. Thus, for developing countries, fertilizers have become too expensive. Many of these poorer countries are turning to the less expensive (and less effective) use of crop residues, that is, reploughing decaying plants back into the soil, and recycling animal and human waste.

Many developed countries have realized the enormous risks associated with increased chemical spraying. Water **run-off** (surface water that collects and then runs into other water sources) is

FIGURE 4-8 World fertilizer use, 1950–1999

This figure shows that worldwide use of fertilizers dramatically increased between 1950 and 1990. In 1950, the total world use was 14 million tonnes (5.5 kilograms per person). By 1990, this had risen to 143 million tonnes (27.1 kilograms per person). However, since that time, there has been a steady levelling off in the use of chemical additives worldwide. Why is this?

contaminated by chemicals and pollutes streams, rivers, and **water tables** (natural underground water reservoirs). Increased concentrations of algae — which reduce oxygen levels in water habitats — have been blamed on chemical additives. Another problem is the amount of time it takes some chemicals to break down. It can take decades for some pollutants to cease being harmful to the lakes in which they are poured.

Greater use of pesticides

Pests cause enormous losses of crops. Worldwide losses of production before a crop can be harvested may be as high as 30 to 40 percent. A further 15 to 22 percent loss may result from poor storage and distribution facilities. In rice alone — the staple food for over 2 billion people — 50 percent losses of the crop often occur.

The farmer's main weapon in the war on pests is chemical spraying with pesticides. The term "pesticides" includes herbicides, fungicides, and insecticides.

FIGURE 4–9 Plant damage caused by insects in rice plants

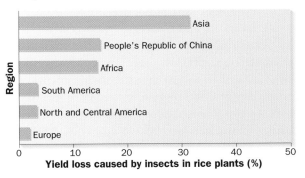

Insects attack all portions of the rice plant and all stages of plant growth. They also attack rice grains in storage. Feeders consist of the root feeders, stem borers, leafhoppers, planthoppers, defoliators, and grain-sucking insects.

One drawback to pesticide use is that, again, it is only the developed, richer countries of the world that can afford it. Many pests eventually become immune to the chemicals that are used (about 200 species of insects are known to be resistant to one or more insecticides), so research must be ongoing to develop new types of pesticide. North America uses approximately 30 percent of all pesticides, followed by Europe at 27 percent, and Japan at 12 percent.

Pesticides can also be harmful to humans. They have a cumulative effect in biological systems. In recognition of the potential harm of these sprays to human environments, more countries are turning to **integrated pest management (IPM)** processes (using knowledge about nature to protect against the enemies of plants). Integrated pest management has been described as "clean" (pesticide-free), sustainable farming. An example of integrated pest management is the use of predatory insects, which, by being allowed to consume their natural foods, help to protect the plant in some way.

Crop rotation (changing what is grown in the same fields from year to year) can also be used to disrupt an insect's normal lifecycle. In addition, crop rotation can allow a farmer to grow nitrogen-fixing plants such as alfalfa which, when ploughed back into the soil, enrich the soil with nitrogen and naturally create a more hostile environment for insects.

Issue briefing

The California grey ant

A welcome guest on the peach trees of Californian farms is the California grey ant. Traditionally, this ant would have been destroyed through insecticide spraying, but California Clean (an organization of farmers dedicated to farming using "clean" methods) discovered that the ant is really an asset. They learned that drops of nectar on their peach trees would attract the California grey ant. Following a snack of nectar, the ant turns its attention to a real meal — the peach tree borer — which normally devastates peach trees. This partnership between farmers and the California grey ant is an excellent example of integrated pest management (IPM).

FIGURE 4–10 Peach trees and the California grey ant form a mutually beneficial relationship.

Using freshwater more effectively

Perhaps the best way to produce more food on existing land is to use freshwater more effectively. This is particularly true if a farmer is growing high-yield, water-dependent crops. Again, the technology for this is not new — about 50 percent of all irrigation programs simply use low-engineered systems, such as a *shaduf* (a water-raising device, shown in Figure 4–11) and drainage ditches.

Some 50 percent of irrigation projects emerge because of the construction of megadams, such as the Aswan in Egypt, the Volta in Ghana, or the Three Gorges in China. All large rivers are targets for development, as dams bring tremendous economic gains in extra energy, flood control, and the availability of freshwater for irrigation schemes. Nevertheless, there are concerns about the effects of dams on natural environments, the social disruptions dams cause, and their mounting costs — the Three Gorges dam, for example, is costing China between US$40 and US$75 billion.

FIGURE 4–11 A *shaduf,* like this one in Egypt (above), consists of a container and a lever. The container is filled with water from a river, canal, and so on, then it is levered up and swung round, to be emptied into an irrigation canal. The Aswan dam (right), also in Egypt, is an example of a megadam. What are the advantages and limitations of each of these methods of harvesting water?

FIGURE 4–12 Organizer — Increasing food yields

	Current situation	Prediction for future	Impact on developed countries	Impact on developing countries
Amount of cropland				
Fertilizer use				
Pesticide use				
Freshwater needs				

There are problems associated with irrigation. It removes water faster than nature can replenish the supply. Also, diseases such as bilharzia (caused by water-dwelling parasites) and sleeping sickness (a fatal disease caused by the bite of a tsetse fly) proliferate around the stagnant water in irrigation ditches.

Overirrigation is another problem. It produces waterlogging and salting of fields. It is estimated that, in India, over 50 percent of the fields are damaged by overirrigation.

Because of these concerns, the era of irrigation is in decline. Between 1950 and 2000, the area of irrigated land worldwide grew from 94 million to 272 million hectares, but now only small amounts of development are taking place.

8. You have been asked by the World Bank to report on methods to increase food production to accommodate the growing global population. Complete an organizer like that in Figure 4–12; then write a paragraph summarizing your thoughts on the various options for increasing food yields.

9. The spread of cities into surrounding agricultural land is a significant problem worldwide. Develop a four-frame cartoon strip that shows the dangers of this process, with regard to disappearing foodlands.

10. Draft an e-mail you could send to the Food and Agriculture Organization of the United Nations about your concerns regarding the diminishing amount of cropland worldwide.

11. a) Work in groups of four, split into two pairs. One pair will represent the commercial companies that produce and promote various methods of controlling pests, weeds, and insects, as a means of increasing global food production. The other pair will play the role of members of a citizens' action group who are worried about this increased usage. Make point-form notes for your arguments, then present them to the other pair and discuss the problem.

b) As a foursome, draft a written statement (to which you all agree) about whether you support increased pesticide usage or not, or ways in which their use could be controlled so that both sides are satisfied. Share these statements with the rest of the class.

Case in point — Sudan

Sudan is the largest country in Africa, covering 2.5 million square kilometres (three times the size of Ontario). It has great diversity in each of its three physical regions. Its northern area — covering about one-third of the country — is desert. Its central portion is mostly semi-arid (semi-dry), with low-rising mountains in the east and west. The south (known as the Sudd) contains large areas of swampland and tropical rain forest.

Sudan's main resource is its large rivers. These south-to-north-flowing rivers supply a lifeline of freshwater to the semi-arid central regions, and to the dry north regions. Sudan has considerable land with fertile soil in an area between the Blue and White Nile rivers, and between the Blue Nile and Atbarah, as well as an estimated 80 million hectares of potential cropland. However, crops are currently grown on only about 5.5 million hectares.

Although there are 2 million hectares of irrigated land in Sudan, most food and most export crops are grown on land that relies on rain instead of irrigation. One of the major causes of food shortages in Sudan has been continuous and severe drought. As a result, the desertlands of northern Sudan have expanded southward. In addition, the stripping of trees and vegetation by local farmers (to create precious farmland or to burn as fuel) has left desert margins very dry and susceptible to soil erosion.

The most important crop in Sudan is *durra* (sorghum), a type of grain, which forms the staple diet of the Sudanese. In 1970, Sudan believed that with this crop, not only would it be self-sufficient in terms of feeding its people for the next 30 years, but would also become the "breadbasket" of Africa — meaning that it would be that continent's major food-growing region. However, with so much reliance on rainfall, this crop has gone through varying cycles of success.

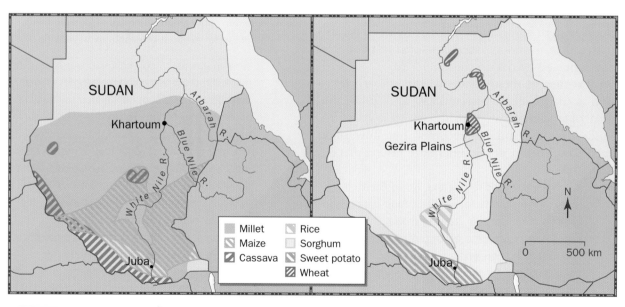

FIGURE 4–13 Where are the main crop-growing regions in Sudan?

Sudan has a long history of irrigating its croplands using water from its large rivers. The most significant effort in this regard was the creation of the Gezira Scheme to irrigate the Gezira plains — an area in northern Sudan that would normally be dry, with desert conditions. Around 2 million hectares of its land are irrigated today.

At a glance — *Sudan*

- Population: 36 080 373
- Population growth rate: 2.79%
- Birth rate: 37.89 births/1000
- Death rate: 10.04 deaths/1000
- Infant mortality rate: 68.67 deaths/ 1000 live births
- Life expectancy: 56.94
- Total fertility rate: 5.35 children born/woman
- Calorie consumption per capita: 2274
- Ethnic groups: black African 52%, Arab 39%, Beja 6%, foreigners 2%, other 1% Religions: Sunni Muslim 70% (in north), indigenous beliefs 25%, Christian 5% (mostly in south and Khartoum)
- GDP per capita: US$1000 (PPP)

An important source of energy was found in the late 1970s when vast amounts of oil and gas were discovered in the south and central areas of Sudan, as well as off the Red Sea coastline. These oil reserves are estimated to hold between 600 million and 1.2 billion barrels. Sudan is currently producing 12 000 barrels of oil per day and, in 2000, became an oil exporter.

Many have blamed the international community, and the policies of the World Bank and the International Monetary Fund (IMF) for Sudan's food problems. When the United Kingdom controlled Sudan (until 1950), it promoted the production of cotton, to supply the United Kingdom's textile mills with an inexpensive raw material. Thus, instead of focussing on growing food for local consumption, Sudan began growing cash crops for export — a practice that would last for more than 50 years. With the collapse of cotton prices in the 1960s, Sudan's main international creditor, the World Bank, allowed Sudan to grow food for local consumption, which worked fairly well. Then in the late 1970s and 1980s, as the country worked to improve its infrastructure, Sudan once again struggled with a crippling debt.

FIGURE 4–14

Climate data for Khartoum, Sudan

	Jan	Feb	Mar	Apr	May	Jun	Jul	Aug	Sept	Oct	Nov	Dec	Avg
Maximum temperature (°C)	32	34	38	41	42	41	38	37	39	40	36	33	38
													Total
Amount of rainfall (mm)	0	0	0	0	2.5	7	53	71	18	5	0	0	156.5

Climate data for Juba, Sudan

	Jan	Feb	Mar	Apr	May	Jun	Jul	Aug	Sept	Oct	Nov	Dec	Avg
Maximum temperature (°C)	37	38	37	36	33	33	31	31	33	34	36	37	35
													Total
Amount of rainfall (mm)	5	15	33	122	150	135	122	132	107	94	36	18	969

The above data shows the difference in climate between the city of Khartoum in the north, and the city of Juba in the extreme south.

So, at the insistence of the World Bank and the International Monetary Fund, Sudan reverted to growing cotton and other cash crops. Cotton is a difficult and expensive crop to farm; it requires constant spraying for insects and is very labour-intensive. During the late 1970s and 1980s, for every US$3 that Sudan relinquished to repay its debt, it earned only US$1 from cash-crop exports. Despite this, the World Bank still believes that Sudan is better at growing cash crops such as sugar and dairy products, for export, while relying on others in the world (mainly the United States) for its food supply.

Social and economic inequalities between the rich minority and the poor majority of the population have also contributed to food shortages in Sudan. The country is home to many millionaire farmers who own thousands of hectares of commercial farmland, while 80 percent of the population consists of poor workers who live off the land. Many have been dispossessed of their land because they do not hold a legal land title. Numerous people work for low wages on their own former land, which is now owned by rich, commercial farmers. Some of these rich farmers belong to an **economic cartel** (a group that controls the price of food and level of wages for the poor). Many poor people migrate to cities like Khartoum, in search of work and food, but there are others who refuse to leave the impover-ished, rural lands and they become victims when famine strikes.

Another reason for Sudan's continued food shortages is a civil war that has continued for decades. Sudan is a country of cultural diversity, with two main cultures — Arab and black African. Arabic-speaking Muslims live throughout the northern part of Sudan, while the southern half of the country contains a variety of religious groups, speaking a variety of languages. Although the Islamic government promised cultural, religious,

FIGURE 4–15 The irrigation scheme in the Gezira region of Sudan is the largest in the world.

and political freedom for the non-Islamic south in 1972, it tried to impose Islamic law on the whole country in 1983. In response, a rebel militia force — the Sudan People's Liberation Movement (SPLM) — was formed in the south, and began fighting to control the region. In 1989, the Sudanese army took control of Sudan and formed a government as the National Islamic Front and, in late 2000, a new rebel group formed the South Sudan Liberation Movement (SSLM).

The civil war has now spread to many regions of the country. It is estimated that at least 1.5 million people have been killed, and millions more forced to flee from their homes. Many villages and farming communities have been abandoned.

Looking to Sudan's future

In 2001, a Food and Agriculture Organization/World Food Programme Assessment Mission studied Sudan's food supplies and found the results worrisome. (The World Food Programme for the United Nations was established in 1963 to fight world hunger.) The mission believes that Sudan will face severe food shortages in the western and southern parts of the country. Poor harvests, the depletion of emergency stocks, and increased local prices for food are still a problem.

With its vast lands and favourable climate, southern Sudan has great potential for increasing the food supply. But rainfall amounts have become erratic and unreliable, and this area is still feeling the effects of the ongoing civil war. It has a weak infrastructure and a debt of US$24 billion (over twice the size of its total gross national product).

Aid agencies believe that more changes, such as land ownership and political stability, are needed for Sudan's food situation to improve.

An estimated 2.4 million Sudanese, most of whom live in the south, need help in obtaining a constant supply of food. In the Bahr El Ghazal region in southern Sudan, as many as 45 percent of the population is malnourished.

12. Refer to the climate data for Khartoum and Juba in Figure 4–14. Is there evidence that precipitation and temperature are of a seasonal nature in both Khartoum and Juba? What might the implications be for the Sudanese?

13. Refer to Figure 4–16. How would you summarize the production trends for sorghum and wheat during these years?

14. Assume that there is a lack of seasonal rainfall in central Sudan, around Khartoum.
    a) How would this affect the growth of sorghum and wheat in central Sudan?
    b) How might the people cope with this problem?

15. a) Using the following headings, explain how each of these factors has impacted food supplies in Sudan: Drought; International community; Social inequality; Conflict.
    b) What steps could be taken in each of these four areas to improve the situation?

FIGURE 4–16 Sorghum and wheat production in Sudan, 1961–2000

Year	Sorghum production (tonnes)	Wheat production (tonnes)
1961	1 433 600	26 400
1965	1 094 427	56 008
1970	1 535 000	115 300
1975	2 143 000	269 000
1980	2 084 000	231 000
1985	3 597 000	79 000
1990	1 180 000	409 000
1995	2 450 000	448 000
2000	2 521 000	214 000
2001	2 488 000	334 000

Remote sensing

Remote sensing is the process of recording information about an object or phenomenon without being in physical contact with that object or phenomenon.

Aerial photography

As used for geographical analysis, remote sensing tends to involve two separate but related technologies — aerial photography and satellite imagery. In aerial photography, photographs are taken from cameras mounted on the underside of an airplane. The photographs can be recorded on film, or digitally onto a computer-storage device. Aerial photographs provide geographers with high-resolution (highly detailed) pictures of a relatively small area.

Most aerial photography uses only visible energy to create pictures. This makes the photographs easy to use and understand — they are simply black-and-white photographs. Visible energy is the small part of the electromagnetic spectrum that is visible to the human eye. It contains the colours of the rainbow and every shade in-between.

Satellite imagery

While aerial photographs are easy to use, they also have significant limitations. They show only a small part of the earth's surface, and record only what the eye can see. Satellite imagery is not restricted in this way. The images are recorded by a satellite in orbit many hundreds of kilometres above the earth's surface. The satellite's array of sensors can record energy from almost any part of the electromagnetic spectrum, allowing non-visible energy, such as infrared, to be recorded. State-of-the-art satellite imagery has a resolution that is comparable to that of aerial photography, while also capturing views of large areas. Depending on how far away the satellite is positioned, it is possible for almost half of the earth's surface to be recorded at once.

Satellite imagery is digital — information is recorded on a digital-storage device such as a hard drive. Images are recorded in a matrix (grid). Every cell in the grid is given a number that corresponds to the information that the sensor has detected. For example, in a given band of energy, the sensor might detect lots of energy for trees, which would be recorded as 1000; water might emit only a small amount of energy and would be recorded as 50. Interpreting satellite imagery takes a lot of training and practice.

Each of the numerous satellites positioned around the world (Landsat 1, 2, 3, 4, 5, and 7, SPOT 1, 2, and 3, Seasat, Earth Observation Satellites (EOS), Geostationary Operational Environmental Satellites (GOES), Advanced Very High Radiometric Resolution (AVHRR) satellites, Metrosat, RadarSat, Ikonos, Caterra, and so on) has special abilities and purposes. For example, Advanced Very High Radiometric Resolution and Geostationary Operational Environmental Satellites are designed for weather forecasting and analysis, whereas Seasat is designed to provide information about marine and coastal phenomena.

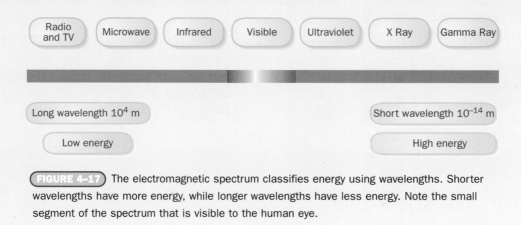

| Radio and TV | Microwave | Infrared | Visible | Ultraviolet | X Ray | Gamma Ray |

Long wavelength 10^4 m

Short wavelength 10^{-14} m

Low energy

High energy

FIGURE 4–17 The electromagnetic spectrum classifies energy using wavelengths. Shorter wavelengths have more energy, while longer wavelengths have less energy. Note the small segment of the spectrum that is visible to the human eye.

Applications of remote sensing in Sudan

To determine Sudan's potential food production, the Food and Agriculture Organization of the United Nations (FAO) uses two different satellites and techniques — the Normalized Difference Vegetation Index (NDVI) and the Cold Cloud Duration (CCD).

Normalized Difference Vegetation Index (NDVI)

This index is based on satellite imagery using infrared energy and some visible energy. The result is a calculated image that shows dark green for areas that are heavily vegetated, and light green for areas that have very little vegetation.

Cold Cloud Duration analysis (CCD)

Metrosat satellite imagery is used to give the size, temperature, and duration of cloud over Sudan; Cold Cloud Duration analyses this to determine the rainfall for an area. The colder the cloud (especially colder than $-38°C$), the more rain. A second part of the analysis measures how long a cloud has maintained a cold temperature — a cloud that has been cold for a long time is more likely to produce precipitation.

Image differencing

The Normalized Difference Vegetation Index reveals the health and richness of the vegetation, and Cold Cloud Duration determines an area's rainfall. How can this information be used in a predictive way?

Image differencing takes advantage of the digital storage of remotely sensed imagery to determine differences between two images of the same area, taken at different times. The numeric values in each corresponding cell of both images are subtracted. The resulting image shows the degree of change — either positive or negative — that has occurred. Differenced images usually have two colours (often red and green) that correspond either to new information, or to information that is no longer present in the image.

a) Create a chart that illustrates the similarities and differences between satellite imagery and aerial photography.

b) How might image differencing be applied to other areas of geography?

c) With your classmates, discuss some of the potential problems that may arise from the ability to predict crop yields — either high or low.

Visit www.gagelearning.com/onthethreshold for activities related to satellite imagery.

FIGURE 4–18 This image shows the difference between the average NDVI for Africa in August 2000, and the average for Africa in August over the last 20 years. Positive change (lusher vegetation than average) is green and negative change (drier than average) is dark red.

Looking to Science for Solutions

Human population numbers have boomed in the last 150 years. As discussed in Chapter 2, many neo-Malthusian demographers predicted "doom and gloom" on the basis that, eventually, we would not be able to feed ourselves. According to the Worldwatch Institute, if the entire world ate the amounts and kinds of food consumed in North America, we would need two additional planets to feed everyone. Here lies the danger: more and more people are eating like North Americans. Does the earth have the capacity to grow enough for this new demand? Is a Green Revolution the answer?

The Green Revolution

The Green Revolution is the use of technology to generate plants that produce high yield with few resources. Such plants must mature quickly, be resistant to disease and pests, and require little water. It has resulted in the development of new varieties of "high-response seeds" that increase crop yields.

First developed in the mid-1940s in Mexico, dwarf varieties of wheat (that channelled growth into the grain rather than the stem) produced yields that were two or more times greater than normal. By 1956, Mexico became self-sufficient in wheat production (meaning they could grow enough wheat to satisfy demand within Mexico, without having to import any) and, by 1964, Mexico was exporting half a million tonnes of wheat annually. In the Philippines in the 1960s, scientists at the International Rice Research Institute duplicated these successes by developing a high-yielding strain of rice.

These advances had dramatic results. India reaped great benefits when it started its high-yielding variety seed program (HVP) in 1966, using five types of these higher-yield seeds (wheat, rice, sorghum, maize, and millet). These seeds, with the exception of rice, were all drought-resistant and had short growing seasons, so crops became immune to monsoon droughts. India's grain production increased fourfold in 20 years, and the country became self-sufficient.

By the mid-1980s, high-yielding varieties made up 50 percent of all grains grown in the world. According to the Food and Agriculture Organization of the United Nations, yields today are 75 percent higher than in the early 1960s.

The Green Revolution increased the opportunity to **double crop** (grow and harvest two successive crops in one year). New plants matured faster because they were less sensitive to changes in daylight; the yields produced were 2 to 4 times greater than normal. Double cropping was possible in many parts of the world, such as India, East Asia, and Central America, where extra food production was needed most.

FIGURE 4–19 Rows of experimental rice plants await further testing at the International Rice Research Institute in the Philippines.

Other advantages brought about by the Green Revolution included higher farm incomes, more varied diets, the development of an infrastructure to cope with increased movement of grains, and a reduction in the cost of food. Over the last 30 years, the cost of food has not risen as fast as people's incomes or purchasing power and therefore food is more affordable. Here, the real beneficiaries are the poor, since food purchases take up a larger proportion of everyday spending for lower-income groups.

Costs of the Green Revolution

The Green Revolution does not come without costs, however.

FIGURE 4–20 The Green Revolution has been helped by sophisticated technology like this blueberry harvester, which gently shakes the fruit loose and collects it for an efficient harvest.

- The increased use of chemicals poses *human and environmental threats*. Many multinational corporations now farm in developing countries where environmental and safety regulations are less stringent, and where many chemicals are not banned. This has been described by opponents of the Green Revolution as a **race to the bottom** — environmental groups see the practice of racing to find a lack of chemical controls as environmentally and socially degrading.
- *Plant diversity has decreased*. While double cropping was possible in some cases, many farms practised monocropping. Here, a single type of plant is the only thing that survives massive chemical applications, which makes the new superplants healthier, but destroys other living organisms.
- Some new super seeds require *three times more water and fertilizer* than traditional crops, and are often too expensive for poor farmers.

- Tenant farmers and **sharecroppers** (tenant farmers who pay a portion of each crop as rent) have not benefitted much from the Green Revolution. In many countries, the gap between rich and poor farmers has increased greatly. Large commercial farmers and companies have bought more land, and the world has seen *an increase in rural, landless poor*.
- As farming becomes more scientific and mechanical, there are *fewer jobs available for the poor*.
- It is estimated that about 65 percent of all agricultural biotech research is being done by private corporations with profit as a motive. In some cases, patents protect important scientific findings, so royalty payments to use this technology will *add to the costs for poorer farmers*.

The New Green Revolution

The Food and Agriculture Organization of the United Nations states that new breakthroughs in food production are needed if hunger levels are to be halved in the next 20 years. Breakthroughs alone are not enough. They must be introduced alongside other initiatives, such as media influence on taste shifts (to promote diets low in inefficiently produced meat and poultry), the reduction of countries' debts, and the facilitation of the political will of farmers and consumers. The Food and Agriculture Organization of the United Nations is encouraging a **New Green Revolution** that will:

- *create even larger yields*
- look at *ways in which food production could be increased in non-grain groups* (such as vegetables, livestock, and fish)
- develop research centres to *create a new generation of plants and animals*
- use the latest methods of **genetic engineering** (altering hereditary characteristics by linking DNA fragments from different organisms), to *create **genetically modified organisms (GMOs)*** (see "Frame of reference")
- further isolate specific plant characteristics and manipulate their blending patterns to *form new species aimed at growth in marginally productive lands*

Not all improvements in science and farming technologies need to be innovations. Today, there is a push to better understand the traditional practices of farming: shifting agriculture to low-latitude forests (where cleared land in the forest will be farmed until the soil becomes exhausted); alley cropping (crops grown between nitrogen-fixing trees such as acacias); and improving soil and water management with traditional ditches and irrigation.

Researchers are working to share knowledge worldwide. There are enhanced learning opportunities for those in rural areas in poor countries — especially women. Many women in developing nations have not had the opportunities to hold jobs that require more education than basic literacy. Today, an increasing number of women are enrolling in agricultural training programs and becoming agricultural scientists.

Working partnerships between researchers and local farmers are encouraged, where insights may be exchanged regarding successes in the past, and what can be improved in the future. Researchers must take into account the fact that farmers' methods are traditional and are often deeply ingrained. Newer methods can be very different, and farmers may offer a great deal of resistance to changing their practices. In some cases, traditional farmers are receiving greater amounts of financial help to buy their own land.

The New Green Revolution recognizes the importance of integrated pest management techniques, which can boost crops without high financial and environmental costs.

Frame of reference

Transgenic/genetically modified organisms (GMOs): These are defined as any organisms that are altered by the addition of foreign genetic material, or by genetic engineering.

Biotechnology: This is defined by the Convention on Biological Diversity (CBD) as "any technological application that uses biological systems, living organisms, or derivatives thereof, to make or modify products or processes for specific use."

Impact of the New Green Revolution

Just as the amount of food available on the planet is a good news/bad news story, so is our ability to use science to increase this amount. Despite promising advances, there are drawbacks to the New Green Revolution.

Advantages of the increasing role of science in food production

- **Stronger plants:** Many varieties will become stronger and more resistant to drought, cooler climates, and poor-quality soil. For example, plants with deeper, stronger roots require less water to survive, and giving plants genes from arctic fish helps them to resist cold.

- **Nitrogren-fixing plants:** Since nitrogren is the main ingredient in fertilizer, these plants — which will become more common — will need less fertilizer.

- **Plants with fewer chemical needs:** Some plants are being developed that require less chemical support, which will make them less expensive and more available.

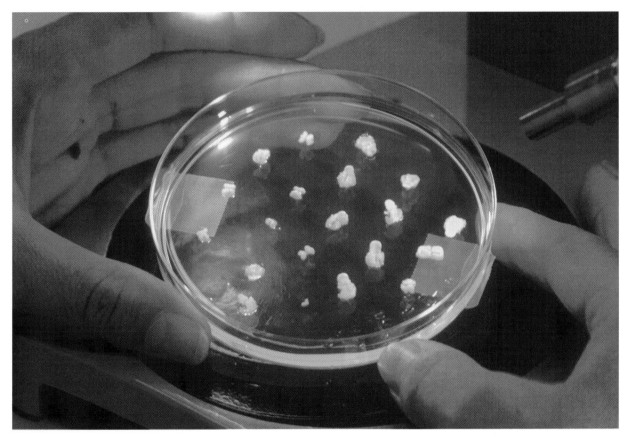

FIGURE 4–21 Genetic engineers analyse corn embryos. What sorts of ethical issues have arisen, or may arise, as a result of genetic manipulation?

Who are they?

The Consultative Group on International Agricultural Research

The Consultative Group on International Agricultural Research (CGIAR) was formed in 1971. It currently has 16 centres around the world. The group's task is to:

- develop seeds that require little fertilizer and that are drought- and insect-resistant.
- develop (or rediscover) non-polluting alternatives to fertilizers and pesticides.

- **Increased spread resistance:** Most crops today do not spread easily outside the farm environment. Genes could be manipulated to further lessen their chance of spreading into the natural habitat, where they could interfere with the wild ecosystem.

- **Availability of less expensive foods:** Agribusinesses believe that less expensive foods can be grown because of **economies of scale.** That is, when there is a great supply of an item, that item becomes cheaper; when the supply is small, the item becomes more difficult and hence more expensive to acquire. Economies of scale are therefore a case of supply and demand.

- **Possibility of higher yields:** Higher yields of some foods will provide more food for growing populations, especially in the developing world where population growth is concentrated.

- **Better nutrition and diet:** Plants can be programmed to provide for specific nutritional requirements. Extensive screening can eliminate possible allergens, or warn consumers about them.

- **Better livestock:** Improvements (faster growth, less body fat for meat production, and better digestive systems) can be made to all commercial animals.

- **Chances to learn from past mistakes:** DNA from plant remains helps scientists to understand what caused major plant epidemics in the past, and helps prevent such epidemics from recurring.

- **Medical help:** Plants and animals may offer new opportunities to fight human diseases. A new type of rice — Golden rice — helps prevent blindness for the millions of people in developing countries who suffer from vitamin A and iron deficiencies.

- **Consumer-designed produce:** Consumers will be able to determine what they desire from food — better flavour, or longer life in the refrigerator. (Experts believe that up to one-third of all fruits are wasted because of ripening spoilage.)

Disadvantages of the increasing role of science in food production

- **Greater chemical needs:** While some plants will require less chemical support, many genetically modified crops need more chemicals to protect them from weeds, insects, and fertilizers. These plants may contain harmful chemical residues.

- **Junk plants:** Plants being produced to feed off very specific chemicals — made by agribusinesses — are called "junk plants." These plants may reject traditional plant foods found in soil, and so make the farmer dependent upon specific agribusiness products.

- **Damaged natural ecosystems:** Genetically modified fish, like salmon grown on fish farms, do not have the migration drive to swim between freshwater and saltwater. If these fish escape into the natural habitat, they could drastically affect stream and river ecosystems by not returning to traditional spawning grounds. Likewise, trees designed for higher-yield growth could spread into the natural habitat and damage forests by growing too fast and thus becoming dominant. This could also result in a reduction in the gene pool, resulting from the forests' loss of native species and traditional strains of plants.

- **Commercial "kill" genes:** Some plants are given a self-destructive gene so that seeds will have to be purchased by farmers each year. This "terminator technology" would prevent use of home-produced seed, which is common practice in sustainable, traditional farming.

- **Destruction of ecosystems:** If self-destructive seeds spread into the natural habitat and mix with the genes in wild plants, they could be devastating to ecosystems. The sterility trait might spread via pollen to surrounding plants, and could make the seeds of these plants sterile.
- **Genetic modification:** Where do we stop? All plants and animals can be genetically modified, which raises ethical questions. How do we determine which plants and animals should be altered?
- **Expensive machinery:** Genetically modified crops grown by intensive agricultural methods need sophisticated, expensive machinery. Many small-scale farmers cannot afford new, more specialized equipment.
- **Loss of export market for poorer countries:** Crops traditionally grown in poorer, developing world countries can be modified to grow more cheaply in developed countries. For example, crops are being developed to withstand colder temperatures and could therefore be grown in northern countries. Perhaps bananas could someday be grown abundantly in the southern United States or southern Europe, lessening the costs and chance of spoilage for northern consumers.
- **Centralized control:** Ownership of new technology and genetic manipulation knowledge will be owned and patented by companies who could make high profits their goal, rather than making the technology affordable for poorer farmers.
- **New diseases:** While some plants are being bred to prevent them getting certain plant diseases, they may develop a resistance and create "super diseases" that are immune to new chemicals and genetic plants.
- **Faster-spreading diseases:** A loss of biodiversity may allow diseases to spread more quickly.

- **Consumer information:** Consumers may not be able to determine the true nutritional value or the age of the food they buy.
- **Increased health costs:** Integrated genes could result in allergies. For example, soybeans that were given Brazil nut genes have caused allergic reactions.

16. Why could it be argued that what science is doing to improve the quality of plants and animals today is not really new at all?

17. How would you define the term "Green Revolution"?

18. Complete a PMI (pluses, minuses, and interesting) chart for the topic "Green Revolution." Write a summary in which you highlight the main points under each heading. Take into account the various individuals and groups (for example, scientists, farmers, consumers) who stand to win or lose from the Green Revolution.

19. How would you compare the older Green Revolution with the New Green Revolution? Make a chart in which you discuss features of each that are both similar and different.

20. Biotech research is undertaken by both private corporations and governments. What do you think the advantages and disadvantages might be of the type of research undertaken by each?

21. Create a poster or Web home page either supporting or opposing the creation of genetically modified organisms.

22. Research the role of one of the large companies that dominate the market in genetically modified organisms. In a short report, suggest both what you like and dislike about this company's policies.

Case in point — Kerala

Kerala, formed in 1956, is one of India's smallest states. It covers an area of 38 863 square kilometres (less than the size of Nova Scotia) on the southwest coast of India. Like most states in India, Kerala struggled with low levels of socio-economic development at the time of its formation. It mirrored the rest of India with its high birth rates, large families, illiteracy, and poverty, and experienced widespread chronic persistent hunger (CPH). Health care was sporadic and there were high levels of infant mortality.

In the 1960s, the state government — which was communist — embarked on a plan of development that shifted tremendous development powers from the central government to local areas — the process of **decentralization**.

The food supply was not abundant, but the government issued a policy for people to share food equitably; food was supplied inexpensively so that everyone could receive at least two full meals per day. Over 15 000 food-ration shops were set up to achieve this target, and even the poor could afford the guaranteed low prices. Kerala did not receive outside help or food aid — unlike much of the rest of India — and became self-sufficient in food, partly because of a rapidly falling birth rate.

Providing free local hospitals and clinics played a vital role in reducing population growth. Free medicines and vaccinations were provided and over 80 percent of birthing deliveries were in hospitals. With a greater number of children surviving infancy

FIGURE 4–22 India

and families feeling more confident of this fact, the number of children per family fell dramatically to two or three children. Today, life expectancy is the same as that of a modern developed country. The state of Kerala spends 37 percent of its budget on health care and education, which has been seen as an important development in improving social conditions — especially eliminating hunger.

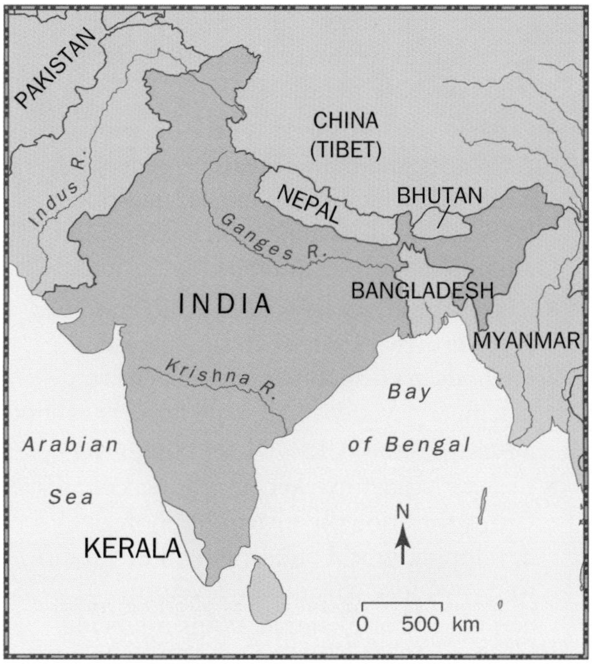

At a glance — India and Kerala

	India (as a whole)	Kerala
Population	1 030 000 000	33 000 000
Population growth rate	1.55%	1.2%
Total birth rate	24.3/1000	18.0/1000
Rural/urban birth rate	29.3/27.6	18.0/17.9
Total infant mortality	63.2/1000 live births	13.0/1000 live births
Rural/urban infant mortality	77/46	13/16
Life expectancy	62.9	72.0
Total fertility rate	3.0 children born/women	1.7 children born/women
GDP per capita	US$2200 (PPP)	US$324 (PPP)

Social changes were planned so that the poor could play a more equitable role in Keralan society:

- The decentralization program became the largest in the world. Over 3 million people (10 percent of Kerala's population) take part in the grama sabhas (local assemblies). These meetings allow citizens to voice their opinions.

- The communist government also recognized the importance of land ownership for all. Inexpensive grants were made to allow families to build their own homes on land on which they felt secure. Over 1.5 million people benefitted from this redistribution: they were provided with clean, safe drinking water and an opportunity to grow their own crops on their own property.

- The Keralan government believes that a literate society will create more jobs and improve the economy. Children are required to attend school; there has been emphasis placed on educational opportunities for girls; and nursery care is provided at school locations. Literacy has risen to nearly 100 percent. This push toward a literate society is supported by free library facilities. Everyone lives within 3 to 5 kilometres of a library, school, nursery, or food-ration shop.

With women taking an equal part in the workforce, there may be smaller families, if more women will opt to postpone having children while they go to school or work. Also, those who delay the decision to have a child may then choose to have fewer children when they do start a family. This, in turn, will significantly reduce the need for increased food production.

Kerala today

Kerala has been praised by international development agencies as a model for others to follow. The focus on education and health care has reaped rewards in terms of manageable population growth. This, in turn has broken the cycle of food shortages and subsequent ill health among the population.

However, the state's methods of development have their critics, who point to the decaying condition of educational and health services, as well as that of roads. Some believe that a state with such a high level of educational attainment should have attracted more non-traditional industries — Kerala is still a predominantly agricultural state, and has not attracted the industrial development it sought. The purchasing power parity of Kerala still lags behind India as a whole. Many educated Keralans have emigrated to other states and countries — especially in the Middle East — which has been viewed as brain drain, in which Keralan investments in education are benefitting other countries.

Kerala has recently adopted the development of a new plan called "the people's plan campaign." This plan has been designed to achieve annual planned targets, and will include further discussion among government officials, elected representatives, experts, and people from the general population about ways to achieve faster and more sustainable progress in education, industrial production, and health care.

23. How is the situation in Kerala different from that in Sudan, and how might these differences have contributed to Kerala's success?

24. How do you think local participation and decision making have helped Kerala?

25. How are factors such as high birth rates, illiteracy, poverty, and sporadic health care related to malnutrition and chronic persistent hunger?

26. Many Canadians feel Canada, like Kerala, is experiencing brain drain, with educated Canadians seeking employment elsewhere — mainly in the United States. The term "brain drain" has negative connotations — do you think it is something a country should be concerned about? How does the concept of brain drain relate to what you learned in Chapter 3 about disparity in wealth? Explain your answer.

27. Do you believe that Kerala's success could be replicated in other areas of the world? Why or why not?

Canadian help in Ethiopia

The Fiftieth Anniversary Convention of the Food and Agriculture Organization of the United Nations (FAO) was held in Québec City in 1995. At that time, it was agreed that Canada would play a significant role in helping poor countries that have regular food deficits. Ethiopia was chosen by Canada as being the country that needed help most. Discussions were held between the Canadian International Development Agency (CIDA) and Ethiopian officials as to what kind of help this should be.

It was agreed that the Canadian International Development Agency would fund a permanent water development in the northernmost region of Tigray, in Ethiopia. A company based in Regina, Saskatchewan — the Prairie Farm Rehabilitation Administration (PFRA) — was chosen to lead the development, since it had extensive expertise in drought-related water projects. It was estimated that the project would take six years to complete.

The Tigray region of Ethiopia

Ethiopia is one of the poorest countries in the world. It has a population growth rate of nearly 3 percent per year. Food production is increasing by only 1 percent each year, and there is a constant need for additional food. Ethiopia receives about 1 million tonnes of food aid most years, even when harvests are good.

The Tigray region has a population of 3.6 million (about the size of Greater Metropolitan Toronto). It is among the most drought-prone areas of Ethiopia. The eastern part of Tigray has 500 millimetres (mm) of rainfall each year, mostly in July and August. Because of the excessive heat, evaporation rates reach 1500 millimetres per year. As a result of high evaporation rates, together with frequent drought, there are very few permanent rivers and streams.

As a result of these climate factors, the Tigray regional government decided that, to guard against famine, the supply of water had to be made more reliable. In support of this priority, the Tigray regional government created the Commission for Sustainable Agricultural and Environmental Rehabilitation of Tigray (SAERT) to increase food security through water harvesting (dam construction) and irrigation. The Commission set a target to develop 50 000 hectares of new irrigation schemes (500 schemes at 100 hectares each) in ten years.

Canada's role is to help give the Commission the technical capability and expertise to develop the project. Some of the initiatives include developing skills in soils agronomy, irrigation extension, hydraulic and structural design, hydrology, hydrogeology, geotechnical engineering, and informatics.

Depending on the success of the project, further work will focus on the Amhara region, to the south of Tigray.

FIGURE 4–23 **Climagraph for Mekele, the capital city of the Tigray region**

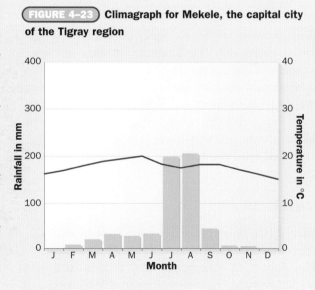

Write a magazine article or create a multimedia presentation about the Canadian International Development Agency's involvement in Ethiopia's Tigray region. Your article must contain the following features:

- a headline for the article
- an explanation of the situation faced by the Tigray population (including reference to the climate data and map provided)
- a description of the Canadian International Development Agency's involvement
- visuals, with effective captions for each
- a discussion of the effectiveness of this kind of project in finding long-term solutions to issues of hunger and food supply
- an evaluation of the need for a combination of international co-operation and local involvement in developing sustainable solutions
- a comparison of this project to the more comprehensive development strategy implemented by the state of Kerala (see pages 110 to 111)

FIGURE 4–24 Ethiopia

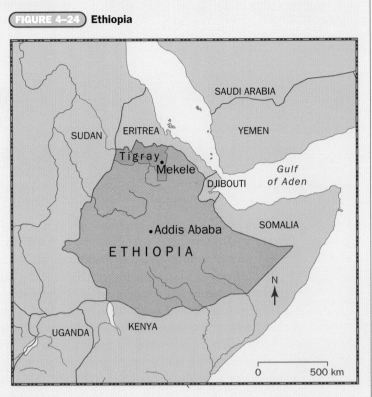

Managing the World's Resources

Humankind has prospered because of a combination of human intellect and the ability to develop and use the riches that the earth provides. In other words, people have prospered by using both human and natural **resources**. A resource is a supply of something that is used to meet the needs of individuals or groups of people. An example of a **human resource** is an architect or craftsperson who has the skills to design and build homes. An example of a **natural resource** is the wood extracted from a forest, used to construct homes. Resources are either **renewable** (they can be sustained under good management) or **non-renewable** (once they are used, they are gone forever).

FIGURE 5-1 *Tamaracks*, **by Tom Thomson**

a) In what ways do forests impact the lifestyles of those living in and around them?

b) Does a forest play any role in your life?

c) How might the Canadian artist who painted this picture in 1916 have viewed a forest differently from a Brazilian aboriginal living in the Amazon rain forest — either then or now?

Expectations

- Evaluate some of the ways of promoting sustainable development and resource management and assess their effectiveness in selected regions.
- Assess the contribution of selected government policies to sustainable resource development in Canada.
- Evaluate the significance of the participation of people in non-violent movements to protect resources and environments.
- Construct scenarios for probable and desirable futures, based on current trends in the human use of the earth and its resources, including trends in technology.
- Produce a case study of a specific situation in which resource development has contributed to the disruption of an ecosystem.

In the past, there was little concern about the way in which the earth's physical resources were used. With small populations and low levels of technology, it seemed that the earth would always provide what was needed. Catching fish from the ocean was never considered a threat to the amount of fish available.

More recently, though, scientists have begun to question humankind's use and management of resources. In fact, resource management has become a global issue because experts are worried that some of the resources on which our lifestyles depend are in danger of running out. Populations have grown so large, and industrial and technological development has become so sophisticated, that many believe that people are demanding too much from the earth's resources. The theory of the tragedy of the commons, outlined in Chapter 1, suggests that this issue will prove a difficult one to solve. The responsibility for good management of crucial resources, such as the wealth of the ocean, seems to lie with no one in particular.

It is important to understand that the issue of resource sustainability involves both renewable and non-renewable resources. It is possible to use up limited stocks, or misuse those stocks that are supposedly renewable. However, in this age of growing consumerism and consumption, our first priority should be to protect those resources that have a limited life and are most threatened because of misuse. This chapter will focus mainly on those renewable resources that are in acute danger of disappearing, such as the world's forests, and those resources — both renewable and non-renewable — that provide us with energy.

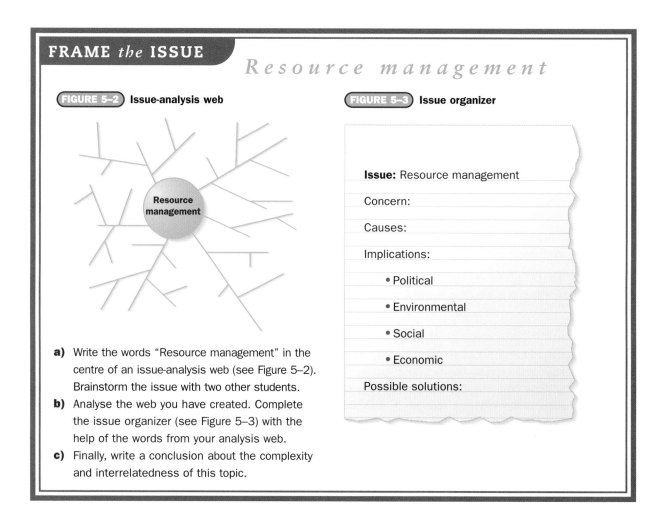

FRAME *the* ISSUE

Resource management

FIGURE 5–2 Issue-analysis web

Resource management

a) Write the words "Resource management" in the centre of an issue-analysis web (see Figure 5–2). Brainstorm the issue with two other students.

b) Analyse the web you have created. Complete the issue organizer (see Figure 5–3) with the help of the words from your analysis web.

c) Finally, write a conclusion about the complexity and interrelatedness of this topic.

FIGURE 5–3 Issue organizer

Issue: Resource management

Concern:

Causes:

Implications:

• Political

• Environmental

• Social

• Economic

Possible solutions:

Renewable and Non-Renewable Resources

Renewable resources are sometimes referred to as **stream resources** or **flow resources** — a constantly renewable supply is always "on-stream." A good example of a renewable resource is a forest. If we plant as many trees as we cut down, we are sustaining the *number* of trees, but is the forest being sustained? Resource management of forests is complicated by questions such as whether the new trees are of the same quality as those cut down; whether the living environment has been harmed; how long it will take the trees to mature; and how many trees will die off in the process.

An example of a non-renewable resource is oil. Once oil is pumped out of the ground and burned — perhaps in a combustion engine — it is gone forever. Eventually, the earth will run out of natural oil. Non-renewable resources are also referred to as **stock resources,** as they comprise a limited stock (supply) that can be depleted. For example, imagine having a warehouse full of office supplies. Once the supplies have been used up, the warehouse is empty. This analogy is not entirely accurate, however, as science may generate synthetic versions of some of the earth's resources, or we may find better and more abundant resources to achieve the same ends. The shift away from oil use to wind, solar, or hydrogen power is an example of the current movement toward alternative energy resources.

William Rees, an environmental economist, describes the earth's resources as **natural stocks,** some of which are renewable. Rees believes that, due to short-term economic greed, we are depleting our natural stocks of both renewable and non-renewable reserves faster than they can be replaced or protected. A renewable resource may be termed a **critical resource** if it is dependent on good sustainable techniques for it to remain unharmed or for its supply to remain undiminished.

Freshwater is a good example of a critical resource. Water is renewable through the **hydrologic cycle** (the cycle of evaporation of moisture from the oceans and land, then of condensation and precipitation, back to the earth's surface). In some places, however, water that is stored underground in aquifers is being pumped out and used at a faster rate than nature can replenish the supply.

A **non-critical resource** is one that can be used without being in any danger of becoming harmed. The radiation from the sun used for **solar energy** is a good example.

Resource management has shown some promising developments. We live in an age where there is a growing demand, and the technological know-how, for extending the life of resources by re-using or recycling materials. Most of us participate daily in some of the many domestic and industrial waste-reduction programs, targeting such items as batteries, aluminum, paper, glass, cardboard packaging, and computer printer cartridges. These initiatives may save some resources from complete depletion or extend the period of time before they are in danger of depletion.

Resources that make our environment a better place to live in are referred to as **scenic resources** or **aesthetic resources,** and these can easily be endangered, too. Urban construction can destroy natural environments. For example, it is unlikely that a wall of highrise hotels along a beach would be torn down to restore the ocean view for everyone behind its "concrete curtain." The fact that these aesthetic resources are now recognized as worthy of protection is a very positive development in resource management.

1. How would you explain the difference between "renewable" and "non-renewable" resources?

2. Explain the difference between critical and non-critical resources, and give three examples of each.

3. Give three examples of "scenic" or "aesthetic" resources.

4. Resources essential to the stability of an ecosystem are worth protecting. Give two examples of such resources.

5. Look around you. Which two everyday items are made from materials that have changed due to advances in technology? For example, many school desks are now made of a plastic composite rather than wood. How may some of the earth's resources have been saved as a result of this technology?

Resource Consumption

When industries turn raw materials into a manufactured product, materials are used or **consumed** in the process. For example, wood is consumed to make pulp and paper, and iron ore is consumed during the steel-making process. The United States Environmental Protection Agency (EPA) states that modern industrial economies such as those of Germany, Japan, and the Netherlands, consume between 45 000 and 85 000 kilograms of natural resources per person, each year. This amounts to at least 133 kilograms every day, and would fill 300 grocery bags every week. According to a 1999 study published by the University of California, the United States, with only 4.7 percent of the world's population, consumes 25 percent of the world's resources.

Canadians follow similar consumption patterns to those in the United States, but consume more energy per person than Americans do. This is because Canadians live in a colder climate (more heating) and have such a dispersed population (more travel and longer shipping distances for goods).

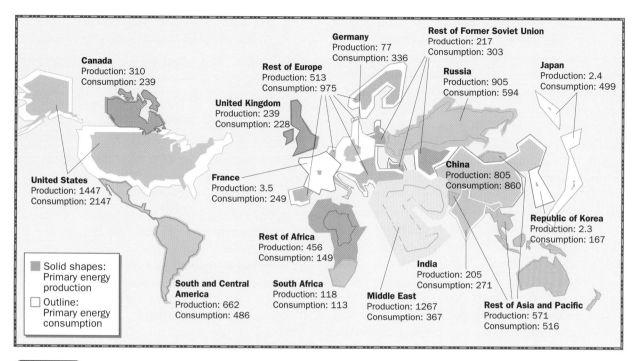

FIGURE 5-4 This map shows a diagrammatic representation of countries and regions proportionate to their production and consumption of commercially traded fuels. All figures are in million metric tons of oil equivalent (mmtoe).

The Organization for Economic Co-operation and Development (OECD) has suggested that industrialized countries look for ways to reduce consumption of resources to 10 percent of their current levels, by managing resource materials more efficiently and using better technologies. According to *The Business Journal* of Portland, Oregon, a recent study found that manufacturing a car generates less waste and uses fewer resources than manufacturing a laptop computer. Modern technological developments, such as replacing copper wire with fibre optics, and improving methods of creating computer chips, are examples of ways in which North Americans can reduce per capita levels of consumption.

In 2001, the National Intelligence Council (NIC), an organization that gathers information about critical global issues for the United States government, described trends that will shape the world in 2015. Two significant concerns were associated with the use of water and energy:

■ *Nearly half the world's population — more than 3 billion people — will live in countries that are "water-stressed"* (have less than 1700 cubic metres of water per capita per year). The majority of these people will be in Africa, the Middle East, South Asia, and northern China. In the developing world, 80 percent of the water is used for agriculture — a proportion that is not sustainable, based on current supplies and patterns of use. By 2015, a number of developing countries will be unable to maintain their levels of irrigated agriculture, because they will have exhausted their water supplies.

■ Sustained global economic growth, along with population expansion, will drive an *almost 50-percent increase in the demand for energy* over the next 15 years. Total oil demands will escalate from roughly 75 million barrels per day in 2000, to more than 100 million barrels in 2015 — an increase almost as large as the total current production of the Organization of Petroleum Exporting Countries (OPEC). Natural gas usage will accelerate more rapidly than that of any other energy source — by more than 100 percent — stemming mainly from an anticipated tripling of gas consumption in Asia. Asia is predicted to drive the expansion in energy demand due to increasing populations and industrialization, replacing North America as the leading region for energy consumption, and accounting for more than half of the world's total rise in demand. By 2015, only one-tenth of Persian Gulf oil will be directed to Western markets, while three-quarters will go to Asia.

According to the National Intelligence Council, **fossil fuels** (fuels obtained from within the earth, like oil and natural gas) are expected to remain the dominant form of energy, despite growing concerns about global warming. **Solar cells**, which provide solar energy, will become more efficient, and genetic engineering will expand the long-term prospects for the large-scale use of ethanol (a renewable energy source, produced when grain is distilled and mixed with small amounts of gasoline). Hydrates (a compound of natural gases and water) will also be used increasingly as fuel. The utilization of nuclear energy is expected to remain at current levels.

Due to the exploration of remote locations, estimates of the world's total abundance of oil — a non-renewable resource — have steadily grown. Recent estimates published by the United States Central Intelligence Agency (CIA) — a government agency responsible for gathering information regarding the security of the United States — indicate that 80 percent of the world's available oil still remains in the ground, as does 95 percent of the world's natural gas. This is particularly good news considering that, only 20 years ago, experts speculated that oil reserves would be depleted before the turn of the century.

6. What factors have caused the growth in demand for the world's resources?

7. a) Refer to the map in Figure 5–4. Which countries or regions show the largest amount of energy consumption relative to what they produce?
   b) Which countries or regions show the largest amount of energy production relative to what they consume?
   c) What conclusions might you draw from this map regarding the consumption patterns of richer industrial countries versus those of the poorer, less-industrialized countries?

8. Why do you think the National Intelligence Council is most concerned about water and energy resources?

9. Assuming that you agree that water and energy are high-priority resource concerns, what third global resource do you think also deserves immediate attention? Explain.

Who are they?

Organization of Petroleum Exporting Countries

The Organization of Petroleum Exporting Countries (OPEC) consists of 11 countries: Algeria, Indonesia, Iran, Iraq, Kuwait, Libya, Nigeria, Qatar, Saudi Arabia, the United Arab Emirates, and Venezuela. The group's role is to co-ordinate oil production amounts that control the world price of oil. OPEC countries collectively supply about 40 percent of the world's oil output and contain more than three-quarters of the known oil reserves on the planet.

Ecological Footprints

Imagine that you may only use the resources within your local community. Will your community be able to sustain itself? Probably not for long. The ecosystems within your community would quickly have insufficient carrying capacity to support the community's ecological demands. (See the simulation demonstrated in Chapter 1, pages 16–17.)

In reality, though, we do not live in isolation; we trade with other communities and countries in order to acquire additional ecological goods and services. Nevertheless, global trade cannot solve all resource problems. Although the pool of reserves grows with trade, it is not infinite. We must consider the planet's total carrying capacity. How much pressure are we putting on our resources and how will this affect their sustainability?

These concerns are heightened in the Living Planet Report, published in 2000 by the World Wildlife Fund (WWF). This report uses a **Living Planet Index** to quantify changes in our ecosystems, and the concept of an **ecological footprint** to measure people's consumption of resources.

The report assumes that there are 10 billion usable hectares of land on earth, and that a population of 6 billion divides this amount. Each of us is left with an average "earth share" of 1.7 hectares (about the size of three football fields).

FIGURE 5–6 Just like shoes, ecological footprints come in different sizes. If you calculate your own ecological footprint and compare it with that of a classmate, the results may differ. How big is your footprint? Check out www.gagelearning.com/onthethreshold and find the link for calculating your ecological footprint.

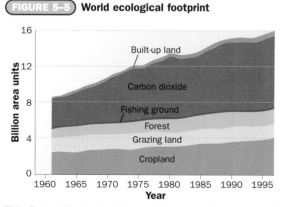

FIGURE 5–5 World ecological footprint

Graph: Billion area units (y-axis, 0 to 16) vs. Year (x-axis, 1960 to 1995). Layers from bottom to top: Cropland, Grazing land, Forest, Fishing ground, Carbon dioxide, Built-up land.

This figure illustrates the world's expanding ecological footprint. When did the earth encounter an ecological overshoot? What trend do you forecast for the twenty-first century?

However, over the past 30 years, human consumption has exceeded what the earth's natural ecosystems can provide by 20 percent! In other words, we are in the midst of an **ecological overshoot**. Our resource demands exceed nature's supply. The report asserts that it is this overshoot that has led to the decline of some of our natural resources.

Because the ecological footprint can be calculated regionally and globally, it can be used to compare regions and countries. According to calculations made by Mathis Wackernagel and William Rees, the creators of the ecological footprint concept, the average ecological footprint size of Canadians is 4.8 hectares: 2.9 hectares for energy, 1.1 hectares for agriculture, 0.6 hectares for forest products, and 0.2 hectares for housing and transportation. This average size is significantly higher than the ideal individual's earth share of 1.7 hectares, as set out in the Living Planet Report.

How long can the earth sustain these countries' demands, in addition to rising demands from other nations that are striving for greater

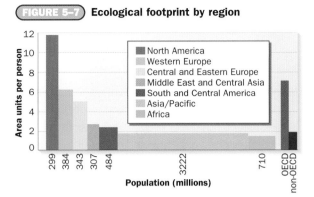

FIGURE 5–7 Ecological footprint by region

Legend:
- North America
- Western Europe
- Central and Eastern Europe
- Middle East and Central Asia
- South and Central America
- Asia/Pacific
- Africa

Area units per person (y-axis): 0, 2, 4, 6, 8, 10, 12

Population (millions) (x-axis): 299, 384, 343, 307, 484, 3222, 710, OECD, non-OECD

This figure indicates the ecological footprint disparity among world regions. According to Wackernagel and Rees, about three-quarters of the world's current consumption is done by only one-third of the world's people. Developed countries have extremely large ecological footprints, due to their high rates of industrialization and consumption — largely of food, forest, and fossil-fuel resources. These resources are taken from within their own borders and beyond.

economic development? Best Foot Forward — a group that measures environmental impacts — suggests that, if China reached the consumption levels of the United States, the global ecological overshoot would increase from its present unsustainable 37 percent to an enormous 250 percent!

Wackernagel and Rees illustrate the severity of this issue in their prediction that, if all individuals around the world lived like North Americans, we would need three more planets the size of earth to meet the resulting resource demands. Where will the footprints of developing nations expand in a world of shrinking resources?

The ecological footprint concept focusses attention on the potential dangers of increasing pressure on the earth's resources. It also highlights the need to achieve ecological sustainability through changes in lifestyle. These changes include: increased use of public transit; improved waste recycling; new environmental policies; global development programs that promote improved living standards for developing countries; and greater resource sustainability for high-consuming societies.

On the other hand, the ecological footprint concept does not attempt to measure the role

technology might play in allowing for a more sustainable extraction of resources.

10. a) Define the term "ecological footprint."
   b) Outline the value and limitations of this concept.

11. How do you think the concept of an ecological footprint can be used to help explain the relationship between a country's wealth and its consumption habits?

12. What do you think will happen if the ecological overshoot increases to the point where resource demands exceed nature's supply?

13. a) Research a local, national, or global resource consumption or waste issue that contributes to a growing ecological footprint, thereby threatening related ecosystems. Issues might be, for example, offshore oil exploration, waste disposal in urban centres, or global warming.
   b) "Frame the issue" by analysing your information in terms of its political, environmental, social, and economic implications. For each of these four criteria, suggest possible solutions to improve your selected issue's ecological footprint.

Sustainable Development

Chapter 1 introduced the concept of sustainability, and the fact that we have to be extremely careful how we use and consume resources. Lester Brown of the Worldwatch Institute describes a sustainable society as one that satisfies its needs without diminishing prospects for the next generation. He also believes that we must not exceed thresholds — the resource limits beyond which supply cannot be sustained. Global efforts to continually raise human quality of life become a major threat to the sustainability of the world's resources, if thresholds will be exceeded in the process.

Scientists are worried about the decline in the world's biodiversity, as well as issues like disappearing forests, unsustainable fishing practices, population growth, and growing levels of industrialization and consumption. Industrialization and consumption levels are rising at particularly high rates in developing countries, which make up four-fifths of the world's population. Even so, experts do not necessarily believe that developing countries have to go through the same gradual progression of economic development as presently industrialized countries. As mentioned in Chapter 3, they believe that, if large amounts of private investment go into state-of-the-art environmental technologies, poorer countries will be able to leapfrog the wasteful stages of development and unsustainable practices that developed countries experienced.

Coal is now burned much more efficiently than in the past, with far less pollution entering the atmosphere. Countries such as China could utilize this technology instead of older combustion methods, which caused high levels of pollution. This assumes, of course, that those possessing newer technologies will be willing to share this expertise, or will allow it to be purchased at a price that poorer countries can afford.

14. With a partner, brainstorm the kinds of new technology that you think may assist developing countries to circumvent the misuse of resources that occurred in the past.

15. What can countries like the United States and Canada do to improve the management of resources nationally or globally? Give three examples and explain how easy or difficult they would be to implement.

16. What can individuals in your community do to help conserve resources? List ten suggestions and explain each one.

17. Research a current Canadian government initiative regarding resource conservation and evaluate its potential effectiveness. Then write a question that you could ask your local federal Member of Parliament about the initiative and Canada's role in helping the world to become sustainable, in terms of its resources.

Global WARNING

A SUSTAINABILITY TRAGEDY

The Earth Council, an international non-government organization that promotes ecological awareness and sustainable development, has observed that many people hope augmented agricultural productivity will be able to save humanity from the ecological squeeze. What many people forget is that high agricultural productivity is mainly possible due to massive *ecological* subsidies: loss of ground water, loss of topsoil, and input of fossil-fuel-consuming fertilizers and other agrochemicals. The case of hydroponic greenhouses (plants are grown in water environments without soil) may be particularly telling. There, the yield per square metre greatly exceeds that of open-field production. However, once the ecological

subsidies are included, the balance turns upside down. The requirement of ecological space for hydroponic greenhouses for the same amount of tomatoes was 10 to 20 times higher than that with more traditional open-field methods. According to the Earth Council, this is a sustainability tragedy: humanity becomes increasingly dependent on an energy and resource-intensive agriculture, while the resources and energy stocks necessary to sustain this agriculture are being depleted.

a) How does agricultural technology, and in particular, hydroponics, challenge the ecological footprint concept?

b) How do you think agricultural technologies can promote greater resource sustainability?

Our Fragile Forests

One of the world's most significant resources currently threatened is our forests. Forests can be a tremendously useful, bountiful resource, if managed correctly. The World Resources Institute estimates that only one-fifth of the world's original forest cover — 3 billion hectares — remains undisturbed. One-quarter has been destroyed in the past 40 years.

The rate of **deforestation** (forests being cut down) does not match the rate of **reforestation** (trees being replanted). According to the World's Forests 2001 report from the Food and Agriculture Organization of the United Nations (FAO), the total amount of forest on the earth declined by 9.4 million hectares in 2001, with the most loss occurring in tropical forests, in developing countries. The organization attributes forest loss to such factors as lumber export, the clearing of additional agricultural land, forest

FIGURE 5-9 An average tree exhales about 0.48 kilograms of oxygen while growing 0.45 kilograms of wood.

FIGURE 5-8 Global deforestation by region

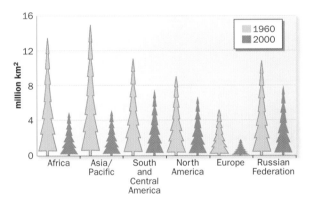

Summarize the regional decline in forest cover between 1960 and 2000.

fires, and poor forest conservation programs by governments and businesses. Rates of deforestation are higher in developing countries, the organization believes, because there is much pressure in these regions for additional land to be cleared, especially from people with few or no resources. In such cases, the cleared, arable land is viewed as the important resource, rather than the forests, which become a wasted by-product. Developed countries also contribute to the decline in tropical forest cover, however. For example, approximately 12 percent of Japan's lumber imports come from Malaysia.

Who are they?

The World Resources Institute

The World Resources Institute is a non-government organization that acts as a think-tank on many political, social, economic, and environmental issues. It works with hundreds of other organizations and governments around the world. The group gathers information, conducts research, and publishes reports on the state of the earth and its resources.

World regions that have experienced the most forest loss are those in the Congo Basin of Africa, and in the Amazon region of South America. According to the World Resources Institute, during the last two decades, 1.1 million hectares (an area the size of Jamaica) has been cleared each year within the Congo Basin — poor people are clearing forests for firewood and farmland. In countries like Brazil, forest cover is being stripped away in the Amazon rain forest to enable subsistence farmers to use the land for crop cultivation, as well as to provide meat-producing commercial operations with land for large-scale grazing. Losing the earth's forests results in a number of critical consequences.

Consequences of forest loss

- When forests are cleared by means of burning, *large amounts of stored carbon dioxide enter the atmosphere.* Carbon dioxide levels have risen by over 30 percent in the past 250 years. This is thought to cause global warming — the earth's average surface temperature has risen by about 0.6 degrees Celsius.

- Trees are contributors of oxygen to the world's atmosphere. Many scientists believe high rates of deforestation will somewhat *decrease overall oxygen levels.*

- The effect of a cleared forest is *devastating to local ecosystems.* According to Environment Canada, even under programs of reforestation in which logging companies replace the trees they have cut down, the diversity of the forest's plant and animal life is not restored to its original amount.

- According to *The Overstory,* an American forestry journal, less plant diversity can lead to *ecological imbalance,* which can cause infestations of "pest" insects that thrive on concentrations of the remaining plant life. These insects can cause a great deal of damage to plant growth. In monitoring the decline of forests, the Food and Agriculture Organization of the United Nations has noted that even in Europe, where extensive use of insecticide sprays is possible, tree infestation is nevertheless on the increase.

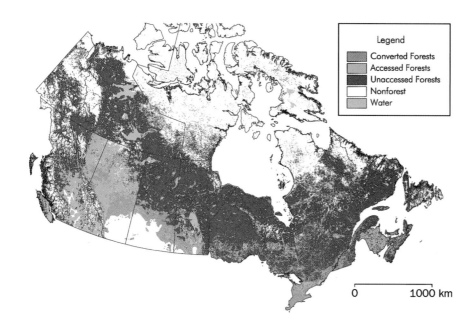

Legend
- Converted Forests
- Accessed Forests
- Unaccessed Forests
- Nonforest
- Water

0   1000 km

FIGURE 5–10 Canada has 10 percent of the world's forests by area. Two-thirds of Canada's 140 000 species of plants, animals, and micro-organisms occur in the forest.

- At times of heavy rain, trees allow the water to flow and sink gradually, thus protecting areas from flooding. Therefore, deforestation can increase the *risk of flooding in some areas*.
- The root systems of trees provide an anchor for soil, protecting steep grades from land erosion. Hills that were stripped of their forest cover in Thailand, Indonesia, and Malaysia experienced *devastating mudslides*.
- Trees collect and then transpire, or breathe out, moisture. In areas that have been heavily deforested, the local climates experience drier conditions. Ethiopia, once covered with 40 percent forest cover, now has less than 7 percent, due mostly to the collection of firewood. This has had an overwhelming impact on the local climate, resulting in *severe droughts*.

The Canadian forest threat

Few countries in the world can match Canada's wealth of forest. The Canadian Forest Service estimates that forest covers about 418 million hectares (roughly the size of Europe) of Canada's land area. That is, 10 percent of the world's forests are in Canada.

Canada produces 1.5 times the amount of forest products as its nearest competitor (the United States), according to the Canadian Forest Service. Canada ranks No. 1 in the world for newsprint production and export, No. 1 for exports of softwood lumber and wood pulp, and No. 2 (behind the United States) for production of softwood lumber and wood pulp.

Canadian Forest Service figures for 2001 show that a total of 842 000 Canadians (363 000 employed directly and 479 000 indirectly) are employed in the logging, lumber, and pulp and paper industries. That is, 1 in 16 working Canadians is employed by these industries to some degree. Natural Resources Canada states that, in total, the logging, lumber, and pulp and paper industries contribute CDN$20.8 billion to the gross domestic product (GDP). Wood products valued at approximately CDN$68.2 billion are generated, of which CDN$38.2 billion (56 percent) are exported, generating a positive balance of trade of CDN$32.1 billion.

Sustaining Canada's forest

Canada has a reputation as a world leader in managing and sustaining forest, while commercially exploiting it on a large scale. However, this reputation is beginning to change. Despite good management by provincial and by federal governments — which own 90 percent of Canada's forests — there is mounting concern that these forests are becoming unsustainable.

According to the federal government, the annual growth of commercial forest is about 250 million square metres. Governmental control of commercial licences has limited the cutting of trees to 247 million square metres annually, which is said to be a sustainable limit. In recent years, only about 170 million square metres of forest has been cut annually, which is good news. Even so, environmental critics believe that softwood trees are being cut down in larger amounts than are allowed, to satisfy the world demand for newsprint, pulp, and construction lumber — only the hardwoods are being spared. As the softwoods decline in number, younger and younger trees are being harvested. Friends of the Earth asserts that, recently, many lumber mills in the forest-rich

Who are they?

Friends of the Earth International

Friends of the Earth is a federation of environmental groups with representation in 66 countries, including Canada. Using the results of their environmental research, the group produces a great deal of educational material for schools, government, and industry.

province of British Columbia have had to meet such a high demand for softwood product that they have been importing wood from neighbouring provinces.

Part of the problem is that the area which is replanted (about 460 000 hectares) amounts to about half of the total area that is actually cleared of trees (about 900 000 hectares). Also, in much of the reforested area, the trees do not grow or regenerate into good-quality trees. Critics believe that excessive logging practices and poor management have damaged nearly 4.5 million hectares of land in Canada.

Friends of the Earth estimates that eight of the largest logging companies — both Canadian and international — have rights to log 247 million hectares within Canada. A few large corporations do most of the logging in Canada, and ten companies control the logging rights to over three-quarters of Canada's forests, including international companies such as Mitsubishi from Japan.

Protecting Canada's forest

Canadian forests are vital for maintaining ecological diversity, yet very few of them are actually protected. About 23 million hectares are protected from logging activity by provincial and federal governments, but this constitutes only 6 percent of the total area. According to the National Forest Inventory, approximately 160 million more hectares are untouched because they are not **commercially viable**; in other words, a profit cannot be made from them. However, if other areas are used up, prices could make these non-viable forests potentially lucrative, and they could become targets for harvesting as well.

Forestry harvesting practices in Canada have caused some controversy. Although provincial governments cover most of the cost for **silviculture** programs (the replanting and care of trees in areas where logging has occurred), the problem, in some areas, is the fact that companies have been allowed to cut down trees in the first place. In British Columbia, where there are strict regulations regarding forest management techniques,

FIGURE 5–11 Police prepare to arrest protestors blocking a logging road near Clayoquot Sound on Vancouver Island in 1993. On what basis could these protestors be arrested?

it is still permitted to cut **old-growth forests** (forested areas that have reached extreme ecological maturity and which contain trees that are extremely old and large). A unique ecological balance between plants and animals in these areas has existed for centuries, undisturbed by humans. Besides the fact that new forest growth cannot replace these environmentally sensitive areas, removing old-growth forests — which are often found on steep slopes — can encourage mudslides and avalanches.

The old-growth **temperate** (moderate climate) rain forests are also under threat of logging, especially those located on Vancouver Island such as Clayoquot Sound — the second-largest lowland, temperate rain forest left intact on earth. These forests are as ecologically diverse as tropical rain forests.

Government experts calculate that 60 percent of this temperate rain forest in Canada has already been lost. According to Friends of the Earth, some of its unprotected commercial areas could be completely stripped by 2020. They further report that only 7 percent of the coastal temperate rain forest in British Columbia has been protected from logging, while about 22 000 square kilometres of old-growth forest has been harvested. The members of the group on Vancouver Island add that parks protect only 4.5 percent of the island's ancient, temperate rain forest, 20 percent of its bog/non-productive forest, and 90 percent of its alpine tundra and mountaintops.

Friends of the Earth is critical of Canada's ability to manage the world's largest temperate and old-growth forests, basing their criticism on:

- the increased logging of old-growth forests, and loss of biodiversity that results
- the Canadian lumber industry's heavy reliance on high-volume exports of low-value products, such as raw (unprocessed) lumber
- unresolved land rights disputes
- doubts about how the government's annual growth increments and annual allowable cuts have been determined and followed

Protesting and the Law

Environmental groups that oppose corporate actions — such as Friends of the Earth in British Colombia, who criticize Canada's forestry industry — may opt to protest against those actions which they see as being harmful to the environment. Protest can be made through the legal court system: protestors can try to legally bring an end to what they perceive as environmentally damaging behaviour on the part of a corporation. In contrast, protesters can opt for a more "grass-roots" method. For instance, a group of residents who are worried that toxic chemicals may leach out of a nearby dump and into their drinking water might attempt to block an access road to a proposed waste disposal site.

In such an instance, those companies involved in constructing or using the waste disposal site can ask the courts to impose a **Strategic Lawsuit Against Public Participation (SLAPP)**. These are used to enforce a company's legal right to access and use the property. The enforcement of a trespass order is an example of this. SLAPPs are therefore used to discourage protest against a corporate action. They are often effective because, in order to fight them, protestors must take part in a potentially lengthy legal process, involving legal costs. Many SLAPP suits have been used to deter protestors seeking to protect the old-growth forests of Clayoquot Sound in British Columbia.

18. What environmental dangers can result from the depletion of forests?

19. Write down five facts that best support the belief of the Food and Agriculture Organization of the United Nations that there is a threat to the world's ability to sustain its forests.

20. What evidence suggests that Canada is not practising sustainable wood harvesting? How are Canadian federal and provincial governments contributing to the problem, and/or helping to remedy it?

21. a) Research and evaluate the role played by non-violent environmental movements, such as British Columbia's Wilderness Committee or local aboriginal groups, in protecting the health of wilderness forests.
   b) How might local loggers, whose livelihood depends on wages from logging, respond to environmentalists' concerns?

22. Contact or research two forestry companies to learn about their policies toward sustainable forestry in Canada and in other countries. What two features about their policy and work stand out as being positive? What two features would you identify as in need of rethinking?

23. Consider a situation in which a rail line has been blocked by protestors. The line is used to transport lumber from an area the protestors consider to be ecologically threatened by the "clear-cutting" methods. A company owns the rail line, has a 50-year lease on the forest, and is considered by its workers to be a good employer.
   a) What SLAPPs do you think the company could ask the courts to impose on the protestors?
   b) If you were a protestor, how would you respond to these SLAPPs?
   c) Research an example of a SLAPP that has been used in Canada, and an example of a similar lawsuit that has been used in another country.

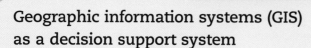

Geographic information systems (GIS) as a decision support system

Would you choose cereal with milk, or toast with orange juice? Which would you support — no commercial fishing, fishing by aboriginal people only, limited quota-based fishing for licensed people only, or open commercial fishing for all? You make decisions every day. Some choices are personal and have no lasting impact (like eating either cereal or toast), while others can impact many people and leave a global mark. How do people make tough regional or global decisions?

Making decisions

It is generally accepted that, in making an informed decision, there are two important factors — a goal, and adequate information. An effective decision can be made by examining the information at hand and choosing the option most likely to lead to the desired outcome. For many organizations, computer technologies called **decision support systems (DSS)** play a role in decision making. Decision support systems tools can provide a variety of options, when given specific parameters to follow.

Geographic information systems — The geographers' decision support systems

Geographers use computer technology to speed up the decision-making processes. Geographic information systems (GIS) are so called because they require geographical information and, when used correctly, create new information which can be used to support decision making.

Problem solving

Geographic information systems problem solving has five phases.

1. **Problem definition** *The problem must be expressed in clear, concise language.* In the example, "Where should I go shopping for clothes?" the language is unambiguous.

2. **Analysis** *The problem is examined to determine what tools are required.* Questions must be asked: Where will the data come from? What level of accuracy is required? What financial and technological limitations exist?

3. **Design** *The attention shifts from the problem to the solution.* More questions may be asked: What will an adequate solution look like? How will I know whether the proposed solution will resolve the problem? What methods will be required to generate this solution?

4. **Implementation/Testing** *The application of the solution is observed.* Observation forms the foundation for tweaking and modifying the solution, so that as much of the problem is solved as possible. Specific geographic information systems software and platforms are chosen here, as well as actual geographic information systems methods. During this phase, a geographic information systems product is created either on paper (for example, a printed map) or digitally.

5. **Conclusion** *A statement is made as to whether the solution generated has been effective.* Shortcomings, restrictions, and limitations are described in this last phase.

Often, the conclusion that will be generated from a geographic information systems problem-solving effort is that there is a range of possible solutions. This range of possibilities is presented to the decision makers and they choose the most suitable.

FIGURE 5–12 **Geographic information systems problem-solving technique**

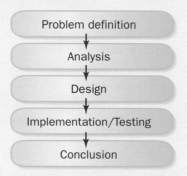

There are thousands of problem-solving techniques available. The right one will provide you with a powerful mechanism to choose the most reasonable options. Here is one such problem-solving model often used in geographic information systems.

Decision support in action — Managing a rain forest

You have been appointed to the Tropical Rain Forest Action Conservation Kinship International (TRACK), whose role is the management and protection of rain forests worldwide. You have been given the position of Rain Forest Manager and have been presented with your first task, which concerns the satellite image in Figure 5–13.

You have been asked to compile information in order to write a report on the effectiveness of TRACK's reforestation program in this part of Brazil. You should also suggest additional prime locations for continued reforestation. Using the geographic information systems problem-solving model, identify and support a decision that resolves the challenge assigned to you.

a) With a group of classmates, go through the phases of problem solving you will use to address the task issued by Tropical Rain Forest Action Conservation Kinship International. The first phase is problem definition. In this case, note that there are actually two problems stated. Be sure to identify and define any ambiguous terms, such as "effectiveness" and "prime."

b) Which do you think is the hardest phase in the geographic information systems problem-solving model? Which phase do you think would be most costly for researchers or scientists? Which would be the most time-consuming?

c) With reference to the "Case in point" on Thailand (pages 130–132), how effective has technology such as satellite imagery and geographic information systems been in protecting the forest? Be prepared to defend your position with examples from this textbook and from other sources.

To see the application of the geographic information systems problem-solving model, check out www.gagelearning.com/onthethreshold.

FIGURE 5–13 The solid dark green areas indicate undisturbed forest; the light brown areas indicate deforestation. The pattern of deforestation along roads is obvious on the left side of the image, in a north-south line. Much of the white haze is not cloud — it is smoke from forest fires. These fires are marked as red dots.

Case in point — Thailand

The World Resources Institute tells us that a portion of tropical rain forest measuring 18 kilometres by 18 kilometres is cut down each day. Some scientists and environmentalists fear that within our lifetime, rain forests could be completely destroyed.

These forests are one of the planet's mechanisms for absorbing carbon dioxide. The Rainforest Action Network estimates that the cutting and burning of tropical rain forests contributes approximately 20 percent of the carbon dioxide (CO_2) that is added annually to the atmosphere.

They also estimate that about 50 000 plant and animal species become extinct each year, largely due to rain forest destruction.

Why is there so much pressure on rain forests? Commercial logging, clearing of land to grow crops and graze cattle, mineral and oil extraction, as well as the building of hydro-electric dams and their expanding reservoirs, are some of the complex causes of deforestation.

Deforestation is one of the most pressing issues facing countries within the Southeast Asian region. As determined by the World Wildlife Fund (WWF), roughly 16 percent of the world's forests are in the Asian/Pacific region, and have been affected by extensive deforestation and decline in quality. In Thailand, forests have been fragmented, and a governmental logging ban has increased logging pressure in the forests of neighbouring Cambodia, Laos, Myanmar, and Vietnam, as well as increasing illegal logging within Thai borders.

Historical background to the current situation

Many Southeast Asian countries experienced rapid economic growth prior to the 1997 Asian financial crisis, and resource extraction of timber and water were significant contributors to Asian economies during this growth period. Thailand's tropical hardwood exports — namely teak — have been valuable components of Thailand's economy since the 1850s. Timber production in Thailand rose steadily during the 1980s, due to growing international demand for tropical hardwood: exports to large furniture markets such as Japan, United States, and France totalled over 60 percent of Thailand's total furniture exports. The Trade and Environment Database (TED) reports that, by the late 1980s, Thailand's exports to the United States had reached US$68 million.

To meet this strong international demand, **clearcutting** measures were used. (Clearcutting is a method of forest harvesting in which no trees are left to decompose. As a result, the soil lacks nutrients and the forest can take over 50 years to regrow.) The Trade and Environment Database also notes that, by 1989, large amounts of Thailand's forest were cleared for expanding cattle grazing and agricultural land. Thailand faced a huge depletion of its tropical hardwood resource.

To help combat this rapid deforestation, in 1985 Thailand's government introduced the National Forest Policy. This aimed to increase the amount of forest land to 40 percent of Thailand's total land area, by allocating 15 percent for conservation (no human use or settlement allowed)

At a glance — Thailand

- Total area: 514 000 km²
- Climate: tropical; forests and woodlands comprise 26% of the land area
- Population: 61 797 751
- GDP per capita: US$6700
- Economy: service industry 47%, industrial 40%, agriculture 13%

and 25 percent as forest use. Protected areas were established without consulting local residents, in particular highland villagers. Many villages were relocated to poor agricultural land. This led to overcrowding, disputes, and increased clearing of forests for new, better agricultural land.

To aggravate matters, during the late 1980s, devastating landslides in southern Thailand — resulting from extensive soil erosion in deforested areas — killed thousands of people and cost millions of dollars in damage. In response, the Thai government banned commercial logging in 1989 and planned to expand protected areas. In the mid-1990s, the Seventh Economic and Social Development Plan increased forest conservation to 25 percent and reduced the target for forest use to 15 percent.

The commercial logging ban had a significant effect on the timber industry: timber production in 1992 was half of the 1998 amount of 4.5 million cubic metres. According to the World Rainforest Movement, Thailand's main logging organization — the state-owned Forestry Industry Organization (FIO) — earned profits of approximately US$4 million prior to the ban, but now has a debt of almost US$12 million.

To help combat this debt, the Forestry Industry Organization is focussing on commercial tree plantations — mainly fast-growing eucalyptus — which can be turned into pulp to meet Thailand's growing demand for paper, as well as for export to Taiwan and Japan. First, however, the Forestry Industry Organization needs its forestry plans to be "certified" by the non-profit group, SmartWood. This certification allows the Forestry Industry Organization to

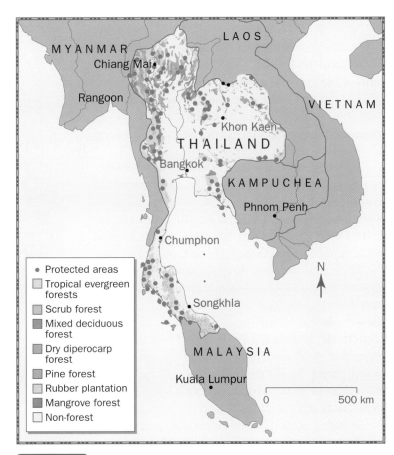

FIGURE 5-14 How would you describe the distribution of types of forest in Thailand? How does this distribution relate to the protected areas?

sell timber products to industrialized countries that are looking to purchase goods from sustainable and well-managed resources. The Forestry Industry Organization, in conjunction with the Thailand Authority on Tourism, has also begun building ecotourism sites to help increase revenues.

Despite this, the Rainforest Action Network states that Thailand's annual rate of deforestation is 8.4 percent, which is considerably higher than Brazil's rate at 2.3 percent and Indonesia's at 1.4 percent. Losing over 300 000 hectares of forest per year, Thailand is ranked among the top ten countries in the world in terms of its rate of deforestation.

Seeking forest sustainability

What can Thailand do to ensure the sustainability of its precious forest? This question has become more difficult for Thailand to solve, as wood from neighbouring Cambodia, Laos, Mynamar, and Vietnam continues to be imported, and as illegal logging continues to take place, particularly along Thailand's northern borders.

As well, the government's efforts at reforestation have had limited success. Approximately half a million villagers living in the remote highland regions of northern Thailand have had to be resettled. These communities have strongly opposed the large-scale tree plantations and, more recently, the ecotourism projects that take over village farmland and forest areas. The efforts of the Forestry Industry Organization have resulted in the degradation of the local forest ecosystem, disrupted watersheds, and altered the villagers' way of life by either forcing them to work on the plantations, or by displacing them to marginal forest areas, which must then be cleared for agriculture — and so the cycle continues.

It is also argued by the Natural Resources and Biodiversity Institute (NAREBI) of Thailand that reforestation can replace neither the number of trees cut down, nor the quality of the forest's ecosystem, in terms of its diverse species, soil, and water resources. Therefore, the Thai government and the Ministry of Agriculture and Co-operatives are looking to the Natural Resources and Biodiversity Institute for help in developing forestry management policies that will guide Thailand into 2016. The main policies include:

- *increasing forest cover to 50 percent of the country,* with at least 30 percent for conservation and 20 percent as economic, in order to try and balance social and economic demands
- *sustaining the forests through laws, monitoring, and careful consideration of the ecosystem,* prior to granting permission for use of forested areas
- *protecting the remaining natural forest areas* by managing reserve forests, increasing the efficiency of forest protection, rehabilitating degraded forests, and preventing the use of remaining healthy, forested areas
- *reducing conflict over the use of forest and other related resources* by developing a master plan for agricultural land reform, issuing land certificates to poor farmers, and allowing people to stay in protected areas if they do not expand the existing use of forests
- *protecting, preserving, and conserving the plant and animal species of the forested areas* by enforcing legal conservation measures, closely monitoring activities that may impact the biodiversity, supporting research, and involving local people in management.

These policies are intended to help Thailand seek ways to balance increasing pressure for greater industrial development with the need to sustain its tropical rain forests.

24. Create a web diagram to outline the complex aspects of the deforestation issue in Thailand.

25. Prioritize the list of forest management policies being considered by the Thai government, in terms of which you feel would have the most impact. Can you add to the list?

26. Outline the contrasting positions of economic development versus environmental protection of Thailand's tropical rain forests.

27. As a member of the World Rainforest Movement (an international network of groups working to "defend" rain forests), you have been asked to provide the Thai government with four proposals to assist in the development of a resource sustainability policy, to guide future management of the rain forests. Use the information from this section, plus additional information from the Internet, to justify your proposals.

Global Energy

Economic and social prosperity is largely dependent on the availability and use of energy resources. However, as some energy sources are declining and others pollute the atmosphere, alternative energy resources are gaining greater attention. According to the Worldwatch Institute's 2000 State of the World report, approximately 75 percent of global energy sources come from fossil fuels such as oil, natural gas, and coal, followed by 19 percent from renewable resources and 6 percent from nuclear power. From 1990 to 1999, the use of global fossil fuels increased dramatically. Coal use (primarily to generate electricity) quadrupled, while oil use increased over 160 times, and natural gas use, over 240 times! Ironically, the same decade also saw more global initiatives being formed to address issues of carbon dioxide emissions and climate change.

The Worldwatch Institute reports that Canadians and Americans — only 5 percent of the world's population — use almost one-third of the world's energy resources. North Americans are also the highest consumers of gasoline per capita, followed by Germany, Japan, Russia, and China. By 2020, China's demand for oil is expected to double to 11 million barrels a day.

Statistics like these highlight the central role that fossil fuels play in our economic growth and way of life. Author E. F. Schumacher sums up just how entrenched our demands for oil are: "There is no substitute for energy. The whole edifice of modern society is built upon it ... It is not 'just another commodity' but the precondition of all commodities, a basic factor equally with air, water, and earth."

Issue briefing

Energized Canada

Here are some facts about Canada's energy production:

- In 2000, energy accounted for almost two-thirds of Canada's large trade surplus.
- Deregulation of the Canadian oil and gas industry in 1985 (thus allowing gas prices to be set by the North American market) and the implementation of the North American Free Trade Agreement (NAFTA) have contributed to an increased volume of energy trade across the Canada/United States border. According to Natural Resources Canada, in 1995, the trade surplus for energy was 2.4 times greater than in 1986. Exports of almost every Canadian energy product have grown, with petroleum exports seeing the greatest increase at 150 percent.
- Canada was the fifth-largest energy producer in the world in 1999, behind the United States, Russia, China, and Saudi Arabia.
- Approximately 60 percent of Canada's energy production is in natural gas and oil, followed by hydro, coal, and nuclear energy.
- Two-thirds of Canada's energy production is in Alberta. However, in 2001, 11 of the 13 provinces and territories were also involved with the oil and gas industry.
- Future oil and gas developments are being looked at in environmentally sensitive areas such as the Mackenzie River Delta, Georges Bank (between Nova Scotia and Cape Cod), and off British Columbia's northern coast near the Queen Charlotte Islands.

North America — Seeking energy in remote areas

North Americans' insatiable appetite for oil continues to be satisfied by government policies, and by searches for petroleum resources. The 2001 United States National Energy Policy encourages oil and natural gas exploration in remote areas like, for example, Alaska's Arctic National Wildlife Refuge (ANWR). In 1960, The Arctic National Wildlife Range was established to protect this wilderness frontier. Twenty years later, United States Congress passed the Alaska Lands Act, which reassigned the area to the Arctic National Wildlife Refuge and doubled its size to nearly 7.7 million hectares (the size of South Carolina). However, the Act also authorized a study of the oil and gas potential of "Area 1002," the northern part of this area, sparking a conservation debate that still continues today.

The United States Fish and Wildlife Service has described the Arctic National Wildlife Refuge as a vast and beautiful wilderness frontier because of its diverse landscape and varied ecosystems. The Refuge is home to hundreds of species of grasses, mosses, and other plants; 36 species of fish; approximately 180 species of birds; and 45 species of mammals.

As determined by the United States Department of Energy, there is a 5 percent probability that at least 16 billion barrels of oil are recoverable from the Arctic National Wildlife Refuge coastal plain, while other estimates suggest a 95 percent probability that 5.7 billion barrels are recoverable. The United States Geological Survey indicated that only 2.6 billion barrels of oil are **economically recoverable** (cost effective for

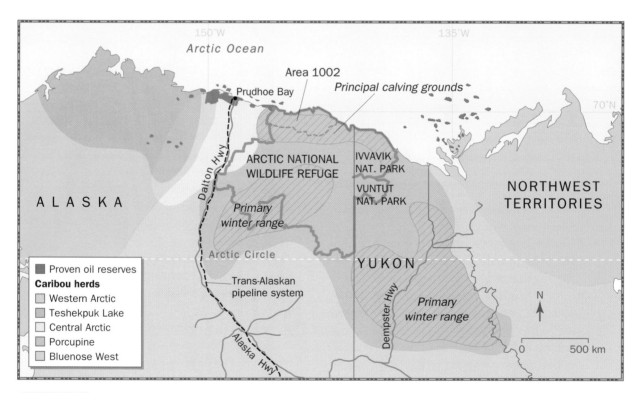

FIGURE 5–15 According to *Canadian Geographic* (May/June, 2001), it is estimated that the Arctic National Wildlife Refuge protects the calving grounds of over 130 000 Porcupine caribou. Research the arguments made by environmentalists that energy exploration should be banned here to protect the caribou, and those made by the oil companies that exploration will not harm caribou populations. Which position do you agree with?

FIGURE 5–16 The oil field at Prudhoe Bay in Alaska, discovered in 1968, is the largest oil field in North America. Oil is transported via pipeline from Prudhoe Bay along the North Slope to south central Alaska, and then transferred to oil tankers.

through Canadian territory, in order to transport natural gas from Alaska's North Slope and to tap into the large reserves from the Northwest Territories' Mackenzie Delta, through the Mackenzie Valley. This pipeline would supply the growing demands of North Americans for fossil fuel, as well as providing Canada with an opportunity to expand its current CDN$39 billion-dollar oil and gas exports to the United States.

28. **a)** How much of the world's energy supply do Canadians and Americans use? Explain why North Americans, a relatively small percentage of the global population, have such a relatively high energy consumption.

   b) Which energy needs do you think are similar, and which are different, between Canadians and Americans?

companies to extract and process) from the Arctic National Wildlife Refuge. With the present United States consumption of oil at near 18.5 million barrels a day, all of the Arctic National Wildlife Refuge oil resources would be able to supply the United States with only 140 days' worth of oil.

The United States Fish and Wildlife Service is concerned that oil development in the area would have major effects on the Porcupine caribou and musk-oxen herds, as disturbances to fragile plant communities would result in long-term habitat changes for these and other animals. Environmentalists and some local aboriginal people want a complete ban on oil and gas exploration on this reserve, as they are concerned that the caribou calves will be forced to graze on poor-quality land as a result of being displaced from better grazing lands. However, oil companies argue that the caribou populations around Prudhoe Bay in Alaska actually multiplied, despite the construction of pipelines and roads.

The United States is also looking to route its proposed multi-billion-dollar natural gas pipeline

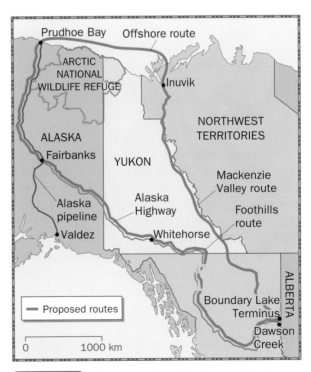

FIGURE 5–17 How would Canada be impacted by the construction of the proposed gas pipeline?

29. Do you agree or disagree that an escalation in oil drilling along Alaska's North Slope, and possibly in Area 1002, would help to meet the goal of the 2001 United States National Energy Policy of increasing the supply of energy at lower prices? Explain your opinion.

30. List all the sources of energy that you use during a typical day. Which energy items could you give up? Use less of? Replace with an alternative source?

31. a) Using Figure 5–17 and a Canadian atlas, complete a PMI (pluses, minuses, and interesting) organizer regarding the proposed multi-billion-dollar natural gas pipeline. Your organizer should consider the direction of the proposed pipeline, the estimated distance of the pipeline in Canada versus the United States, the location of existing communities and infrastructure (for example, highways), and the proximity of pipeline to physical features, protected lands, and natural habitats.

b) Share your findings with a partner and add any additional information to your organizer.

c) Based on information from your organizer, write a statement (in two or three sentences) in which you take a stance regarding the proposed pipeline.

Case in point — Alberta

While Canada's provinces mainly control its energy resources, it is the federal government's job to develop policies and guidelines regarding the overall development and management of these resources. Over time, Canadian policy has shifted from being primarily concerned with supply and demand to focussing, in the 1993 policy, on the economic and environmental aspects of energy. Canada now has commitments to the North American Free Trade Agreement and to the reduction of greenhouse gas emissions. Since 1997, a sustainable energy policy has been developed to help prevent pollution and mismanagement of resources. Canada's energy policy continues to evolve and may see still more changes, in response to the new United States National Energy Policy.

The depletion of conventional oil resources, the rise in oil prices, and the development of improved technologies have given rise to oil exploration in more remote regions. Alberta — Canada's leading oil producer — is looking to further explore and extract its oil-sands deposits near Fort McMurray and the surrounding Athabasca River region.

The sands cover an area greater than New Brunswick, and may contain 2.5 trillion barrels

FIGURE 5–18 The Alberta oil sands make up one of the two largest oil deposits of this kind in the world. (The other is in the Orinoco Belt in Venezuela.)

of oil, 300 billion of which are recoverable. An amount of 2.5 trillion barrels of oil is greater than existing supplies in Saudi Arabia!

Oil sands are a mixture of bitumen, sand, water, and clay. Bitumen is a thick, tar-like hydrocarbon that surrounds the sand and water; it is separated and upgraded to high-quality oil called "synthetic crude." Oil sands are not extracted by drilling, but by removing approximately 15 to 20 metres of "overburden," comprised mostly of soil and trees, which cover the sands.

The development of the Alberta oil sands is expensive. Large-scale equipment and technical operations are needed to extract and upgrade the bitumen into usable oil. According to recent articles in *Maclean's* and *Canadian Geographic*, it is estimated that CDN$5.1 billion dollars will be invested between 1996 and 2010, with output targets of 170 million barrels a year by 2007. Long-standing Canadian companies in the oil-sands business — namely Suncor and Syncrude — argue that they are just "scratching the surface," in terms of oil-sands output. The National Energy Board of Canada estimates that, by 2025, about 70 percent of Canada's oil production will come from Alberta's bitumen deposits located in the Fort McMurray area.

Extracting synthetic crude from the oil sands is not a new concept. Its development resurged in the mid-1990s, when federal and provincial governments offered tax and royalty breaks, improved technologies became available, world oil prices rose, and there were ongoing fossil fuel demands from strong North American economies. Rising political pressure from the United States National Energy Policy, and recent corporate consolidation in the oil industry have strengthened the prospects for future development of the oil sands through large-scale investments of money and technology.

Social and environmental consequences

Beside the economic costs, how else is Alberta's oil-sands development impacting the sustainability of the area? From a social aspect, the population of Fort McMurray has increased from only a few thousand residents 30 years ago, to over 40 000 people in 2001. Over the past few years, Fort McMurray has experienced a "growth spurt," with new people arriving to satisfy the demand for workers in the oil-sands industry. This has led to a need to expand the existing infrastructure. Also, it has became difficult for employers in the area to find employees for lower-wage jobs, because oil companies offer significantly higher pay.

From an environmental aspect, there is apprehension over the extensive strip mining involved in the extraction of oil sands. This method scrapes away and discards overlying vegetation, soil, and rock. The proximity of mines and processing

At a glance —
Fort McMurray's oil sands

- Community of over 40 000 people
- Located 450 km northeast of Edmonton, where the Athabasca and Clearwater Rivers meet
- Oil sands often described as a "hydrocarbon triangle," spanning almost 78 000 km²
- First oil-sands boom in 1964, with the construction of the Great Canadian Oil Sands plant
- Second boom in 1973, when Syncrude Canada Ltd. built a large-scale oil-sands mine, which is currently operating
- Many of the workers come from neighbouring Cree and Chippewa communities
- Region contains differing ecological systems within its boreal forests (primeval forests that almost completely encircle the northern part of the globe)
- New projects are exploring the use of underground extraction wells called "situ projects" to minimize impact of open-pit mining, and to access deep oil-sands reserves

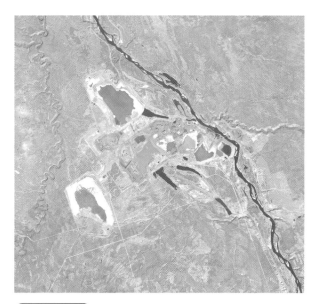

The area between Fort MacKay and Fort McMurray (shown above) contains the Suncor and Syncrude oil-sands mines and processing plants. What are some of the positive and negative impacts of the oil-sands development for the local area?

Energy Board also suggests that the development of oil sands will contribute up to one-quarter of Canada's excess greenhouse gas emissions (according to levels set by a 1997 international agreement called the Kyoto Protocol).

As the development of Alberta's oil sands expands, and North America's economic and personal dependency on oil continues, questions about the sustainability of this oil boom persist.

32. How do oil sands differ from conventional oil resources?

33. Describe where Alberta's oil-sands deposits are located. Refer to Figure 5–18.

34. Outline the factors that have contributed to the resurgence of the oil-sands development in Alberta.

35. In a chart format, contrast the costs and the benefits of Alberta's oil-sands development.

36. Work in a group of four. One half will defend, while the other half refutes the argument that Alberta's oil sands are the answer to meeting North America's future demands for fossil fuel. Use the text, as well as research material, to support your stance. Present and debate both sides of the argument. After debating the issue, set aside your opposing roles and, as a group, attempt to come to a conclusion.

37. As a journalist for an energy resources magazine, you are asked to write a one-page feature article on the direction energy development is taking in North America. Use information from this chapter and from other current sources for your feature. Your article should outline:
    • the purpose and current direction of Canada's National Energy Program
    • the pros and cons of energy exploration in remote regions
    • your thoughts as to where energy use and projects are heading in the twenty-first century

    Be sure to include an eye-catching and appropriate title for your article.

plants to the Athabasca River is also of concern. Sulphur dioxide and nitrogen dioxide emissions from the mining and refining processes raise fears of increasing acidification of nearby lakes.

Air pollution is the greatest worry, however. According to *Canadian Geographic*, Suncor and Syncrude are now the fourth-largest sources of carbon dioxide emissions in Canada. The amount of these emissions doubled in less than ten years, and it is estimated that these two companies combined will emit up to 8 to 10 megatonnes by 2002. This is an issue: carbon dioxide emissions are thought to contribute to global warming.

Suncor and Syncrude have made attempts to reduce emissions by investing in expensive smoke-stack scrubbers, which remove some impurities before emissions are released into the atmosphere. However, as oil sand companies' production levels rise, so do their greenhouse gas emissions, which the National Energy Board of Canada calculates will approach 49 megatonnes by 2015. This is double the output measured in 2000. The National

Turning to Alternative Energies

What happens when the demand for fossil fuel exceeds the development of new reserves? A geological survey expert, Colin Campbell, calls this situation the **big rollover**, where the demand for oil exceeds the rate at which new sources are being developed. According to the *New Internationalist* (dated June 2001), Campbell confirms how scarce fossil-fuel resources are becoming, and states that oil companies are finding only one new barrel of oil for every four barrels currently in reserve or being used. Furthermore, the *New Internationalist* forecasts that world energy consumption will rise 60 percent by 2020.

Two critical questions arise:

- How can we lessen our dependency on fossil fuels?
- How quickly can we adopt alternative sources of energy into our daily lives?

Moving away from the extensive use of fossil fuels may take some time, but as people pay higher prices economically, environmentally, and socially for energy consumption, there will be more incentive to explore alternative energy solutions that do not utilize non-renewable resources.

FIGURE 5–20 Wind farms, like this one in Pincher Creek, Alberta (above), and solar farms like this one in California (right), are examples of green energy sources. What is meant by "green energy"?

As the demand for clean, renewable sources of energy grows, along with new technological developments and greater government and corporate initiatives, the use of **green energy** (that is, solar power, wind power, nuclear power, geothermal energy, biomass energy, and hydro-electricity) is expected to rise.

38. Why were green energy sources not more intensively explored and implemented before now? Why are they gaining the world's attention today?

39. Which, if any, alternative fuel types have you seen or heard promoted in the media? How effective were these promotions in educating you about alternatives?

40. a) Form groups of six. Each member should research and report on one of the sources of alternative energy outlined in "Frame of reference." Check www.gagelearning.com/onthethreshold for more information on these energy sources and for links to other relevant sites. Share your report with the rest of the group.

b) Which of the six sources of alternative energy listed would be "most likely to succeed" in terms of your daily energy consumption? Select two or three of these sources of green energy and explain your reasons for selecting them.

c) As a group, create attractive slogans for each type of alternative energy, for use in an advertising campaign to enlist support for alternative fuel sources. Your slogans need to be concise while still informing the public about the alternative energy's benefits and about its importance in meeting future energy demands. Be prepared to present your slogans visually and orally, and to explain what you found most challenging about this exercise.

Frame of reference

Solar energy: This is energy derived from the sun. It can be used passively to heat air or water for commercial and residential use. It can also be harnessed by using photovoltaic cells to convert it to electricity — like a solar calculator, on a much bigger scale.

Hydrogen energy: This is a rich source of energy. It is a promising alternative, since hydrogen can act as an "energy carrier" that stores and transports usable energy. Also, pure hydrogen is clean-burning. Current research is focussing on using hydrogen fuel cells in cars and buses.

Nuclear energy: This method generates large amounts of electricity through the process of nuclear fission. Even though nuclear power has been criticized for its construction and maintenance expense, as well as its use of radioactive materials, it is a form of energy that does not emit greenhouse gases.

Tidal energy: This energy source works by harnessing the tides to generate electricity. A dam is built across the tidal basin, which contains the incoming water, and pushes it through turbines, thus activating a generator. The dam includes a sluice (gate) to hold the water in the basin and keep the turbines moving during low tide.

Wind energy: This is a means of generating power from the wind, and is a fast-growing form of "green energy" because it is inexpensive. This is not a new technology, but modern wind turbines, with their propeller-like blades, can generate electricity that can be transferred to a local community's power grid.

Biomass energy: This involves the use of a biomass (organic matter) to provide heat, fuel, or electricity. Energy derived in this way is called "bioenergy." Ethanol (a substance derived from the fermenting of crops or crop waste) can be mixed with petroleum to create a gasoline substitute for cars known as "gasohol."

Megadam sustainability

The Three Gorges hydro-electric dam, which is being built along China's Yangtze River, is heralded as the world's largest hydro-electric project, and is projected to be completed by 2009. Some Chinese call it the "modern Great Wall" — it is an impressive engineering feat. The megadam will be 185 metres high, with a 2-kilometre concrete wall stretching across the world's third-longest river, the Yangtze.

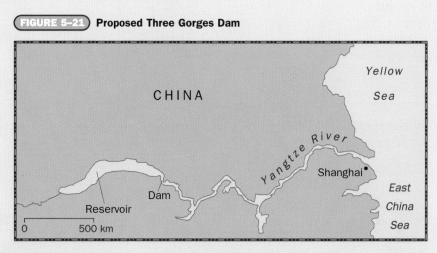

FIGURE 5–21 Proposed Three Gorges Dam

By 2003, it will begin to fill a reservoir that will ultimately be 1.1 kilometres wide, 600 kilometres long, and will hold 40 billion cubic metres of water. This reservoir will encompass a large area called the Three Gorges, which currently includes the Qutang Gorge, the Wu Gorge, and the Xiling Gorge.

The Three Gorges Dam is being constructed to provide China with inexpensive energy to support and strengthen its economic and social development. The dam's two power stations are expected to operate 26 of the world's largest turbine generators. The total generating capacity of the dam will be 18 200 megawatts — equivalent to the energy produced by 18 nuclear power stations or by 40 million tonnes of coal.

By controlling the flow of the Yangtze River, the dam will enable ships to navigate these turbulent waters more effectively, thus expanding the amount of shipping along this central part of the river by 10 million tonnes to 50 million tonnes annually, while cutting shipping costs by 30 to 37 percent. The dam is also intended to help control the frequency of floods, from once every ten years to once every 100 years, thus reducing the significant damage faced by downstream areas of the Yangtze River Delta.

The construction of large-scale dams in China is not a new idea. The country has been building dams and reservoirs since 1949, and these have displaced a total of over 10 million people. The Three Gorges Dam reservoir will flood an area of 632 square kilometres, which will impact 365 townships in 21 cities, districts, or counties in Sichuan and Hubei Provinces. The International Rivers Network (IRN) — an organization established in 1985 by activists and specialists to raise awareness and oppose what the Network considers to be economically, environmentally, and socially unsound river intervention projects — estimates that the dam will displace 1 million to 2 million people. The Network classifies such people as "reservoir refugees." The project's preliminary stages have been hampered by poor resettlement attempts, inadequate resettlement funds, and lack of consultation with resettled people.

FIGURE 5-22 The city of Wushan lies within the proposed reservoir boundaries. In 2009, the area below the arrow (shown above) will be under water.

It is expected that 28 400 hectares of fertile valley farmland will be flooded. Some people who used to live along the Yangtze River have been resettled to sites built on 25 degree slopes, making it very difficult for them to farm and develop a community. Others have been resettled as far away as Shanghai and Xinjiang Province in China's northwest. The half-urban and half-rural resettled populations will need either new jobs or high-quality farmland to make a living.

The flooding will also cover more than 1000 factories, hundreds of tourist and cultural sites, and ancient temples and monuments such as the Qu Yuan Temple, the Han Watchtower, and the historic Moya Cliff carvings. This area also contains important burial grounds of farmers and other rural dwellers.

This dam project is being highly criticized for its enormous cost. The official estimate for completing construction is approximately US$25 billion; unofficial estimates are targeting US$75 billion. The International Rivers Network calculates that the project is 800 percent over its original estimate, resulting in money having to be removed from other programs, as well as threatening China's economic stability. Due to the economic, environmental, and social concerns, the World Bank and the United States Export-Import Bank have not provided direct funding for this project. However, large international corporations and financial institutions, such as Merrill Lynch and General Electric, have underwritten bonds, and provided other financial support and equipment to help with the project's ballooning costs.

A further criticism of the Three Gorges Dam project is that it will change the river ecosystem for fish and wildlife, and may be a threat to endangered species such as the Chinese sturgeon, the Chinese tiger, the Yangtze dolphin, and the giant panda.

Since the once fast-moving river in the Three Gorges will be transformed into a lake, the more than 50 types of pollutants from human and industrial waste that are dumped into the lake will not be washed away. Chongqing — China's largest metropolitan area with over 30 million people — fears a tremendous backup of sewage. The location of the Three Gorges Dam along a fault in the earth, which makes the location more susceptible to earthquakes, is also disconcerting.

Because of these concerns, there is intense opposition to this project by locals and by prominent international organizations such as the International Rivers Network and Amnesty International (a grass-roots activist organization).

Supporters of the Three Gorges Dam project argue that, by controlling the flow of water, the lives of over 15 million people downstream will be protected, since the threat of a flood will be remote. They stress the ultimate aim of the project — to provide China with large amounts of hydro-electric power so that it will no longer need to rely on power from coal, which damages the environment.

Sustainability report

You and a partner have been contracted by the Worldwatch Institute to provide them with an up-to-date "sustainability report" about the Three Gorges megadam. Your report will include the following:

a) A cost/benefit analysis: Use the information from this text, as well as other research, to complete a cost/benefit analysis of China's Three Gorges Dam. Under separate headings, record the political, environmental, social, and economic costs or negative aspects of the project, as well as the benefits or positive aspects of the Three Gorges Dam.

b) A sustainability ranking: Create an organizer to record information on the Three Gorges Dam project. Within your organizer, rank this project, based on each of the following criteria:

- extraction/harvesting methods
- resource uses/demands
- amount of energy generated
- environmental impacts
- conservation considerations

Rank each criterion on a scale of 1 to 3, whereby 1 is the least sustainable criterion and 3 is the most sustainable. In which of these areas is the Three Gorges Dam most sustainable and in which is it least sustainable? How sustainable is this project overall? Are you a supporter or a critic of the project? Add your conclusions and recommendations regarding this megadam to your report.

c) A sustainability comparison: Complete the same ranking system for the Alberta oil-sands project, using the same criteria and scale. Which of these two projects do you feel is the more sustainable? Why? In the final section of your report to the Worldwatch Institute, record your conclusions regarding comparative sustainability of the Three Gorges Dam project.

CHAPTER 6

Global Water Supply

Gerry White's story

Gerry White is an entrepreneur who wants to sell Canada's water to the world and sees no reason why he should be prevented from doing so.

Specifically, he wants to sell water from Gisborne Lake in Newfoundland. The lake is 16 kilometres long and 10 kilometres wide, near the south coast of Newfoundland. White flew over Lake Gisborne one summer day in 1996 and nearly didn't notice it because the water is so clear.

White quickly developed a plan to skim 500 000 cubic metres from Gisborne Lake each week and ship it in bulk to overseas customers. He argued that draining this much water would lower the lake by a couple of centimetres, but this would be replenished naturally within 10 hours.

He also argued it would be a benefit to jobs-poor Newfoundland, especially the small community of Grand Le Pierre, 30 kilometres down the hill on the Atlantic shore. Grand Le Pierre used to be a thriving cod-fishing town. Then the cod disappeared and now the unemployment rate is more than 40 percent.

White convinced the town's mayor, Edward Fizzard, to back the plan. Fizzard imagined a water pipeline from Gisborne Lake, a bottling plant in Grand Le Pierre, and work for locals loading tankers to take the water to distant ports.

When environmentalists got wind of the plan, they successfully argued that allowing Gisborne Lake water to be sold in bulk would make Canadian water a "commodity" and thus subject to the terms and conditions of the General Agreement on Tariffs and Trade (GATT) and the North American Free Trade Agreement (NAFTA). White's grand plan was scrapped.

Early in 2001, Roger Grimes, the new premier of Newfoundland, revived the plan to sell water from Gisborne Lake. Mayor Fizzard of Grand Le Pierre couldn't be happier. "The water is just running into the Atlantic Ocean. No one is getting one nickel out of it," he told a visiting reporter in May 2001. "Why shouldn't it help us?"

Maude Barlow's story

Maude Barlow is chair of the Council of Canadians, a citizens' group with 100 000 members. "There is a common assumption that the world's water supply is huge and infinite," Barlow has said. "This assumption is false. At some time in the near future, water bankruptcy will result."

She endorses a 1999 paper from the Canadian Environmental Law Association (CELA) that says: "Water is an essential need, a public trust, not a commodity. It belongs to everyone and to no one." The CELA paper continues:

"Even large-scale water exports cannot possibly satisfy the social and economic needs of distant societies. Water shipped halfway around the world will be affordable only to the privileged and will deepen inequities between rich and poor. International trade in bulk water will allow elites to assure the quality of their own drinking water supplies, while permitting them to ignore the pollution of their local waters and the waste of their water management systems."

Commenting specifically on the Great Lakes Basin, CELA says: "Changing water levels and flows will have unpredictable and harmful consequences to basin habitat, biodiversity, shorelines, jobs and culture, particularly to First Nations."

Barlow maintains that if Newfoundland is allowed to export bulk water, it becomes a commodity under NAFTA. This would allow any other company in Canada to do the same.

a) Which position do you support on this very contentious issue? Why?

b) Do you see any possible "middle ground" on the issue of exporting Canadian water? Can you suggest a solution that might satisfy both sides of the debate?

- Demonstrate an understanding of how human-induced changes in natural systems, such as aquifers and seas, can diminish their capacity for supporting human activity.
- Identify ways in which countries of the world are becoming increasingly interdependent.
- Evaluate the effectiveness of the Law of the Sea, which has been designed to protect the global "commons."
- Use maps to analyse change over time in a place.
- Demonstrate an understanding of the role of satellite imagery in the monitoring of water and water-related resources.
- Demonstrate an understanding of how scarcities and inequities in the distribution of resources like freshwater contribute to uprisings and conflict.

When viewed from space, earth could be described as "the blue planet." This is because we have an abundance of water everywhere — in our ocean and atmosphere, and on the surface of our land. Even our bodies are made up of 70 percent water!

If we have so much water, why is our water supply one of the most serious concerns facing the world's population today? In this chapter, we will look at issues regarding the ocean, as well as discussing our most precious resource of all, freshwater.

FIGURE 6–1 With so much water on earth, how can ocean and freshwater resources be a pressing global issue?

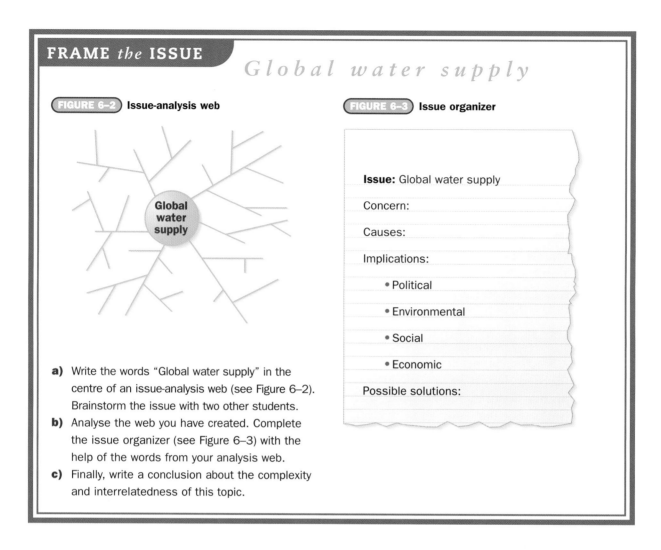

FRAME *the* ISSUE

Global water supply

FIGURE 6-2 **Issue-analysis web**

Global
water
supply

FIGURE 6-3 **Issue organizer**

Issue: Global water supply

Concern:

Causes:

Implications:

• Political

• Environmental

• Social

• Economic

Possible solutions:

a) Write the words "Global water supply" in the centre of an issue-analysis web (see Figure 6–2). Brainstorm the issue with two other students.

b) Analyse the web you have created. Complete the issue organizer (see Figure 6–3) with the help of the words from your analysis web.

c) Finally, write a conclusion about the complexity and interrelatedness of this topic.

The Ocean

The 362 000 000 square kilometres of ocean — the Atlantic, Pacific, Indian, and Arctic Oceans — that cover 71 percent of this planet's surface remain largely unexplored and mysterious to humankind. We have long held the opinion that the ocean is so big it could never be harmed; we believed that it could absorb anything poured into it, and could supply an endless amount of food and resources. We are learning now how wrong these assumptions were. We have polluted the ocean and over-harvested the fish stock. Detailed study is vital if we are to understand the limits within which we may co-exist with the ocean.

Life in the shallows

Water environments have as much geographic diversity as land environments. While the average depth of the ocean is 3795 metres, it also contains deep chasms and trenches that reach a staggering depth of 11 700 metres. In comparison, the average height of the land is only 840 metres. The ocean is made up of expansive sandy plains, which are as lifeless as the great deserts, as well as rich shallows, which are home to vast numbers of plant and animal species. There are large, unexplored areas waiting to be discovered, as new technologies provide us with the means to access them. Scientists predict that these vast,

FIGURE 6–4 In this map, greater depths are shown as dark blue, while shallower depths are lighter blue. According to the Marine and Environmental Education and Research Centre in California, continental shelves provide about 90 percent of the world's fish harvests.

unknown areas contain remarkable ecosystems of species and plants that can survive in the darkness and the near-freezing temperatures of very deep waters.

Eighty percent of all life on earth is found beneath the ocean's surface. Of this amount, only a small portion is found in deep waters. The richest living environments of the ocean are at its edges, where ocean meets land. Here, at the submerged edges of the continents — called **continental shelves** — marine plant life is as productive as many agricultural crops on land.

Prior to the 1970s, the resources of the ocean were open for anyone to exploit. This led to friction between those countries wanting to control their own shallow, offshore waters. Many countries with shorelines created boundaries at certain distances from the shorelines and claimed to control the areas within these boundaries. In response to this trend, a United Nations (UN) conference convened in 1973 to discuss the rights of countries with regard to their shorelines.

In 1982, the United Nations finally passed an agreement termed the **Law of the Sea**. This agreement stipulated that a set distance from a shoreline would form a boundary that all countries had to recognize. The area within this boundary is described as a country's **Exclusive Economic Zone (EEZ)**. Specifically, the Law of the Sea states that a country can "exploit, develop, manage, and conserve all resources — fish or oil, gas or gravel, nodules or sulphur — to be found in the waters, on the ocean floor, and in the subsoil of an area" extending 320 kilometres from its shore. The law prevents countries from entering the coastal area of another country and exploiting it.

1. Explain why ocean shallows are so important.

2. Refer to the world map of shallows in Figure 6–4. Describe the location of what you consider to be the six most extensive continental shelf margins.

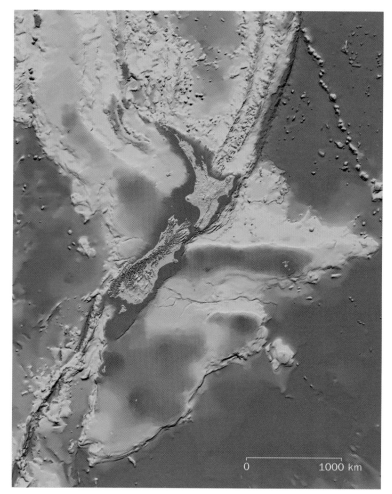

FIGURE 6–5 Orange, yellow, and green represent progressively deeper underwater shelves in this image. New Zealand's marine assets include fisheries, oil, gas, and minerals.

3. a) Using the map in Figure 6–5, trace an outline of:
   • the shape of New Zealand
   • the continental shelf area (indicated by the colours orange, yellow, and green).
   b) Using the line scale, measure a distance of 320 kilometres from the actual coastline of New Zealand. Mark this imaginary line around the country. The area between this line and the coast represents the Exclusive Economic Zone for New Zealand.
   c) How well does the Exclusive Economic Zone match the continental shelf of New Zealand?

4. What problems could a country face when its Exclusive Economic Zone does not enclose the country's entire continental shelf?

5. Do you believe that the Law of the Sea is effective, regarding the control of a country's offshore regions? Explain your answer.

Ocean pollution

Not long ago, the most prevalent theory concerning ocean pollution was the **dilution theory**. This theory was based on a belief that the ocean was so vast and deep it could be used as a waste area. It was thought that even poisons would be diluted so much that they would not pose any threat. Time has shown how wrong this theory was!

Airborne contamination accounts for 33 percent of all ocean pollution. A further 44 percent reaches the ocean via rivers and streams. According to the environmental action group People and Planet, the Black Sea is rapidly becoming a "dead" sea; its biological diversity is being destroyed, due to pollution. The water below 150 metres has little or no oxygen because of pollutants, and can sustain only micro-organisms.

It is estimated that 85 percent of all ocean pollution is first generated on land. Huge volumes of **agricultural run-off** end up in the ocean. Chemicals in pesticides, herbicides, and fungicides not only contaminate groundwater, but also follow natural drainage systems into the ocean. Fertilizers that are rich in nitrates cause accelerated production of algae, which reduces oxygen levels in marine waters.

A large amount of urban development in coastal locations also contributes to ocean pollution. A total of 3.2 billion people live within 100 kilometres of the ocean, and 13 out of 15 of the world's megacities are built either next to

FIGURE 6–6 Coral reefs are only found in the shallow, warm waters of the tropics where there is enough warmth and light for coral organisms to survive.

the ocean, or near major rivers that flow into the ocean. These cities dump large amounts of waste into the ocean — approximately 6.5 trillion kilograms each year.

Industry is tightly regulated by environmental controls in most developed countries, but is less so in developing countries. Many large multinational corporations are accused of participating in a "race to the bottom," (described in Chapter 4) as they shift production investments to countries where regulations are less costly. In these countries, large amounts of waste from industrial production seep into the groundwater systems and end up in the ocean.

Many of the world's large oil refineries have coastal locations. According to the Worldwatch Institute, about 1 million tonnes of oil escape through accidents or decayed infrastructure (any structure used to collect, refine, move, or store oil) each year, polluting nearby coastlines, estuaries, and salt marshes. The Worldwatch Institute asserts that shipping discharges, accidental oil spills, and ocean dumping account for 22 percent of all ocean pollution.

Pollution — A threat to the coral reefs

A major concern to many ecologists throughout the world is the serious threat to one of nature's most valuable ocean resources — its coral reefs. The World Resources Institute believes that almost 60 percent of the world's 600 000 square kilometres of coral reef is at risk of being permanently damaged or lost within the next 40 years. In South Asia, some 80 percent of its reefs are in serious danger. Why should we be concerned about the loss of coral reefs?

- Coral reefs cover only about 2 percent of the ocean floor, but they provide a habitat to roughly 4000 species of fish, that is, 25 percent of the world's total fish species.

- Reefs give shelter to hatching fish, thus supplying a rich harvest of food to the developing world. The World Resources Institute estimates that coral fish are caught at a rate of 15 tonnes per square kilometre, each year. Approximately 25 percent of all harvested fish worldwide are from coral habitats.

- Coral contributes to the maintenance of the pH balance (acidity level) of the ocean.

- Reefs provide shoreline protection from heavy waves.

- The beauty of coral reefs provides employment through tourist snorkelling and diving.

Factors which add to the destruction of coral habitats include:

- *growth in the amount of sewage dumped into the ocean* from the urbanization of coastlines and expansion of coastal cities

- *land reclamation* (waste and building materials dumped into coastal waters to extend the shoreline artificially)

- *dredging and expanding harbours*

- *run-off from agricultural fertilizers*, which accelerates algae growth and so reduces sunlight penetration

- *overfishing*, especially via the method of underwater blasting with dynamite. Overfishing can also set in motion a food chain reaction that eventually damages the coral. In the Caribbean, overfishing decimated the number of herbivorous fish that helped to keep algae levels healthy.

- ships that clean their storage areas while at sea, often *dumping sizable amounts of leftover chemicals or oil* overboard.

- *tourism* (through the dropping of anchors by snorkelling and scuba-diving boats, and coral mining — the harvesting of the reef for souvenirs)

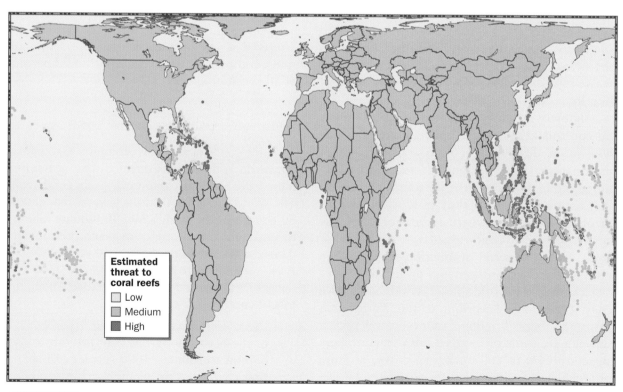

Estimated threat to coral reefs
- ☐ Low
- ☐ Medium
- ■ High

FIGURE 6–7 Where are coral reefs most under threat?

Global WARNING

POLLUTION IN THE MEDITERRANEAN SEA

The Mediterranean Sea, which is a popular tourist region, is one of the most polluted water passages worldwide. According to the World Wildlife Fund (WWF), although the Mediterranean covers less than 1 percent of the world's total ocean area, 25 percent of global oil transportation passes through it.

Almost a self-contained sea, with two narrow passages at either end, the Mediterranean stretches from Spain/Morocco in the west, to Turkey in the east. With its hot summers and very mild winters, this region has developed unique ecosystems: its vegetation and climate support 13 000 species exclusive to the region. Its significant wetlands support up to 5 million migratory birds each year and, while it contains only 1 percent of the world's saltwater, it is home to 6 percent of all marine species.

The Mediterranean is surrounded by 22 countries, most with industrial areas and large urban concentrations. There are also significant rivers — outflows from industrial heartlands — that empty into its waters.

Due to pollution and overfishing, the Mediterranean has become unsustainable. Pollutants include sewage, industrial metals, agricultural run-off, and oil from ships. The WWF calculates that its fish stocks are down by 20 percent and that Mediterranean wetlands — important breeding and nesting sites for a variety of creatures — are threatened.

According to the WWF, specific pollutant problems included the following:

- Beach resorts and communities are growing at an explosive pace. A total of 85 million people live in the coastal cities. By 2025, the resident coastal population could be 170 million, while the annual tourist population could number 200 million.

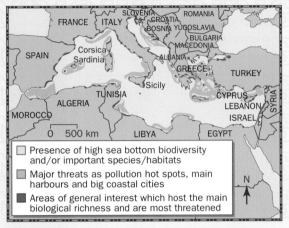

FIGURE 6–8 Which countries' contributions would be vital to a discussion on protecting areas within the Mediterranean that are threatened by pollution?

- A total of 650 million tonnes of sewage is discharged into the sea each year, 70 percent of which is untreated.
- Industrial metals such as mercury (60 000 tonnes) and lead (3800 tonnes) are poured into its waters each year.
- Agricultural run-off accounts for 36 000 tonnes of phosphates draining into the Mediterranean annually.
- One million tonnes of oil enter the sea from ships cleaning their tanks, and from tank spillage or leakage.

a) Solving the Mediterranean's pollution problem will require international co-operation from both rich and poor countries. Proposals suggesting tough financial penalties for polluters have been put forward. Research some of these proposals.

b) With a partner, brainstorm some key arguments for and against accepting these proposals.

Fish — An endangered resource

The ocean provides a classic example of an "environmental commons" that is open to free exploitation (see Chapter 1). This has resulted in significant overexploitation of a major food resource — fish. The Food and Agriculture Organization of the United Nations (FAO) reports that about 80 million tonnes of fish are caught each year, providing protein for nearly 1 billion people. The demand is expected to grow to 120 million tonnes by 2010, to match the worldwide growth in population. Some 75 percent of fish caught in the world each year is for direct human consumption. The remaining 25 percent is used to make fish by-products such as fish meal and oil for animal consumption and the cosmetic industry.

To satisfy this rise in demand, fishing technology has become very efficient. Long-range trawlers are excellent hunting machines that use state-of-the-art sonar and high-tech sea-floor mapping. Guided by aircraft, it has become easy for trawlers to reach the location of a fish harvest.

How long can increased catches continue? It is difficult for fish populations to replenish themselves at the same rate as they are being caught. In many cases, catches have overtaken the sustainable limit of replenishment. The Food and Agriculture Organization of the United Nations has found that 25 percent of all fish stocks are at their biological limit, meaning that they are at their sustainability threshold. Another 35 percent are in serious decline. Of 17 major fisheries, 15 are in serious danger of collapse — just like the cod fishery off the East Coast of Canada.

In response to demand, the number of fishing jobs available has increased significantly (to over 21 million) in the last ten years. However, when fisheries collapse, the impact on employ-ment is quick and severe, and many multinational corporations are worried about the repercussions of such job losses. For example, Unilever (a major fish processor and maker of products such as detergent, soap, and toothpaste) has co-operated with the World Wildlife Fund (WWF) to create the Marine Stewardship Council, which advises countries on sustainable fishing practices and seeks to ensure healthy fish stocks. According to the World Resource Institute, Unilever has pledged that by 2005, it will buy fish only from sustainably managed stocks. Also, the Marine Stewardship Council will certify fish that are harvested according to their standards. Products certified by the Council will promote this fact on their labels ("eco-labelling"), which will give them more consumer appeal. Eco-labelling should therefore offer producers an incentive to harvest their fish in accordance with the Council's requirements.

FIGURE 6–9 Sea-floor "mining" using huge dragnets catches everything in a trawler's path, even unwanted fish. According to the Food and Agriculture Organization of the United Nations, an estimated 30 million tonnes of fish are thrown back into the sea each year as unusable.

Grow your own fish

Most of the world's fish stocks are caught within their natural habitat. However, **aquaculture**, or fish farming, is increasing significantly — about one-third of all fish are now farmed. Globally, 2 kilograms of fish are produced on fish farms for every 5 kilograms of beef protein produced. The increase in fish farming has caused serious environmental concerns. The New Internationalist estimates that 5 kilograms of ocean fish must be caught to feed and produce 1 kilogram of the farmed species. For example, krill is used to feed salmon because it contributes to the salmon's pinkish colour, which appeals to consumers. Thailand — one of the world's biggest producers of farm-raised fish — has lost half of its mangrove forests due to shrimp farming. In British Columbia, according to the journal *Science*, salmon farms produce as much waste (from fertilizer, fish meal, and effluent) as half a million people.

FIGURE 6–10 Fish farms that raise fish in fenced-in areas of natural water like this one in British Columbia affect the ecosystem both within the fenced-in area and in the open water beyond it.

6. Describe the most common ways in which the ocean has become polluted.

7. Why are coral reefs important?

8. What are the major threats to coral reefs around the world?

9. a) Visit the Web site of a coral watchdog group, such as the International Coral Reef Initiative or the Global Coral Reef Monitoring Network. Identify three steps such groups are taking to protect coral reefs from further damage.

   b) Evaluate the effectiveness of these strategies.

10. The international fishing industry is a classic case of "the tragedy of the commons." Explain or refute this statement.

11. Research corporate initiatives that are being developed to help sustain global fisheries. An excellent site to start with is that of the Marine Stewardship Council.

Freshwater

Approximately 70 percent of the earth's surface is covered by water. About 97.5 percent of this is saltwater, forming the seas and the ocean.

FIGURE 6–11 Freshwater availability

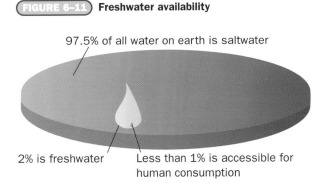

97.5% of all water on earth is saltwater

2% is freshwater

Less than 1% is accessible for human consumption

Only 2.5 percent of all the earth's water is freshwater. About 70 percent of this is frozen in Antarctica and Greenland. Less than 1 percent of all freshwater is usable for human consumption; 60 percent of this is frozen, underground, or in rivers that flow through uninhabitable regions.

What is left is available for our use and, fortunately, it should be enough. There is enough freshwater on this planet to allow every human 7000 cubic metres of water (enough to fill 49 000 bathtubs) each year.

The problem is that the freshwater is not evenly distributed. The Amazon River alone carries 20 percent of the planet's freshwater run-off. In desert regions — which comprise about 40 percent of the land on earth — only 2 percent of freshwater run-off is found. The amount of freshwater available in each country varies greatly,

from over 600 000 cubic metres per person in Iceland, to less than 75 cubic metres per person in Kuwait. In Canada, the supply is equivalent to 98 462 cubic metres per person. Other countries are not so fortunate. For example, in Lebanon today, where there is only 1842 cubic metres per person, water rationing and recycling is a fact of life.

In theory, all freshwater is renewable and therefore sustainable. The earth receives 110 000 cubic kilometres of precipitation, part of the water cycle of precipitation and evaporation. Of this, 9000 cubic kilometres is available for our use. Most of the rest is either lost to seasonal run-off, flows through uninhabited regions, or is trapped underground. To the accessible 9000 cubic kilometres, we can add about 3500 cubic kilometres stored within the dams we build. We use about 50 percent of the total 12 500 cubic kilometres available.

FIGURE 6–12 Predicted vulnerability to water scarcity, 2025

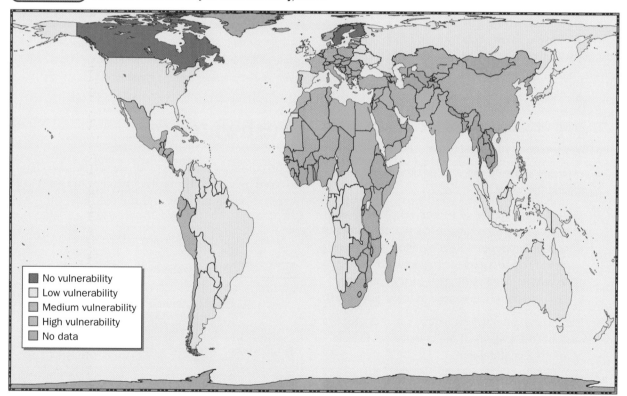

Legend:
- No vulnerability
- Low vulnerability
- Medium vulnerability
- High vulnerability
- No data

Like other resources, we misuse and overconsume water relative to our needs. As a result, 30 percent of all countries have water shortages today. According to the World Resources Institute, this number is expected to grow to nearly 70 percent by 2025.

Ecosystems and water supply

Water is vital for all ecosystems. It cycles through all the natural biomes on earth and is needed by all species:

- Wetlands and estuaries need water so that their rich habitats and diverse life forms can thrive.
- A healthy ocean is needed for the aquatic life within it.
- Humans must have clean drinking water to survive.
- Freshwater systems contain 40 percent of the world's fish species; freshwater rivers and lakes provide 6 percent of the world's total fish catch.

Yet, through wastage, ineffective use, and lack of preservation, humankind attacks this vital resource at a frightening pace. The number of major rivers and waterways that have been physically altered for use by boats and ships has risen from 9000 in 1900, to 500 000 today. Dredging and widening of waterways, and the resulting changes in water flow, severely affect ecosystems.

Pollution and waste have made access to safe drinking water a worldwide issue. About one-fifth of the world's population — most of them poor — do not have safe drinking water, and approximately one-half of the global population does not have adequate sanitation. As a result of these two factors, half of the total world population regularly suffers from water-borne diseases. These diseases, which include cholera (an infectious disease of the stomach and intestines) and bilharzia (caused by water-dwelling parasites), are common epidemics in some parts of the world.

The natural environment suffers too. Agricultural and industrial wastes pollute many of the world's lakes, rivers, and aquifers. The polluted water runs off into the ocean and becomes a serious threat to all marine ecosystems. According to Environment Canada, over 14 000 lakes in Canada contain enough acid (through acid rainfall) to have lost a significant number of fish.

The United Nations Department for Policy Co-ordination and Sustainable Development believes that water should be seen as:

- a vital element for the survival of biodiversity and human societies
- a vital resource for the development of economic activities
- a natural resource, which has economic value because of its scarcity
- an environmental resource, which has a common heritage that society should use, preserve, and conserve, and which highlights related cultural and spiritual aspects of society

The Department believes that all world inhabitants should be guaranteed equal access to **potable water** (water fit for drinking) and sanitation as a fundamental right. To achieve this end, sustainable methods for using water must be adopted globally.

Freshwater — Use and misuse

When we consider how we use freshwater, we usually think in terms of our personal use of water in the home. But we "consume" a large amount of freshwater elsewhere. Besides satisfying thirst, it is also important to maintain freshwater to grow food for the over 800 million people in the world

FIGURE 6–13 Regional differences in water use

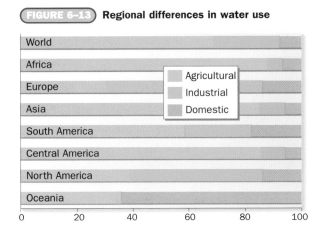

who do not receive adequate food supplies. The Green Revolution helped by creating high-yield varieties of plants, but most of these require higher-than-normal amounts of water to sustain them. About 40 percent of all food production comes from land that is irrigated, which amounts to about 17 percent of all cropland.

In the Middle East, where freshwater shortages are a part of life, scientists have attempted to make irrigation more efficient. Israel pioneered **drip irrigation** techniques, by which water is routed through small pipes directly to a plant's feeding mechanism — its roots. Small drips of water are fed to the roots over a long period of time (see Figure 6–14). Whereas traditional spraying of plants means a water loss of 35 to 45 percent through evaporation, drip irrigation is 95 percent efficient. As a result of this technique, Israel's present water use per irrigated hectare is 40 percent less than it was in 1955.

12. Why are freshwater ecosystems a vital resource that must be protected?

13. a) What proportion of the world does not have access to safe drinking water and effective sanitation?
    b) What health hazards are produced from such conditions?

FIGURE 6–14 Why are these innovative drip irrigation methods used in some areas but not in others?

14. a) Which three regions shown in Figure 6–13 would you describe as being "high demand" regions for agricultural freshwater?
    b) How would you describe the patterns for North America, Europe, and the rest of the world?

Groundwater

Groundwater (water that seeps through the ground into springs and wells) supplies one-third of the world's population with freshwater, and is the main or only source of water for rural dwellers in many parts of the world. Some 50 percent of all domestic supplies in Asia comes from groundwater reserves. The other two-thirds of the global population gets its water from **standpipes**. Standpipes are vertical pipes that hold water and maintain water pressure. Groundwater sources are being heavily overused in a number of regions, with water being pumped out faster than nature can replenish the supply. The Worldwatch Institute believes that the excessive use of groundwater is likely to increase over the next 30 years.

A large amount of groundwater is also lost through wastage. It is believed that, in the warmer climates of the midlatitudes, about 60 percent of all irrigation water is lost through evaporation before it can be used for crops.

Overpumping

A lot of the world's water supply that is used to irrigate cropland comes from groundwater sources such as aquifers, which contain water known as "fossil water." The Ogallala Aquifer, which extends from Texas to South Dakota, supplies one-fifth of the United States' irrigation water. However, since its depth was first measured in the 1940s, its water level has fallen by 20 percent due to overpumping.

In many areas of the world, overpumping groundwater has dropped water levels by tens of metres, making it increasingly difficult and expensive for people to access water. In a number of regions, depletion has forced people to use lower-quality groundwater sources, which con-

FIGURE 6–15 Sprinkler irrigation systems, like this one in Idaho, are used mainly in North America.

tain natural contaminants. For example, if groundwater is overpumped in coastal locations, saltwater from the ocean seeps in and contaminates the remaining groundwater.

Overpumping groundwater, especially during dry periods, can have a serious effect on the **base flow** (the part of a river flow that enters the channel from underground water supplies, as opposed to surface run-off) of rivers. Base flow is vital for aquatic ecosystems. Wetlands act as sponges that help to control flooding, purify existing water, and provide a habitat for thousands of fish, birds, and other species. As wetlands dry out, or are drained for development, the natural environment can be irreparably harmed.

Another problem associated with the overpumping of groundwater is its effect on **land subsidence** (land stability). For example, many of Mexico City's historic monuments stand about 3 metres above ground level; because of overpumping of water from beneath the city, these monuments need extra support.

Freshwater pollution

The Great Lakes contain 18 percent of the earth's surface freshwater. Like the ocean, the Great Lakes have been harmed by agricultural and industrial waste. According to the Environmental Protection Agency (EPA), 25 percent of American, and 7 percent of Canadian agriculture takes place within their collective drainage basin. This basin — home to over 33 million people — has received significant doses of inorganic fertilizers through stream and river run-offs. This, and the fact that industrial chemical waste also makes its way into the water system, has sparked significant concerns about the quality of this vital freshwater source. It is an important habitat for many aquatic species, as well as a major North American source of drinking water.

Agriculture is by far the greatest polluter of freshwater. Groundwater often includes high levels of phosphorus and nitrogen from fertilizers. High levels of nitrate in drinking water decrease the ability of the hemoglobin in our blood to carry oxygen, and can threaten the health of infants. Nearly all of Europe's major rivers are now high in nitrate content.

When agricultural run-off water reaches the ocean, "red tides" — also called "algae blooms" — are created. Algae blooms are algae or phytoplankton that grow very fast or "bloom" and accumulate into a dense mass. Algae with reddish pigment will form a "red tide" of algae. Such algae decrease the oxygen supply for other life forms. This is termed "eutrophication." About 50 percent of Europe's water systems suffer in this way.

It is gauged that nearly 500 cubic kilometres of waste is dumped into the world's streams, rivers, and lakes. Well over 100 000 chemicals pollute our waters. Many of these chemicals are banned in developed countries, but substances such as DDT and PCB — because of their relatively low cost and high level of efficiency — are still used in poorer countries. In developing countries, about 60 percent of all infant mortality deaths can be traced back to water-borne diseases and unsafe sanitation.

The United Nations estimates that 90 percent of all waste water in developing countries is discharged into their run-off systems without adequate treatment. In Karachi, Pakistan, the inefficiency of the infrastructure of pipes and sewage-treatment plants means that only 20 percent of the system is operating at any one time.

FIGURE 6–16 Populations without access to safe drinking water

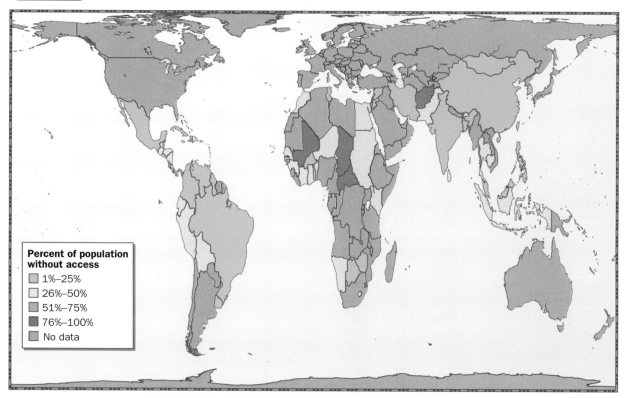

Percent of population without access
- 1%–25%
- 26%–50%
- 51%–75%
- 76%–100%
- No data

Governmental regulations involving freshwater

There is also concern about the management and safety of freshwater supplies in developed countries. Some experts consider the aging pipes and infrastructure that deliver freshwater to consumers a problem; others are concerned with governmental regulations involving the purification and delivery of freshwater.

Government laws and regulations define how private and public organizations should operate. Some people believe that there are too many laws and regulations, and that they slow processes and deter businesses and individuals from making changes and improvements.

In response, some governments are looking at **deregulation** (reduction or elimination of regulations). For example, the government of British Columbia publicized its deregulation objectives in 2001, stating their goal:

To eliminate or at least reduce the burdens imposed on companies, organizations, and citizens by the various policies and procedures of government agencies that impair people's legitimate desire to conduct their affairs in an efficient and helpful manner.

While many applaud these objectives, others caution against such reform. Organizations such as the Canadian Environmental Law Association believe that the environment, and ultimately the public, may suffer as a result of deregulation. Events in Walkerton, a town in southern Ontario, may support this belief.

In Walkerton, during May 2000, some 2300 people fell ill, and seven people died as a result of drinking water contaminated with E. coli bacteria. Following a public outcry, an Inquiry was held, costing Ontario taxpayers some CDN$9 million.

A report was brought out in early 2002 in which it was suggested that a number of things had gone wrong:

- The water in Walkerton had been contaminated by cattle waste seeping into the groundwater around the town.
- The managers of the Walkerton Public Utilities Commission mismanaged the utility and the problem when it arose.
- Safety and monitoring measures that required local utilities to report adverse water samples had been deregulated and were therefore unavailable.

15. How does excessive use of an aquifer, like the Ogallala, diminish its ability to support human life?

16. How may groundwater reserves be affected by future demands?

17. How may future demands for groundwater affect local ecosystems?

18. What could local authorities do to cope in areas where there are groundwater shortages?

19. Refer to Figure 6–16. How would you summarize the regional differences with regard to the availability of safe drinking water?

20. What are some of the effects of contaminated groundwater, streams, and rivers? Have any such effects been reported in the media in your area recently?

21. Define the term "deregulation" and offer reasons governments sometimes opt for these changes.

22. Research ways your province or municipality is lessening regulatory controls on business and individuals. What might the environmental and economic impacts of these changes be?

Case in point — The Aral Sea

The Aral Sea is located in central Asia and is shared by the countries of Uzbekistan and Kazakhstan. Once the fourth-largest inland sea in the world, it has turned into what has been described as an environmental disaster, and is a classic example of how shortsighted planning can devastate a major source of freshwater.

For 30 years, two major rivers that replenished the Aral Sea have been diverted for use as a means of irrigating agricultural land. These rivers — the Syr Dar'ya and the Amu Dar'ya — provide large amounts of water within their river valleys for the growth of cotton and rice. However, providing water to surrounding farmlands became unsustainable in 1960, when the Kara Kum Canal diverted large amounts of water from the Amu Dar'ya into the desert of Turkmenistan to water millions of hectares of land. This was done to create more farmland from arid desert by adding irrigation.

FIGURE 6–17 The Aral Sea and surrounding region

At a glance — *Uzbekistan and Kazakhstan*

	Uzbekistan	Kazakhstan
Population	25 155 064	16 731 303
Birth rate	26.1 births/1000	17.3 births/1000
Death rate	8 deaths/1000	10.61 deaths/1000
Languages (% of population)	Uzbek 74%, Russian 14%, Tajik 5%, other 7%	Russian 60%, Kazakh 40%
Economy	Exporter of cotton (world's third-largest exporter), gold, natural gas, mineral fertilizers, ferrous metals, textiles, food products, automobiles	Large, untapped fossil fuel resources. Exporter of oil (40%), ferrous and nonferrous metals, machinery, chemicals, grain, wool, meat, coal
GDP per capita	US$2400 (PPP)	US$5000 (PPP)

Up to that time, the sea was fed with 50 cubic kilometres of water per year but, by 1985, this amount had fallen to zero. The sea shrunk from 68 000 square kilometres in 1960, to 28 000 square kilometers in 2001. Its composition changed: the salt concentration in the water grew from 10 g/L in 1960 to 45 g/L in 1998. This has dramatically altered the shape of its shoreline, as shoreline ecosystems have evolved toward supporting plant life that is more suited to salt and drought.

Overall, the environmental and economic impacts in this area have been dramatic.

- Local climates have changed, with summers becoming hotter and drier, and winters becoming colder and lasting longer.
- The region's air quality has become a great concern. Approximately 30 000 square kilometres of lakebed have been exposed; massive amounts of chemical residues from pesticides and fertilizer, which were once washed into the lake, are now dry and lie exposed on the lakebed. The chemicals have become mixed with salt and are collected by huge dust storms that occur throughout this region. Sediment from this area has been found as far away as Pakistan and the Arctic. Many illnesses affecting locals, such as tuberculosis and anemia, have been directly blamed on this problem; there has also been a large increase in the rate of infant mortality.
- The livelihood of people in the surrounding areas has changed. Whereas the lake used to provide huge catches of fish, the fishing industry in 2001 has shrunk and can no longer employ 60 000 people, as it once did.

Seeking solutions to the Aral Sea problem

Five countries are directly affected by the Aral Sea problem so finding solutions has proved difficult. The Aral Sea is shared by Uzbekistan and Kazakhstan, but any water conservation decisions made regarding the Sea also concern Turkmenistan, Tajikistan, and Kyrgyzstan, which all share tributary water basins. These countries pledged to contribute 1 percent of their gross national product to the Aral Sea Fund but, in spite of the fact that they signed various agreements, there has been little development or money collected so far. Already, there are political tensions in the region: boundary disputes and water rights have caused conflict.

It has been suggested that farmers in the area should grow smaller amounts of cotton and make a shift toward growing rice, which requires 30 percent less water. A move toward genetically modified crops that need less water may be another solution. Offering another water efficiency solution, a team of Israeli water engineers visiting an Uzbek cotton farm demonstrated how two-thirds less water could actually increase cotton yields by 40 percent, using drip irrigation techniques.

Nevertheless, many of the possible solutions, including drip irrigation, would require large sums of money. This is a poor region — Kazakhstan's per capita gross national product (GNP) is only $5000 and Uzbekistan's is $2400. The region continues to weigh options and struggles to find feasible solutions.

23. Refer to Figure 6–21, on page 163, showing the satellite images of the Aral Sea in 1970 and in 1996. Using a piece of paper, trace around the edge of the Sea as it was in 1970. Accurately position the paper over the second image, and trace the 1996 outline. Using a light colour, shade the area of the lake that was lost between 1970 and 1996.

24. Use the data from Figure 6–19 to draw trend lines for each set of data.
   a) Estimate the percentage change between 1960 and 2010, for each set of data.
   b) Predict the data that might be expected in 2020 and in 2030.

25. Under four headings — *Environmental, Economic, Cultural,* and *Political* — analyse how complex the Aral Sea problem is. Use the Internet to gather further information.

FIGURE 6–18 Once supporting a thriving fishing industry, the Aral Sea has left many fishing boats "high and dry" and their crews have been forced to find new ways to earn a living — not an easy task in this poor region.

FIGURE 6–19 Aral Sea data

Year	Area (km²)	Volume (km³)	Sea level (m)	Salinity (g/L)
1960	68 000	1 040	53	10
1985	45 713	468	41.5	23
1990	38 817	282	38.5	No data
1995	35 374	248	37	No data
1998	28 687	181	34.8	45
2010	21 058	124	32.4	70

TECH IT OUT

Satellite imagery and water

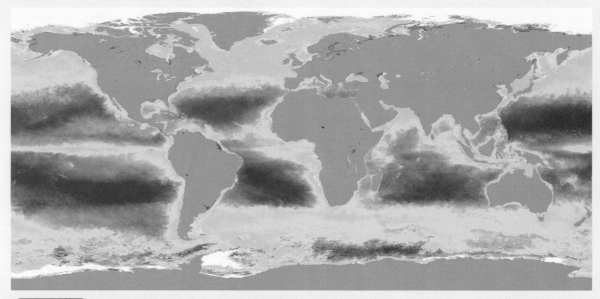

FIGURE 6–20 The variations in the concentration of chlorophyll (from plankton) can be seen in this SeaWiFS image. Blues indicate low concentrations while greens and reds indicate higher concentrations (red is the highest). Water motion such as currents, drifts, and eddies can be tracked by monitoring plankton distribution.

Remote sensing is the process of recording information about an object or phenomenon without being in physical contact with that object or phenomenon. Satellite imagery uses remote sensing in the monitoring of water and water-related resources.

Below the surface — Ocean remote sensing

There are two types of satellites that are used for monitoring the behaviour of large bodies of water — meteorological satellites and oceanographic satellites. Meteorological satellites (or metsats for short) are used primarily for determining weather patterns. They can also be very useful in examining some of the characteristics of large areas of water — they can determine the temperatures of the ocean and its prevailing flow patterns. Metsats are also able to distinguish the transition zones between water and land.

The use of metsats for anything other than weather analysis and modelling creates a problem, however, as they cannot map water features in detail. Generally, weather satellites are positioned in geostationary orbits

— that is, they are positioned above the same area of the planet all the time. For a satellite to be in such an orbit, it must be located about 36 000 kilometres above the earth. Although the satellite coverage of an area at this altitude is excellent, the detail captured is not. Other satellites, such as the Landsat series which orbits the earth at 940 kilometres, are therefore better choices for detailed mapping of water features.

Oceanographic satellites — the second type used — are highly specialized satellites that study large bodies of water in detail. There are only a few of these satellites specifically earmarked for ocean research, including Seasat, Nimbus-7, MOS, and Orbview-2. Many oceanographic satellites are not dedicated to ocean research; rather, they carry sensors such as the Coastal Zone Color Scanner (CZCS) and the Sea-viewing Wide Field-of-view Sensor (SeaWiFS), which can be used to accomplish some very impressive tasks. While they cannot view the position of fish or other sea animals in the depths of the ocean, they can detect the location of one of the main sources of food for marine animals — plankton.

Plankton consists of microscopic plants or animals that live near the surface of the water. Plant plankton, such as algae, contain chlorophyll — the substance that gives green plants their colour. Chlorophyll absorbs blue and red energy in the visible spectrum and, as such, is highly detectable using remote sensing techniques. Both the Coastal Zone Color Scanner and the Sea-viewing Wide Field-of-view Sensor can detect the chlorophyll in plankton and can be utilized to create images of plankton concentration. Such images have direct relevance for any research or industry needing to know where high concentrations of plankton may be found and, consequently, where fish are likely to gather.

Turning water into sand — The Aral Sea

Once the fourth-largest lake in the world, the Aral Sea has greatly declined in size over the last few decades. A range of satellite sensors were used to illustrate the reduction in its volume, area, and level. The enhanced satellite images in Figure 6–21 dramatically illustrate the astounding change in the Aral Sea's amount of water.

These satellite images represent the quickest way, as well as one of the most accurate ways, to monitor environmental change. Governmental, environmental, and private agencies have used this type of imagery to study a variety of water-related issues such as commercial fish stocks, coral-reef bleaching, coastal management and, in this case, lake or river desiccation (drying out).

a) How could oceanographic imagery be of immediate importance to the commercial fishing industry?

b) Environmentalists use satellite images to show the damage that is being done to the environment. Do you think it an invasion of privacy to use satellite imagery from one country to monitor environmentally damaging activity in another country? Defend your answer.

c) With classmates, brainstorm five ways in which remote-sensed imagery that deals with water could be misused. Suggest some international standards that an organization like the United Nations (UN) might put in place, to avoid the malicious use of remote-sensed imagery.

For more activities on the Aral Sea's water levels, visit www.gagelearning.com/onthethreshold.

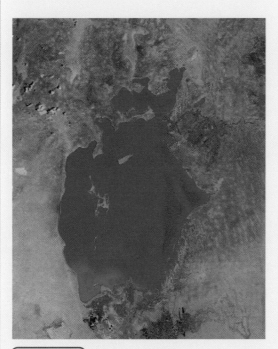 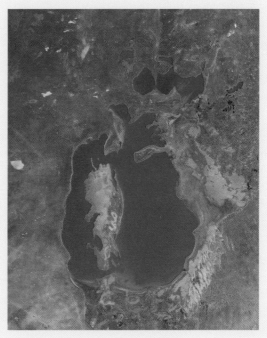

FIGURE 6–21 This pair of images shows the Aral Sea in 1970 (left) and in 1996 (right).

Flooding

The threat of floods is a reality for many people. Most of the world's population lives in fertile regions where food can be easily grown. For many, this means living in river valleys, which are prone to flooding. Approximately 20 million people in Asia face this threat. In China alone, according to the World Health Organization, over 5 million people have been killed in floods during the past 120 years. One of the world's largest engineering projects has been constructed in China to prevent such damage — the Three Gorges Dam. (See Chapter 5.) It was designed, among other reasons, to prevent the flooding of the Yangtze River, which caused such devastation in the past.

Floods are caused by both natural and human activity:

Natural causes of flooding

- Heavy rainfalls, such as monsoons, can cause floods in cases where an intense period of rain is more than rivers can handle.

- The rapid melting of accumulated snow can cause floods when huge amounts of moisture are "banked" throughout the winter and released in the spring.

- Flash floods can occur around steeply sloped areas. Most lives are lost during this type of flooding, which is severe and fast.

Human causes of flooding

- Urbanization can create flash floods in cases where paving and roofs do not allow the ground to absorb water, or where storm run-off systems cannot handle intense conditions.

- Rivers and streams that may have been "straightened" within an urban design or rerouted to facilitate road networks can lead to flooding. The water can flow at a faster pace and cause more erosion, especially in the spring, when rivers and streams are fuller.

- Deforestation can expose soil. As rain runs down the exposed soil, it creates deep channels that concentrate the water. The run-off accelerates down the slope and causes flooding where the area downstream cannot cope with the large volume of water.

Bangladesh — The flooding of a country

Bangladesh is a low-lying country into which three rivers — the Jamuna-Brahmaputra, Meghna, and Ganges-Badhma — discharge their water. The terrain is mainly flood plain and delta, built up from sediment carried down from the Himalayan Mountains. It is a flat country; most of it stands no more than 1 metre above sea level. During the summer months, when the land heats up and draws in the air from the ocean, the country is hit by heavy monsoon rains. When this moisture is

FIGURE 6–22 Flooding in Bangladesh, 1998

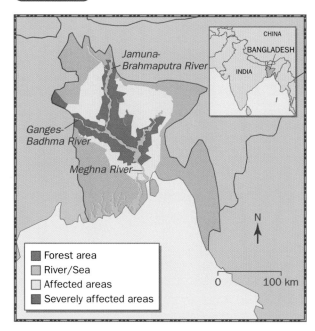

In 1998, 75 percent of Bangladesh was flooded, killing 2500 people. This caused huge devastation to crops, affecting up to 7 million people. How extensive was the flooded area? Use the line scale to measure the widest points of flooding.

added to meltwater from the Himalayas, up to one-third of the country is prone to flooding.

There are two words in the Bengali language for "flood" — *barsha*, used for the annual beneficial floods, and *bona*, used for the large, destructive floods. This densely populated country (135 million people in an area just twice the size of New Brunswick) has learned to live with the annual floods. On the positive side, there is little need for agricultural fertilizer here, as mixed silt has enriched the soil. Floods have flushed away pollutants from urban areas and groundwater reserves have been well replenished. However, this country is also subject to disastrous, larger floods.

Flood action plan

In the early 1990s, the World Bank proposed a project for Bangladesh called the Flood Action Plan (FAP), which included:

- embankments covering 8000 kilometres set back from the sides of the main rivers, to help protect them from the erosional force of the rivers
- sluices on the embankments to help control river flow or to allow for "controlled" flooding
- storage dams and reservoirs in the Himalayas
- increased food production in a contained network of "compartments" between the banks and the river, to help pay for the project

The Flood Action Plan was projected to take up to 20 years to implement, at a cost of $10.2 billion. Since its drafting, a further study of the issue was undertaken by Rivers Network International (RNI), who suggested that this plan was problematic for the following reasons:

- The most damaging floods along coasts are caused by storm surges, driven by fast-flowing, cyclonic winds. The Flood Action Plan has not designed a means of protection against such coastal floods.

- Earthquakes can be expected in this region, threatening the embankments with destruction.
- The Bangladesh economy cannot afford to maintain the embankments.
- Embankments are not strong enough to deflect severe floods, as they contain no bedrock to anchor them. Foundations would have to be sunk into the soft alluvial earth (soil made by sand or mud left by flowing water), which would add greatly to their expense.
- The embankments will channel the water to downstream areas, increasing the risk of severe floods in those areas.
- The fast-flowing rivers may form new river channels, making the embankments obsolete.
- The embankments will have to be continually raised to combat the rises in the river bed, from increased sediment within the river.
- Up to 8 million people will have to move to accommodate the construction of the embankments. These will consist of mostly poor people who have few other options.
- Some poor people may actually "cut through" the embankments to allow freshwater to flow onto their crops.
- Up to 80 percent of the population rely on a fish diet. Many fisheries will not be replenished with water, and most fish stock use the floodwater for spawning routes.

Alternative suggestions by Rivers Network International and the World Bank for the Flood Action Plan include:

- replanting coastal mangrove forests, which many feel would be effective because they would soak up excessive amounts of water
- instituting flood-preparedness programs, such as community centres built on high ground containing emergency stockpiles of tents, food, water, and medicine

- implementing flood forecasting and warning systems that would warn locals, providing them with time to harvest crops and move to safety

26. Why would people continue to live in areas that are prone to flooding?

27. Refer to an atlas and study Bangladesh. Describe the relative location of the country. What physical features (landscape, drainage, and climate) contribute to the frequent flooding of Bangladesh?

28. You are an expert on floodwater management, on contract to the University of Dhaka. You have been asked to evaluate the World Bank proposals and the criticisms made by Rivers Network International, and to publish a suggested plan of action on behalf of the university. Before beginning your evaluation, research two other flood-control plans relating to Bangladesh or to any other flood-prone region in the world. Write a report in which you:

   a) review the flooding problems facing Bangladesh

   b) suggest a plan of action for the country by referring to the World Bank, Rivers Network International, and the other relevant flood plans you have researched.

Case in point — Winnipeg, Manitoba

The Red River winds its way northwards from northeast Dakota, through Minnesota, and into Manitoba, where it pours into Lake Winnipeg. The river drains an area estimated to be 10.4 million hectares; this drainage basin is relatively flat and therefore prone to flooding. Often, the Red River's northward flow is blocked by ice near Lake Winnipeg, making matters worse. Most people in Manitoba prepare for these annual floods. There are thousands of drainage ditches throughout this region, many dating back to early settlements in the 1880s.

The city of Winnipeg, where the Assiniboine meets the Red River, is no stranger to flooding; it stands in the Red River's northward-flowing path. The worst flood of all was in 1826, where flow rates were estimated at 6 372 000 litres per second. Following the 1950 flood (3 058 560 litres per second), it was proposed that a huge engineered ditch be dug around the city, to divert future floodwater.

At a glance — Winnipeg, Manitoba

- Population: 637 000
- Total area: 462.1 km^2
- Red River frontage: 87.3 km
- Assiniboine River frontage: 36.45 km
- Height above sea level: 232 m
- Location: 64 km south of Lake Winnipeg, 97 km north of Canada/US border
- Past massive floods: 1828, 1852, 1861, 1950, and 1997

FIGURE 6–23 School buses form a barrier against the Winnipeg flood of 1997, in case the floodway offered insufficient protection. If it had not, what other tactics could the community have undertaken to avoid disaster?

Red River Floodway Channel

In 1962, work began on the **Red River Floodway Channel**. The 47-kilometre ditch, dug around the eastern edge of the city, was completed in 1968. The floodway can be opened just south of the city in order to take half of the water from the rising Red River and divert it northward, around the city.

The channel's effectiveness was challenged in 1997, when the city was faced with what was described as the "flood of the century." Serious floods were forecast in February of 1997. In addition, a blizzard dumped 50 centimetres of snow in this region. With bulldozers, trucks, and about 6.5 million sandbags, the 40-kilometre Brunkild Dike was built to the south and west of the city, extending the West Dike. The floodway was opened and immediately removed 1 700 000 litres of water per second from the Red River.

This left a further 2 124 000 litres per second still flowing north. Without the floodway, it is estimated that a total water flow of 3 824 000 litres per second would have crested at a height of 10.45 metres. At this level, 80 percent of Winnipeg would have been submerged, and over 550 000 people would have had to have been evacuated. Instead, only 6000 people had to be moved from south Winnipeg. The damage was estimated at CDN$150 million.

29. Using an atlas, draw a map showing the location and route of the Red River. Locate and label significant tributaries, lakes, and settlements on the map.

30. Why did planners decide to dig a floodway around the city of Winnipeg?

31. The 1826 flood was said to have peaked at 6 372 000 litres per second. How does this compare with the flood of 1997?

32. Statistically, a flood with levels like those in 1826 will only occur once in 360 years. How do you think the people of Winnipeg and the flood-control planners should view this statistic?

33. What strategies used in Winnipeg are/could be applied to Bangladesh?

FIGURE 6–24 The amount of dirt removed while digging the floodway was more than that removed during the building of the Panama Canal!

FIGURE 6–25 This Radarstat image was taken on May 1, 1997, at 6:00 a.m. River levels at this time were about 2 metres above peak levels recorded in 1979 at the floodway inlet.

Weather modification

It is early morning. You check the weather forecast — a critical factor in determining how you will dress. The forecast predicts a warm, sunny day. You dress accordingly, only to learn later in the day that the forecast was wrong. It is cool and rainy, and your jacket is at home.

Weather forecasting is based on complex computer modelling in order to "predict" what kind of day the current conditions will generate. However, even with all our technological sophistication, we still seem to be at the mercy of nature. Is there some way in which we can guarantee weather patterns? Rather than trying to predict the weather, can science actually make it rain or be sunny whenever we like?

The basics of precipitation

One method of making rain is cloud seeding (weather modification). To understand how cloud seeding works, it is essential to understand how rain (or any other precipitation) occurs. Rain begins as clouds, and clouds are tiny droplets of water that form around condensation nuclei (microscopic particles of dust, smoke, and soil). These nuclei allow for the conversion of water from its gaseous form (water vapour) to either liquid water droplets or solid ice crystals.

There is always some water vapour in the air. The level of moisture in the air is called "humidity." Generally speaking, higher humidity means that there is a greater possibility of precipitation. In warm clouds, precipitation forms when enough water vapour coalesces around a nucleus for the droplet to become too heavy to remain suspended in the cloud. In the case of cold clouds, the nuclei can take the form of ice crystals, and it is these crystals that increase in size. Regardless of whether clouds are warm or cold, when the nuclei are too heavy to remain suspended, they begin to fall. Depending on the temperature in the lower part of the atmosphere, the precipitation can be predominantly in liquid form (rain) or in crystal form (snow). There are several less common forms of precipitation — hail, freezing rain, sleet — each of which requires highly specialized conditions.

How does cloud seeding work?

Often, clouds form in the atmosphere, but these clouds lack enough nuclei to form precipitation. Scientists discovered that, by placing artificial nuclei in the clouds, it is possible to "force" them to convert more water vapour to liquid or solid form.

To achieve this, a precipitation "starter" is placed in suitable clouds to set the process of precipitation in motion. Many different starters are used to stimulate precipitation in different situations. In the case of warm clouds, chemicals such as salt crystals are used, whereas for cold clouds, several chemicals are used, including dry ice (CO_2) and silver iodide.

In the early days of cloud seeding (during the 1940s), scientists assumed that it would be possible to force rain to occur anywhere, at any time, and under any conditions. However, this proved to be false. It is very difficult to determine how effective seeding is because it is impossible to know what would have happened within the clouds if seeding had never occurred. Also, it is possible to "overseed" a cloud and cause it to dissipate without creating any precipitation at all. Overall, however, it is recognized that cloud seeding can help in the creation of precipitation when the conditions are ideal.

Conditions for cloud seeding

Recognizing ideal conditions for cloud seeding requires not only identifying suitable clouds (those with a critical mass of water droplets and acceptable temperature variables), but also accommodating a myriad of variables such as barometric pressure, humidity, wind patterns (both speed and direction), time of day, choice of chemical seeding agent, and choice of delivery mechanism. These mechanisms could be ground-based generators (which rely on the wind for delivery) or launching systems that employ airplanes and flares for the delivery of the chemical seeding agent.

Cloud seeding has been successful in several applications. These include snow generation for ski resorts, rain generation for farms, and hail avoidance (where clouds likely to produce hail are seeded to force them to rain and prevent the creation of hail). Clearly, however, cloud seeding is not a perfect solution. Many difficulties exist and even legal issues loom over the use of this technique. Despite little scientific evidence, there are those who believe that seeded clouds rob nearby regions of what would be naturally occurring rain.

a) Cloud seeding requires a range of additional technology for it to be effective, including laser-optical probes for determining the size of cloud droplets. Determine other technologies that are required for cloud seeding to work and analyse the true cost of seeding.

b) As mentioned, it may be possible that areas that are practising cloud seeding are robbing other areas of their natural rain. Is rain a "right"? Debate this with your classmates.

Check out www.gagelearning.com/onthethreshold for some interesting activities on precipitation.

Steps for cloud seeding

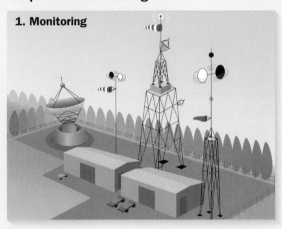

1. Monitoring

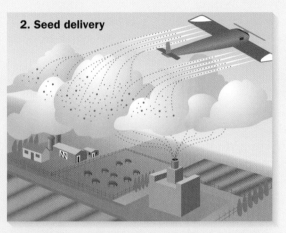

2. Seed delivery

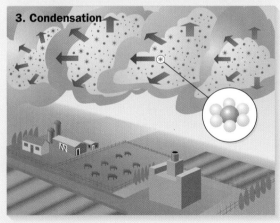

3. Condensation

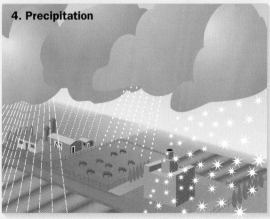

4. Precipitation

FIGURE 6–26 This diagram illustrates the steps required to coax clouds to produce precipitation.

The water of the Middle East

If the situation in parts of the Middle East regarding the supply of freshwater remains unresolved, there will come a point where the population cannot survive. No country in the region can resolve its water problem independently without encroaching upon the resources of its neighbours. No comprehensive plan for water development can take place without peace, and no peace is possible or sustainable without such development.

You are about to attend an important summit meeting regarding the supply of freshwater within Middle Eastern countries. You will each represent a country and your task is to make decisions with delegates from other countries about freshwater supplies.

In order to familiarize yourself with the situation, refer to the map in Figure 6–27, read the briefing notes, and study the regional hotspots.

Form groups of seven people and assign each delegate one of the roles listed on pages 174–175. Whatever your role, you will be working in the best interest of your country and its people, but solutions must satisfy all parties at the summit.

The summit

Gather in your groups of seven. You may then wish to gather with members of other groups who share the same role and discuss your shared position on the situation. Then, re-form into your summit committee groups.

The meeting will be an open-ended discussion. You may decide on rules by which the meeting should proceed, and on whether or not to elect a chair. Your objective is to draft an action plan that will direct policy within this region for the next 25 years. In the meeting, you will:

- summarize what you consider to be the major problems
- formulate an action plan to address the problems (which will only be complete once everyone in your summit group has signed it, indicating that each one accepts the conditions)
- create a map of the area that indicates your suggested solutions spatially

Briefing notes

- Arguably, the most immediate and serious threat to the international environment is water scarcity.
- In regions such as the Middle East, water supply has reached a crucial threshold, as many nations are vying for extremely limited resources.
- Every major water source crosses international boundaries, making it impossible to determine to whom the water belongs.
- Water consumption in the area will rise by 2 to 3 percent per year.
- Climatic changes during the last 20 to 30 years contribute to water shortages; the greenhouse effect could increase shortages in the future.
- Along with drinking water, irrigation supplies are also deeply affected by water shortages. Irrigation uses the largest amount of water by far, and this usage continues to expand — its needs have already grown tenfold during the last century. Where scarcities loom, cities and farms are beginning to compete for available water and, when supplies tighten, it is farmers who typically lose out. A solution must be reached to assist farmers and their crops in the Middle East.
- Pesticides, fertilizers, and sewage contaminate much of the available water supply.

FIGURE 6-27 **The Middle East**

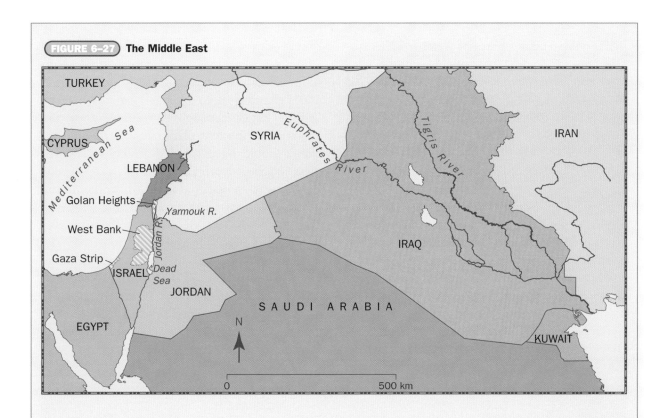

Regional hotspots

The Jordan River

The Jordan River provides water to Syria, Lebanon, Israel, and Jordan. Equitable distribution is insufficient to prevent Israel and Jordan from exhausting the supply, due to the needs of their populations. Although Syria controls much of the headwaters (the sources of the river), Israel diverts water via a National Water Carrier pipeline to its southern deserts, where most of Israel's 30 desalination plants operate (removing salt from the water, making it potable).

Despite its importance in the region, the Jordan is a relatively small river, measuring about 230 kilometres. In total, it discharges

FIGURE 6-28 Trees line the Jordan River near Galilee, Israel.

1500 million cubic metres of water from its system per year. Its flow is seasonal — in the summer and fall, when water is most needed for agriculture, it carries only 3 to 4 percent of its yearly flow, and this is sometimes reduced further by drought. When the water enters the Dead Sea (which is seven times saltier than the ocean), it becomes too salty for agricultural use.

The Yarmouk River

Rights to the Yarmouk, a tributary of the Jordan River, are hotly contested. It measures 42 kilometres and contributes 400–500 million cubic metres per year to the water basin. The Yarmouk flows in a southwesterly direction, forming part of the border shared between Syria, Israeli-controlled territory (the West Bank of the Jordan River), and Jordan. In response to Israel's diversion of water into their National Water Carrier pipeline system, a 1964 Arab summit permitted three states — Syria, Jordan, and Lebanon — to channel water from the Jordan River through Syria and into the Yarmouk tributary. This new arrangement, which would have allowed Jordan to control these waters, depriving Israel of a key water source, was an essential point of conflict in the June 1967 war between Israel and its Arab neighbours. Israel's victory gave them control over the Golan Heights and more of the Yarmouk; they began to extract four times as much water as they had taken prior to the war.

The Yarmouk is vital to Jordanians because of its impact on irrigation, which is crucial to their economy. Jordan is mainly desert and is therefore the country most threatened with

FIGURE 6–29 The Euphrates Dam in Syria does not work at full capacity due to divergence of the river in Turkey.

water shortages. Water rationing is a fact of life there. Jordan views the Yarmouk and Jordan Rivers as matters that could affect the region's future security.

The King Abdallah Canal (KAC) in Jordan takes water from the Yarmouk for irrigation. Recently, Jordan and Syria proposed that they jointly build dams on the Upper Yarmouk because they are concerned about the amount of water being taken by the Israelis. Israel rejected the idea that further dams be built, however, and continues to lobby the World Bank and the United States to refuse to help finance the project. Meanwhile, Jordan and Syria are pushing hard to obtain funding for these dams.

Syria and Jordan are themselves arguing over the construction and operation of smaller Syrian dams on feeder streams to the Yarmouk. Jordan feels that these dams are restricting water flows and contaminating the fresh water supply further downstream, where Jordanians get their water.

The West Bank mountain aquifers

There are three aquifers — the Western Aquifer (which has the largest flow toward Israeli territory); the Eastern Aquifer (which lies entirely within the West Bank); and the Northeastern Aquifer.

In 1967, Israel occupied the West Bank and the Gaza strip. The Palestinian people believe this to be their land, and have been working to claim it from the Israelis since that time. Intense negotiations and violence have resulted; both sides are emotionally attached to this land. (Because this situation continues to evolve, you should research the current political situation in this area, using major news sites on the Internet.)

Israel, which satisfies 50 percent of its water needs from mountain aquifers and currently has

to recycle water to meet these needs, is attempting to prevent the Eastern Aquifer from being shared with its Palestinian neighbours. After the 1967 conquest of the West Bank territory, Israel began to tap waters from the Eastern Aquifer (which had previously been used exclusively by Palestinians) to support new Israeli settlements in the occupied territory. Because the Jordan River is almost unusable in the lower sections due to its high salt content, the Eastern Aquifer provides almost all water consumption in the West Bank. Agriculture is very important to the Palestinian economy, accounting for over 40 percent of Gaza's gross domestic product, but it consumes the largest proportion of freshwater. By 2040, the Palestinian demand for water in the West Bank will equal that of the Israelis. The Palestinian Authority (the government of the territory controlled by Palestinians) believes the Eastern Aquifer water to be theirs, and that Israel is "stealing" the resource.

The Euphrates River

The struggle for control over the Euphrates could result in conflict between Turkey, Syria, and Iraq. Iraq and Syria are dependent on the Euphrates, but 90 percent of its flow originates in Turkey — the only country in the Middle East with more water than it needs. Iraq is an oil-rich country, but agriculture represents 20 percent of its gross national product (GNP) and 1–2 million of its people rely on the river for irrigation and survival. For Syria, the Euphrates is the only major river with reliable annual flows. Iraq and Syria agree that Turkey's unilateral control of the water supply is dangerous. Syria has a large dam on the Euphrates, but because of Turkey's use of the water, only two of the dam's eight turbines are operating.

At present, Turkey holds an economic and military edge over the other two nations in the fight over the Euphrates; Turkey has the capability to use military strength against Iraq and Syria, and could offer economic incentives in return for the acceptance of an agreement. Nevertheless, Syria and Iraq do have a few bargaining tactics themselves. Turkey wants to develop markets in Iraq, and Syria is supporting the Kurdish Workers Party — Turkey's most serious internal security threat. (The Kurds are an ethnic group that wants to create its own state, Kurdistan, taking about 30 percent of Turkey's territory.)

Summit participant roles

Role 1: The American Officer of the World Bank

- You are told by the Board of the World Bank that, based on the problems of involvement with Indian and Chinese megadam projects, you cannot commit World Bank funding for large-scale solutions.
- You are asked to suggest localized, less expensive solutions to this water resource problem.
- You are under enormous pressure from the United States government not to commit too much United States funding to any proposed solution. However, you do recognize that it is in the United States' best interest to have ongoing peace in the Middle East region.

Role 2: Member of the Syrian Security Council

- You believe that you have the right to use the water of the Yarmouk for your exploding population numbers.
- You oppose Turkey's plans for the Euphrates River because they would mean that Turkey could cut off your main water supply for up to eight months.
- Your government cannot afford to fund megaprojects within the next 15 years.

- Syria demands the return of the Golan Heights area before any peace treaty can be negotiated.

Role 3: CEO of a major Jordanian food corporation

- You wish to maintain and increase water supplies for the southern King Abdallah Canal zone where lands require a growing amount of water for irrigation.
- You are concerned about Syria's use of the Yarmouk where diversion dams are being built.
- You would support an independent state of Palestine, which would help to alleviate the number of refugees entering Jordan.
- Jordan is committed to a massive infrastructure development within Amman and cannot afford to contribute to megaprojects to solve this water problem.
- Jordan would like to build dams on the Yarmouk to amass water during the time when there is an increased flow.
- Jordan is upset with Syria for building small dams along the tributaries of the upper Yarmouk, as these are depleting the water supplies downstream and are adding to pollution.

Role 4: Designated Minister of Resources and Development for the Palestinian People's Authority

- You are unhappy with Jordan's claims to the Jordan River.
- As a potential "nation-state," you are desperate for financial help and cannot afford a huge financial commitment to megaprojects (desalination plants, dams, and so on).
- You believe that Israel overpumps aquifers during droughts.

Role 5: Chair of the Israeli Water Commission

- Your task is to secure water supplies for the tremendous growth in population (including new settlements on the West Bank), industry, domestic use, and irrigation of the southern, arid areas of Israel, which are needed for future food supplies. You do not wish to be dependent on other countries for food.
- Because of large military expenditure, you are not able to contribute to any future megaprojects to solve the water problem.
- Israel is unhappy that the King Abdallah Canal takes water from the Yarmouk to irrigate southern Jordan.
- You think that drip irrigation and cloud seeding will help the situation in the future.

Role 6: Senior Executive Officer to the Iraqi Foreign Office

- You wish to establish better trade relations with the outside world.
- You need help in repairing the infrastructure that was destroyed during the Gulf War, and you maintain that the United States should bear the cost.
- You are very concerned about Turkish water developments on the Euphrates River.

- You accept that megaprojects are required to prevent future conflict over water.
- You believe that it is the world's responsibility to help finance any large scheme for future canals, dams, or desalination plants.
- You seek an agreement with the international community ensuring that water from upstream countries cannot be held back from downstream countries.

Role 7: Turkish Foreign Minister

- You seek to protect Turkey's right to harness and use the Euphrates River's water flow.
- You defend the right to continue with a large agricultural development in southeast Turkey (the South Anatolia Project), which will use even more water than current plans originally estimated.
- You oppose Syrian support of the Kurds and have the capacity to respond to this by severely reducing the flow of Euphrates water into Syria and Iraq.
- You are not willing to contribute to any project outside of Turkey.
- You are very reluctant to jeopardize Turkey's long-range water needs, even though Turkey has more than it currently needs.

CHAPTER **7**

Global Warming

As Hurricane Floyd wended its way up the eastern seaboard and Hurricane Gert hovered not too far behind, it became clear that North America faced a record year for hurricanes and tropical storms. Between June and September 1999, North Americans were hosts to several unwelcome guests, namely Arlene, Bret, Cindy, Dennis, Emily, Floyd, and the prospect of Gert.

While property damage and loss of life are major concerns when these ferocious storms approach, another big concern is the link between these severe weather events and global warming. Are they side effects of the global warming caused by burning fossil fuels? If so, are we facing a future in which we will see more hurricanes, evacuations, and economic losses year after year?

There is consensus among scientists that global warming is underway. 1998, for example, was the warmest year in the past millennium. Some studies state that hurricanes are likely to intensify as the world warms. In particular, scientists predict that global warming will cause warmer ocean temperatures, thus putting greater moisture into the atmosphere — two variables that work to power hurricanes. In other words, we could see more intense hurricanes that would cause even more damage when they hit land.

a) Which kind of storm do you think creates more total damage — a tornado or a hurricane?

b) Do you think a larger number of hurricanes means that the earth's temperatures are rising?

FIGURE 7–1 Hurricanes and global warming — What's the connection?

■ Analyse global climate trends and evaluate their effects on people and environments at the local, national, and global levels.

■ Explain why it is difficult to make accurate predictions and why some predictions are more (or less) accurate than others.

■ Analyse cause and effect and sequence relationships in geographic data.

■ Identify awareness levels and viewpoints relating to global warming by conducting a survey in the school.

■ Produce an action plan for a local initiative that contributes to the sustainability of the atmosphere.

■ Demonstrate an understanding of the interdependence of ecology and economics.

The atmosphere surrounding the globe, on which all life depends, is getting warmer. Climate data that has been collected by sophisticated scientific means has produced convincing evidence of this fact. As a result, the earth is experiencing what many consider to be one of the most serious threats to the natural environment — the heating of the atmosphere, or global warming.

Global warming (also known as the enhanced greenhouse effect) is an issue that grabs people's attention in newspaper headlines everywhere. Instances of coastal flooding and powerful hurricanes are often blamed on global warming, and the threat to species due to land degradation and changing ecosystems are also considered to be consequences of this phenomenon. Due to climate changes — again blamed by many on global warming — diseases are changing their normal geographic patterns and some scientists believe that global warming and its effects will change our relationship with the planet forever.

Like other challenges facing the planet, however, the issue of global warming is not without controversy. There is a lot of discussion among experts and scientists about what is *really* causing the atmosphere to warm up — whether it is due to an enhanced or exaggerated warming trend, or due to a natural change, caused either by a slow shift in ocean circulation or by a variation in solar intensity. There is also considerable debate about how seriously we should heed the dire predictions of experts and the press. Is global warming inevitable, or is the apparent warming trend one we can and should alter?

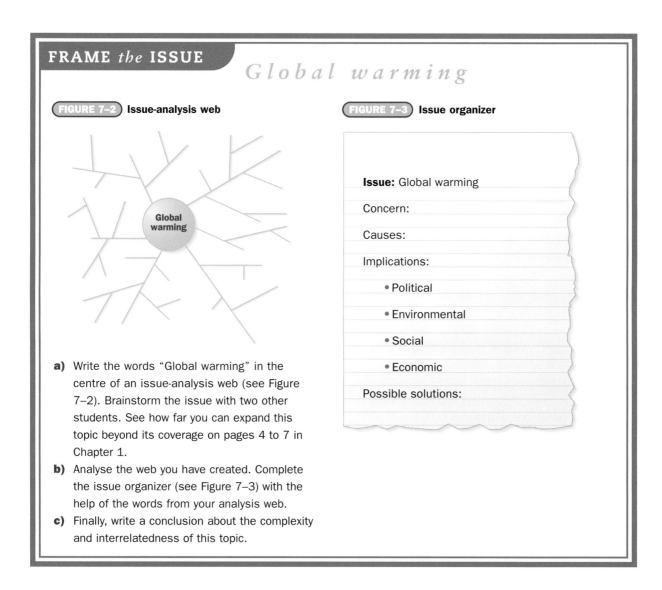

FRAME *the* ISSUE

FIGURE 7–2 Issue-analysis web

FIGURE 7–3 Issue organizer

Global
warming

Issue: Global warming

Concern:

Causes:

Implications:

• Political

• Environmental

• Social

• Economic

Possible solutions:

a) Write the words "Global warming" in the centre of an issue-analysis web (see Figure 7–2). Brainstorm the issue with two other students. See how far you can expand this topic beyond its coverage on pages 4 to 7 in Chapter 1.

b) Analyse the web you have created. Complete the issue organizer (see Figure 7–3) with the help of the words from your analysis web.

c) Finally, write a conclusion about the complexity and interrelatedness of this topic.

The Atmosphere — Nature's Blanket

An atmospheric blanket made up of many gases surrounds the earth. The earth's atmosphere consists of four layers, one of which — the **troposphere** — is the layer within which we live. The next layer of atmosphere is the **stratosphere**, above this layer is the **mesosphere**, and the outermost layer is the **ionosphere** (sometimes called the thermosphere). Without these gas layers, life on earth could not exist. The atmosphere protects earth from the harmful effects of solar radiation.

The most common atmospheric gases are nitrogen (78 percent) and oxygen (21 percent). Argon accounts for 0.9 percent and the remaining gases — called "trace gases" — are carbon dioxide, ozone, and water vapour. Even though these trace gases are found in only small amounts, they are extremely important. They help to control temperature on the earth's surface and in the atmosphere.

With this much gas surrounding the earth, some people think that it would be difficult to change the composition of the atmosphere enough to threaten the existence of life on earth. However, most atmospheric scientists believe this to be a dangerous opinion.

FIGURE 7–4 The earth's atmosphere

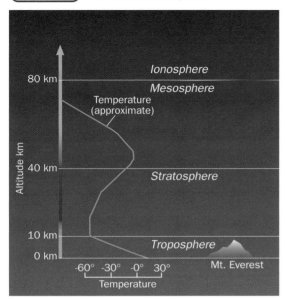

The total thickness of atmospheric gases is about 1000 kilometres, according to Environment Canada. Over 75 percent of the atmosphere's total mass is concentrated within 10 kilometres of earth.

The natural greenhouse effect

The term **greenhouse effect** was introduced when scientists compared the warming of the earth's atmosphere to the transfer of the sun's heat into and out of a greenhouse. Most of the time, the term "greenhouse effect" is associated with every negative prediction concerning how the changing climate will affect us. In reality, the greenhouse effect is essential to all life on earth. Without it, conditions on earth would be like those found on the planet Mars, and we would all perish from extreme cold.

The earth's atmosphere provides us with oxygen and nitrogen — both essential to life. It also traps most of the energy we receive from our most vital energy source, the sun. At the same time, however, the atmosphere also acts as a protective shield: ozone absorbs the majority of the sun's dangerous ultraviolet rays, which are harmful to human skin and eyes.

Much of the incoming **solar radiation (insolation)**, travelling as short-wave radiation, passes through the earth's atmosphere and warms the earth's surface. The atmosphere absorbs about 20 percent of it, through clouds, ozone, **aerosols** (fine supensions of liquid or solid particles), and so on. The earth's surface and oceans absorb 49 percent of it. The atmosphere also reflects about 22 percent of this radiation back toward space, while the earth's surface reflects only 9 percent of it. That is, the atmosphere reflects more of it than the earth's surface does.

FIGURE 7–5 Contributions to global warming

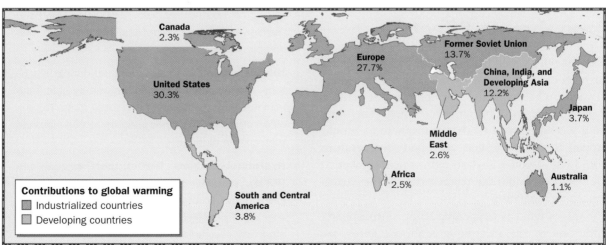

Areas have been drawn in proportion to the amount of carbon emissions from fossil fuel combustion, 1900–1999.

Global Warming **179**

When heat energy (generated within the atmosphere and at the earth's surface through the absorption of incoming sunlight) is reflected back toward space, it travels as **infrared** (long-wave) radiation. Not all of this reflected energy escapes the earth's atmosphere. According to Environment Canada, some of the gases within the atmosphere — those referred to as **greenhouse gases** — absorb part of the infrared radiation and redirect it back to the earth's surface. That is, some energy passes through and is lost into space, while some is kept within the atmosphere. The retained energy helps both the atmosphere and the earth's surface to stay warm, even at night when no incoming solar radiation is being received. If all of the reflected radiation were to escape into space, the earth would experience a rapid cooling down as soon as the sun set.

1. Write a short summary describing the earth's atmosphere. Include information about the types of gases and the different layers that exist. You may want to research an explanatory diagram from the Internet.

2. Draw a diagram showing the distribution of the energy that is received from the sun. Use arrows to show the flow of energy.

3. Write a brief explanation of the term "greenhouse effect," in which you convince the reader that it is necessary for life on earth.

The Enhanced Greenhouse Effect

Without the greenhouse effect, all living things on earth would perish due to freezing temperatures. However, what happens if the comfortable blanket of greenhouse gases becomes too thick? The same thing would happen to the atmosphere as would happen to you — just as your body temperature would rise if you added an extra-thick blanket to your bed, so would the temperature of the earth's atmosphere increase.

This is what is happening to our atmosphere. Additions to the existing greenhouse gases are creating an enhanced greenhouse effect (also called "global warming"), and as a result, the earth's temperature is rising. Yet, we continue to add to our greenhouse gases. When we burn down forests, use coal or oil to fuel power stations, or drive cars, we are adding to the existing amount of greenhouse gases. Of these, the main culprit is thought to be the burning of carbon-based fuels, which releases carbon dioxide into the atmosphere.

Frame of reference

Greenhouse gases: Greenhouse gases are gases that absorb long-wave, infrared radiation, some of which they reflect back toward the earth. These include naturally occurring gases — water vapour, carbon dioxide, methane, nitrous oxide, and ozone — and gases generated by industrial processes. Each greenhouse gas differs in its ability to absorb heat. Often, estimates of greenhouse gas emissions are presented in units of millions of metric tonnes of carbon equivalents (MMTCE), which weight each gas according to its Global Warming Potential (GWP) value.

Carbon dioxide: This gas is released during the burning of solid waste, fossil fuels (oil, natural gas, and coal), wood, and wood products.

Methane: This gas is emitted during the production and transport of coal, natural gas, or oil. Methane emissions also result from the decomposition of organic waste in municipal solid-waste landfills; the raising of livestock; and rice production. Methane traps over 21 times more heat per molecule than carbon dioxide.

Nitrous oxide: This gas is emitted during agricultural and industrial activities, as well as during the combustion of solid waste and fossil fuels. Nitrous oxide absorbs 270 times more heat per molecule than carbon dioxide.

Hydrofluorocarbons (HFCs), perfluorocarbons (PFCs), and sulphur hexafluoride (SF6): These gases do not occur naturally — they are generated by a variety of industrial processes. SF6 and PFCs are the most heat-absorbent of all greenhouse gases.

Carbon

Nature tries to maintain an ideal balance of greenhouse gases. Oceans and plants act as sponges, absorbing about half of all carbon dioxide emissions humans produce. When these storage reservoirs absorb large amounts of carbon, they are described as **carbon sinks**; when they release more carbon than they can absorb, they are called **carbon sources**.

Oceans

During the last 100 years, the world's oceans absorbed about 90 billion tonnes of carbon on average, but released about the same amount. This means that they were neither long-term carbon sinks, nor carbon sources. However, over the past several decades, the oceans have become a small sink. During the 1990s, for example, they absorbed about 2 billion tonnes of carbon per year more than they released; thus, in the short term, they have acted as carbon sinks.

Land

Land-based **carbon budgets** (the balance between sinks and sources) can be examined in the same manner. For land areas, **photosynthesis** (the process by which plant cells make sugar from carbon dioxide and water, in the presence of chlorophyl and light) has resulted in a global absorption of about 60 billion tonnes of carbon. However, until recently, vegetation and soil respiration, as well as oxidation (for example, fire) have, on average, released just as much carbon back toward space. For the past 1000 years, global ecosystems have been neither net sources nor sinks but, during the past few decades, the global land system has become a carbon sink. There is some concern about how much land-based sinks can absorb before they reach their capacity.

Atmosphere

Experts know that the amount of carbon dioxide that is released into the atmosphere is increasing. They also believe that there is a direct relationship between the amount of carbon in the atmosphere and the climate conditions experienced around the world. Historical evidence is one way of providing support for the theory of this relationship. By digging up ice samples from deep within the ice sheets of Antarctica and Greenland (thus exposing ice that originally fell as snow thousands of years ago), scientists have been able to study past climatic and atmospheric conditions. They have discovered, by studying the chemistry of the ice and trapped air bubbles, that when temperatures were warmest, the carbon and methane concentrations were also high. Scientists also know that the amount of carbon in today's atmosphere is the highest it has ever been in the past 400 000 years.

According to the Intergovernmental Panel on Climate Change (IPCC), the average concentration of carbon dioxide in the atmosphere was approximately 280 ppm (parts per million) before the age of industrialization. By the 1960s, when science started to measure this data in detail, it had reached 315 ppm, and is now estimated to be at around 370 ppm. The United States Environmental Protection Agency (EPA) estimates that an increase in heat energy of 1.5 watts (a 1 percent increase) is now distributed for each square metre of the earth's surface.

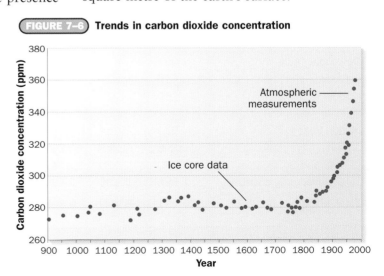

FIGURE 7–6 **Trends in carbon dioxide concentration**

Plants

The world's plant life also helps to control global carbon dioxide levels. Plants and soils, through respiration and oxidation, breathe out ten times more carbon dioxide annually than we add globally through burning fossil fuels. However, since plants also take up about the same amount of carbon dioxide through photosynthesis, the released carbon dioxide is part of a natural cycle that is in near balance. Some experts believe that the burning of forests adds significantly to the buildup of carbon dioxide levels, but this is arguable. Environment Canada states that the release of carbon dioxide into the atmosphere from forest fires is made up for by the absorption of carbon by vegetation regrowth in places where the fire has occurred. A carbon surplus would result only if there was no new plant growth in the burned area.

Humans

Emissions relating to human activity are a mostly one-sided addition to the cycle. The burning of fossil fuels in automobiles, homes, factories, and during the production of cement are major reasons for carbon increases. Carbon is also released

FIGURE 7-7 Total world carbon emissions from fossil fuel combustion and cement production by region (million metric tons)

Region/country	History			Projections			Average annual percent change 1995–2015
	1990	1995	2000	2005	2010	2015	
North America	1 561	1 664	1 793	1 894	1 973	2 039	1.0
United States	1 337	1 424	1 515	1 587	1 644	1 688	0.9
Canada	137	143	156	165	173	180	1.2
Mexico	87	97	122	142	156	171	2.9
Western Europe	1 016	1 014	1 059	1 109	1 155	1 209	0.9
Japan	308	361	388	412	439	457	1.2
Oceania	100	112	111	118	122	126	0.6
Total industrialized countries	**2 985**	**3 151**	**3 351**	**3 533**	**3 689**	**3 831**	**1.0**
Former Soviet Union (FSU)	1 029	653	703	744	784	811	1.1
Eastern Europe (EE)	309	240	264	269	272	276	0.7
Total FSU and EE countries	**1 338**	**893**	**967**	**1 013**	**1 056**	**1 087**	**1.0**
Developing Asia	1 091	1 474	1 693	1 935	2 161	2 394	2.5
China	625	821	930	1 040	1 162	1 294	2.3
India	159	221	252	301	345	384	2.8
Other Asia	307	432	511	594	654	716	2.5
Middle East	203	254	244	254	264	276	0.4
Africa	205	248	251	264	277	290	0.8
Central and South America	189	220	243	275	309	343	2.2
Total developing countries	**1 688**	**2 196**	**2 431**	**2 728**	**3 011**	**3 303**	**2.1**
Total world	**6 011**	**6 240**	**6 749**	**7 274**	**7 756**	**8 221**	**1.4**

Which region(s) of the world should we be most concerned about with regard to carbon emissions?

through the seepage of gas from landfills (during the decay of wood, paper, and other biomass products); and through deforestation, where humans burn trees and expose soil that would otherwise store and accumulate carbon through photosynthesis. Such emissions are imbalances within the natural carbon cycle.

It is believed that the carbon budget imbalance will get worse. The factors that will determine future human-related emissions are: how fast our human population and economies grow; how efficiently we use energy; the type of energy we use; and how fast we strip our forests. Depending on which combination of these factors occurs, carbon dioxide emissions will be between 30 and 150 percent higher by the year 2100 than they are today. The Intergovernmental Panel on Climate Change gauges that, since the Industrial Revolution, the increase in atmospheric carbon dioxide concentrations from past human emissions has been approximately 31 percent.

Methane

Carbon dioxide is not the only greenhouse gas whose level is increasing. Human activity generates very large quantities of methane. According to the United States Environmental Protection Agency, methane concentrations have risen by about 30 percent in the past 40 years. The Intergovernmental Panel on Climate Change believes the increase to be 151 percent since the Industrial Revolution.

- Methane takes a decade or so to dissipate.
- Each molecule of methane gas is 21 times more effective at trapping heat than CO_2.
- Rice production, cattle and sheep farming, coal mining, and drilling for oil and gas produce about two-thirds of all the methane that is released.
- Nature produces the other third. For example, the digestive process of termites is a methane producer. About 80 percent of

FIGURE 7–8 Cattle farming, like that practised on this ranch in Argentina, is a major source of methane. How could this particular global methane source be lessened, and what would the consequences be for both developed and developing countries?

all methane generated by termites comes from the midlatitude grasslands and tropical regions.

- In Canada, landfill is the largest source of human-related methane emissions.
- Methane alone has produced an additional 0.5 watts of the energy that strikes each square metre of the earth's surface.

Other greenhouse gases

Emissions of other gases are also adding to the existing concentration of greenhouse gases.

- Chemical companies are producing large amounts of a new group of greenhouse gases called **halocarbons**, which are mostly used in the production of refrigeration and air conditioning. These gases are extremely powerful in trapping heat within the atmosphere.
- **Nitrous oxide** (laughing gas) is discharged through industrial processes and agricultural activities. According to the Intergovernmental Panel on Climate Change, its concentrations have risen by 17 percent since the Industrial Revolution.

Although an increase in greenhouse gas emissions is a global problem, it is the industrialized countries of the world that must accept the major responsibility. The United States alone is responsible for more than 20 percent of all greenhouse gas emissions in the world today.

4. Develop an organizer in which you list the greenhouse gases and explain how they are produced, comparing their relative heat-absorption abilities.

5. Write a brief report for your local newspaper in which you explain "enhanced greenhouse effect," showing why this term is different from the term "greenhouse effect."

6. Refer to Figure 7–7. Construct a graph that shows energy-related carbon emission totals from 1990 through to the projection for 2015, using the totals for each major group (for example, Total industrialized countries). Which group experienced the most growth in emissions between 1995 and 2015? Why should this be a concern?

7. There is a large focus on carbon dioxide as the main cause of the enhanced greenhouse effect. However, why should we also be concerned about the effect of other trace gases on the atmosphere?

Consequences of global warming

The enhanced greenhouse effect has become a major worry to many scientists and politicians. Scientists who study the facts about global warming are concerned about the physical changes that it will make to the earth's life-support systems. Politicians are worried because they may have to make tough decisions — some of which may be very unpopular — in order to prevent many of the consequences predicted by the scientists. An example of an "unpopular" decision might be compelling car producers to add features to cars that will make them more fuel-efficient and make their exhausts less dirty. By raising taxes on gasoline, governments may also try to encourage the use of mass transit, rather than the private car.

One of the most significant changes predicted due to the enhanced greenhouse effect is climate change. Climates have always been variable, because of aspects such as variations in the sun's radiation over periods of time. For example, we know that Canada was covered in massive sheets of ice up until about 10 000 years ago. We also know that the Canadian Arctic was once warm enough to support semi-tropical vegetation. Ice ages have come and gone a number of times, but always over long periods. For the most part, ecosystems and species had opportunities to adapt during these gradual climate changes.

What is different now is that the climate patterns of the world are predicted to change much more rapidly because of the enhanced greenhouse effect. The Intergovernmental Panel on Climate Change has reached this conclusion after having studied more than 400 plants and animals, and carefully measuring features such as the retreat of the world's ice sheets.

FIGURE 7–9 Variation in annual temperature compared to 1961–1990 average, northern hemisphere

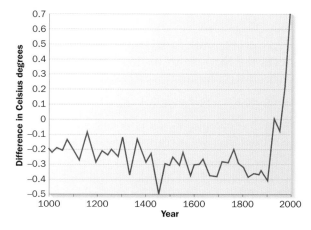

The average global temperature varied little up until the year 1900, but the twentieth century saw a rise of almost 1 Celsius degree.

As the atmosphere heats up, impressive swings in climate patterns are expected around the world. Scientists are predicting that average global temperatures will rise by 0.6 to 2.5 Celsius degrees over the next 50 years, and by 1.4 to 5.8 Celsius degrees within 100 years!

Worldwatch Institute has found that evening temperatures are rising twice as quickly as daytime temperatures; that temperatures are expected to rise faster over land than oceans; and that some regions of the world will warm up much more than others — in fact, some areas will actually experience a cooling trend. How can this be? Scientists believe that in regions of the world where there are large emissions of aerosols such as sulphates, the effects of global warming may be lessened. Most aerosols have a cooling effect on the climate: they tend to reflect incoming solar radiation back into space. They also contribute to increased concentrations of water droplets in cloud formations, offering even more protection from the sun's rays.

While floods, heat waves, severe **El Niños** (changes in tropical Pacific ocean currents that affect weather patterns), and other extreme weather events are expected to increase as the world warms, it is not possible to link any particular climate or weather event *definitively* to global warming at this time. Data on climate extremes in many regions of the world is inadequate, making it difficult to draw definitive conclusions about possible changes that may have occurred on a global scale. The link between the frequency of extreme events and global warming can only be determined through statistical analyses of long-term data, because the natural climate system can also produce uncharacteristic weather and climatic events.

Nevertheless, after gathering data for the 2001 Intergovernmental Panel on Climate Change from all the existing computer simulation models that have been run, scientists seem to have reached a consensus about the following results of global warming:

- *There will be increased evaporation due to heat, which will lead to more precipitation.* Moisture in the soil will evaporate more in warmer regions. However, there will also be more violent and intense rainstorms, which will cause quick erosion and flash floods. The earth is already receiving 1 percent more precipitation than it did 100 years ago.

- *There will be higher sea levels*, as warmer temperatures cause mountain glaciers to melt and add extensive run-off to the oceans. The huge ice sheets of Antarctica and Greenland may also melt, adding extra water to sea levels, particularly over many centuries. Sea levels have already risen by 10 to 20 centimetres over the last 100 years. The Intergovernmental Panel on Climate Change predicts that sea levels will rise 9 to 88 centimetres more by 2100 (depending on levels of increased emissions and how the climate responds to such increases). The United States Environmental Protection Agency estimates that sea levels have a 50 percent chance of rising 45 centimetres over the next century.

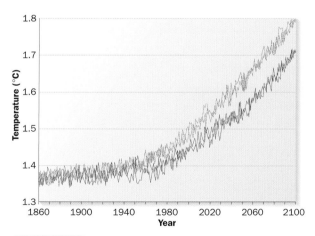

FIGURE 7–10 The orange lines on this graph represent a composite of four different predictions for temperature increases to the year 2100. When the cooling effect of aerosols is included, a smaller global temperature rise is predicted; this is shown by the red lines.

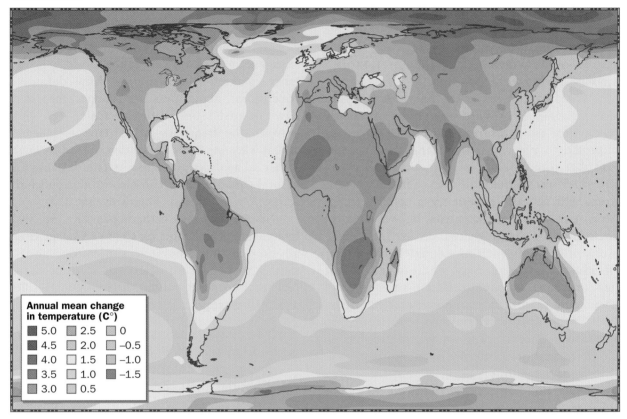

FIGURE 7-11 Predicted change in annual temperature, 2041 to 2070

Annual mean change in temperature (C°)

5.0	2.5	0
4.5	2.0	−0.5
4.0	1.5	−1.0
3.5	1.0	−1.5
3.0	0.5	

These climate model results are based on an average of four temperature experiments using a computer model. The map shows the midrange predicted change in annual temperatures for the years 2041 to 2070.

FIGURE 7-12 Predictions made by the Centre for Climate Prediction and Research

	Present	2020s	2050s	2080s
CO_2 concentration (ppm)	365	441	565	731
Temperature change (C°) (greenhouse gases only)	0	1.2	2.1	3.2
Temperature change (C°) (greenhouse gases and sulphate aerosol)	0	1.0	1.6	2.6
Precipitation change (%)	0	1.6	2.9	4.5
Sea-level rise (cm)	0	10	26	44
Population (millions)	5.266	8.121	9.759	10.672

FIGURE 7–13 Predicted change in precipitation, 2041 to 2070

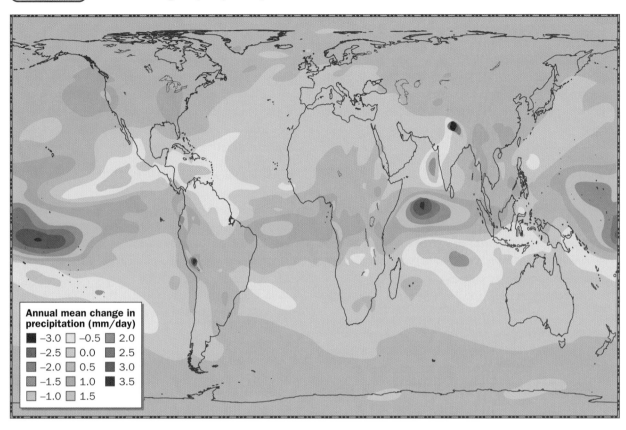

Annual mean change in precipitation (mm/day)
-3.0 | -0.5 | 2.0
-2.5 | 0.0 | 2.5
-2.0 | 0.5 | 3.0
-1.5 | 1.0 | 3.5
-1.0 | 1.5

This model shows the midrange prediction for changes in levels of precipitation between 2041 and 2070.

Nevertheless, this increase cannot come directly from the atmosphere itself. The amount of water held in the atmosphere is only equivalent to 1 millimetre of increased sea level. The additional water will come from the expanding oceans, through the melting of polar ice caps and mountain glaciers.

■ *There will be a significant reduction of freshwater supplies*, if mountain glaciers start to melt. In Lima, Peru, the population depends on the annual summer melt of a nearby glacier for their freshwater supplies. This glacier, which is like a frozen reservoir, is now melting at a much faster rate and as it shrinks, it threatens Lima's future water supply.

8. Refer to the maps in Figures 7–11 and 7–13. Create an organizer in which you describe those regions of the world that will experience lower or higher temperatures and more or less precipitation by the year 2050.

9. Assume that you are the director of a centre for climate prediction and research. Write a report on the apparent increase in average global temperatures. Your report should:
   a) include evidence of temperature increases
   b) give your opinion about the rate of temperature increases
   c) suggest how the world's population may experience climate change

Computer modelling

Computers can be excellent tools for creating models of some of the phenomena in the real world. Computer models are used by scientists to provide answers to a variety of practical and theoretical problems. Often the results generated from a computer model are used to support complex decisions.

What is a computer model?

By definition, a model is an abstraction of reality — it exists to capture the essence of a concept or idea. We see a variety of models around us every day, from model airplanes to models for solving problems (such as the "Frame the issue" model used in this book), but they are a simplification of a complex concept.

Typically, there are three uses, goals, or advantages that models provide.

- First, *models are used to facilitate understanding*. To make a model of a complex problem, you need to dissect the problem into its component parts and show an appreciation for the relationships between them. Whenever a problem is analysed in this way, your understanding of the problem's interrelatedness is heightened.
- Second, *models often provide a common language for people to use*, which improves communication dramatically.
- Third, *models are used to predict the future*. Although no model can be 100 percent accurate, a successful model will approximate most facets of reality. Often, a model is used to explore a problem which is either impossible, extremely difficult, or dangerous to explore in real-world conditions.

How do computer models work?

An effective model will represent reality accurately. To create such a model, several conditions must be understood and met:

- The correct boundaries must be set for the model.
- The variables within the model must be identified.
- The relationships existing between these variables must be recognized.

The accuracy of the model's prediction(s) depends on how well these conditions are met.

It should come as no surprise that computer models require impressive computer hardware to operate. The computers of choice for weather forecasting, for example, are the Cray Inc. Supercomputer series or the Japanese NEC Supercomputers. Both of these supercomputers are capable of performing 1 trillion calculations per second.

Forecasting the weather

Weather forecasting requires the use of a highly complex model. The weather has many variables, ranging from time of year to aberrant meteorological occurrences such as typhoons. Various weather-predicting models are used around the world, and many of them are fairly accurate. Today in Canada, global climate change models (which evolved from weather forecast models) are one of the tools used to predict weather a month or more in advance.

The long-range forecast

Given that scientists have evidence of increasing environmental temperatures worldwide, it is important to try to determine what the outcome of these increases in temperature might be, in order to predict their impact. This is a perfect scenario for the use of computer modelling.

Globally, there are more than 30 models designed for the purpose of examining the climate change and its potential results. These models operate using mathematical equations to show the interrelationship among all of the variables that impact the climate's stability. Using a grid of points placed systematically on the earth's surface, the state of the atmosphere for each unit of time can be predicted. The prediction of climate changes requires the integration of a wide variety of data concerning earth and water, usually displayed in three dimensions and over time.

Such models are called General Circulation Models (GCMs). They incorporate processes such as the greenhouse effect, thunderstorms, all kinds of precipitation, wind, atmospheric pressure, and many other atmospheric variables. Oceanographic processes such as currents, temperature, and the thickness of ice on the oceans are often included in General Circulation Models, because of the relationship between the oceans and the atmosphere.

For General Circulation Models to work, many assumptions guiding the rules of the model must be made. Varying these assumptions (or rules) will change the outcome or prediction. When the processing is over, it is difficult to know how much we can rely on the result. There are three ways to measure the effectiveness of a General Circulation Model:

- Feed the model historical data and use it to predict today's climate.
- Model what the climate was like in the past.
- Compare the results of the model to the results of similar models.

Canada is a forerunner in the field of climate research and climate modelling. The Canadian Centre for Climate Modelling and Analysis (CCCMA) has generated several climate models that are recognized globally. They have also created models for looking at specific regions of Canada.

Internationally, other important climate modelling organizations include the Hadley Centre for Climate Prediction and Research, the Australian Commonwealth Scientific and Industrial Research Organization, the German Climate Research Centre, the USA Geophysical Fluid Dynamics Laboratory, and the Japanese Centre for Climate Research.

a) Canada, the United States, Germany, and Japan all have climate-predicting models. What industrial and economic characteristics do these countries have in common? Why are these countries so interested in climate? Share your answer with a classmate.

b) Climate modelling is very expensive. The costs to employ the hardware and expert personnel (scientists and computer scientists) can be prohibitive. In a debate with your classmates, justify the spending that is necessary to create this climate "guesstimate."

c) In what other areas of geography could models be used? Brainstorm a list of possibilities; then use the Internet to see if, in fact, models are applied in these areas.

FIGURE 7–14 Projected change in global temperature, 1990 to 2060

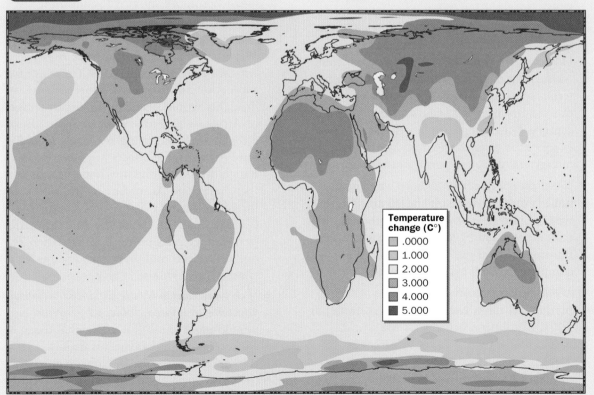

Temperature change (C°)
- .0000
- 1.000
- 2.000
- 3.000
- 4.000
- 5.000

The difference in average temperature between 1990 and 2060 illustrates the impact of greenhouse gas and aerosol emissions.

Criticisms of the Global Warming Theory

Evidence shows that global warming is a reality, and that we had better prepare for its effects. Yet there are some who caution that perhaps there are other explanations as to why the earth's temperatures are rising.

- *What do temperature statistics really show?* Because data has been collected mostly near growing towns and cities, and these areas are getting warmer from the urban "heat-island" effect, statistics may reveal that temperatures are rising. (The "heat-island" effect is caused by asphalt, roads, and buildings, which absorb more heat than the surrounding countryside. As a result, they tend to have higher temperatures.)

- *What do upward trends on graphs indicate?* When we see the increase in pollution, carbon emissions, and temperatures, there is little doubt that a global trend exists. However, this may reflect only a recent trend — the data could be showing part of a long-term oscillation. Temperatures that rise in this century may fall again in the next century. For example, the earth has experienced a sequence of ice ages with interglacial warming periods in-between.

- *What do computer models prove?* These models only show results based on data that was fed into the computer. Even though the data is prepared by leading scientists, it may illustrate part of one trend instead of a complete, natural cycle of change.

- *What makes headlines?* Dramatic predictions make headlines. For example, in 2001, headlines warned that the world would warm by 5.8 Celsius degrees by 2100. However, this figure was based on a number of assumptions: a global population of 15 billion, all following the consumption patterns of North America, with no international treaties in place to help control this consumption. Each of these assumptions seems exaggerated when contrasted with the most recent United Nations (UN) reports on population growth and consumerism.

- *What happens to the extra carbon dioxide we produce?* We are still unsure about the capacity of carbon sinks (such as our forests or oceans) to absorb carbon dioxide.

- *What is the role of the oceans in world climate?* According to Wright, this is a crucial question. He believes that until we fully understand such things as carbon capacity, the effects of weather patterns such as El Niño on ocean currents, and how the oceans affect our climate, we cannot draw any conclusions.

- *What happens if the ice melts?* We cannot assume that sea levels will simply rise. More precipitation throughout the world will also mean that more snow will fall on the existing ice caps, and this may maintain the balance between melting ice and new ice.

- *Who would lose the most from the enhanced greenhouse effect?* There are two aspects to consider. First, more severe droughts would occur in the desert fringes of Africa, where food shortages are already a reality. Second, rising sea levels would have catastrophic effects in places like Bangladesh or in the low-lying islands of the Caribbean. According to the Intergovernmental Panel on Climate Change, if sea levels rise by 40 centimetres (a midrange possibility) by 2100, then 75 million to 200 million people in low-lying coastal areas will be at risk.

- *If changes caused by the enhanced greenhouse effect are so unpredictable, why bother monitoring it at all?* If it is true that the enhanced greenhouse effect is mainly responsible for the rise in global temperatures, the consequences are enormous. If we add the fact that it has made us aware of the benefits of reducing air pollution, this theory is worth further investigation.

FIGURE 7-15 Rising sea levels would threaten low-lying areas like the Caribbean island of Antigua (above), while severe droughts could become more common in other areas. What would this mean for Canadian farmers like Vern Pancoast (right), here seen walking provincial and federal agriculture ministers through his drought-stricken fields in July 2001?

Critics point to other flaws in the enhanced greenhouse effect theory:

- Satellites used to measure the temperature of the troposphere (lower atmosphere) show that temperature readings have not risen anywhere near the levels predicted a decade ago. Computer models showed that these atmospheric temperatures would rise faster than those at ground level; this did not happen.

- The warming trend we are experiencing may be perfectly normal. Some scientists suggest that ice ages occur approximately every 100 000 years and that significant warming of 4 to 8 Celsius degrees naturally follows during periods between ice ages. These interglacial periods last about 10 000 to 20 000 years. Within this cycle, smaller temperature variations of 1 to 2 Celsius degrees also occur at regular intervals.

According to Environment Canada researchers, the majority of the global scientific community believes that global warming is a reality we must address. However, even though we experience floods, heat waves, a severe El Niño, and other extreme events, sceptics assert that it is not yet possible to link any particular climate or weather event definitively to global warming. The link between the frequency of extreme events and global warming can only be determined through statistical analyses of long-term data, since the natural climate system also produces weather events that appear to be uncharacteristic of the recent climate. Generally, sceptics believe that we should wait and see what happens. What do you think?

10. a) "Global warming is real, and we should be very concerned about it." In groups of three, prepare an argument to either support this statement (concerned scientists) or refute it (sceptical scientists). Debate the issue with an opposing group.

   b) At the end of the discussion, write down three points that you found most impressive in the opposing team's argument. Present these points to the rest of the class.

11. Find two articles about global warming that contradict one another. Summarize the differences between these two articles. Note the source(s) for each article and describe how a source may affect the viewpoints expressed. Comment on what this exercise illustrates about the importance of bias awareness to the general media-consuming public.

12. With a partner, consider some of the facts that the general scientific community seems to agree upon, and some of the theories that are much disputed. Why is it so difficult for scientists to agree on predictions regarding global warming and the earth's climate?

Case in point — The North and South Poles

The United States Environmental Protection Agency (EPA) suggests that evidence about the effects of global warming gathered on the polar ice sheets indicates that people should be concerned not only about the health of the North and South Poles, but also about what changes in these remote regions will mean for the rest of the planet.

Climate models used to predict the future effects of global warming indicate these high-latitude regions — particularly the Arctic — to be most at risk.

The Arctic

The Arctic region is predicted to see the greatest increases in temperature (relative to current conditions) within the next 50 years. The United States Environmental Protection Agency has found that temperatures in the Arctic during the last two decades were the highest they have been in the past 400 years.

Satellite photos show that snow cover in the Arctic has declined by 10 percent in the past 40 years, while ice cover on rivers and lakes has shortened its duration by two weeks. When there is open water for longer periods, this indicates a warming trend. In the past 50 years, sea ice has

FIGURE 7–16 Rate of ice level change, Greenland

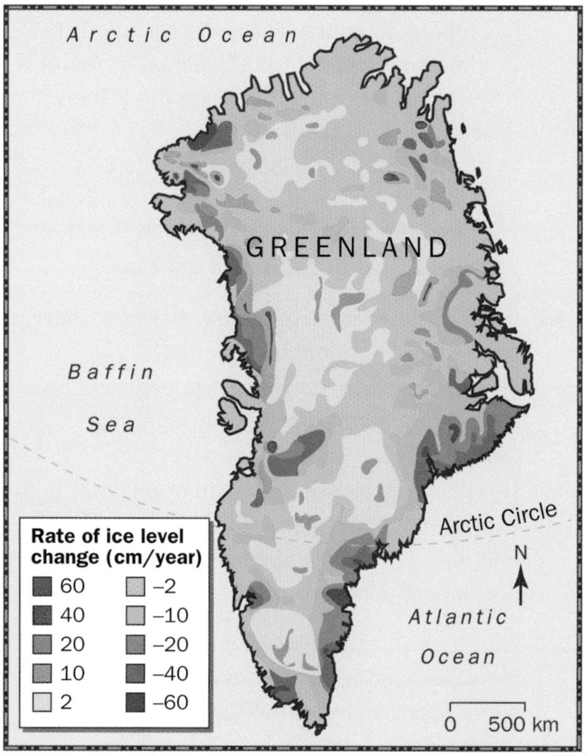

Most of Greenland lies within the Arctic Circle. Which parts of the country are experiencing the most ice loss?

At a glance — The Arctic

- Size: 14.056 million km², including Baffin Bay, Barents Sea, Beaufort Sea, Chukchi Sea, East Siberian Sea, Greenland Sea, Hudson Bay, Hudson Strait, Kara Sea, Laptev Sea, Northwest Passage, and other tributary water bodies. It has a coastline of 45 389 km.
- Climate: extremely cold, ice desert conditions. (A desert has less than 200 mm of precipitation per year.) The average temperature is below 0°C with a summer of 6–8 weeks.
- Population: difficult to determine due to sparse population distribution. In Canada, approximately 60 000 people live in the Arctic, 17 000 of whom are Inuit.
- Ownership: covers all the lands located north of the Arctic Circle. In addition to the Arctic Ocean, it includes territory in northern Canada, Alaska, Russia, and Norway, as well as most of Greenland, Svalbard, and Iceland.
- Economy: sand and gravel, fish, marine mammals (seals and whales). Oil and natural gas deposits are found around Alaska's Prudhoe Bay, Canada's Beaufort Sea and Ellesmere Island, and northern Siberia, in Russia. The economy includes resource exploitation, tourism, and government and communication services.

declined by 10 to 15 percent, and there has been a 40 percent reduction in ice thickness. With less ice and snow to reflect the energy received from the sun, greater warming trends are expected to occur. With a reduction in its reflective base of snow and ice, the land will absorb more of the sun's energy, in turn warming the atmosphere above it.

The Antarctic

Climatic conditions in the southern hemisphere are also critical. Scientists are worried about the northern fringes of the Antarctic continent (where the summer temperatures are around 0 degrees Celsius and rising), but it is the fragile nature of the West Antarctic Ice Sheet on the mainland that is giving most concern. If this sheet were to melt, it might raise sea levels by as much as 5.7 metres.

There are other indicators of future problems. In the past 50 years, Antarctic temperatures have risen by 2 Celsius degrees — a substantial temperature change. As a result, in the past 20 years, the annual melting season of Antarctica has been extended by two to three

FIGURE 7–17 The chunk of ice labelled B-15A in this NASA TERRA image is about to break away and become a new iceberg in the Ross Sea — a severe hazard to shipping.

At a glance — The Antarctic

- Size: about 14 million km² (97 percent covered by ice sheets, 280 000 km² ice-free). About 90 percent of the world's freshwater is held in Antarctica's icecap.
- Climate: very cold, ice desert conditions, especially in eastern Antarctica due to its high elevation. The average temperature is below 0°C. The coldest temperature recorded here was –89.2°C in 1983. It is also the windiest continent on earth, with winds of over 300 km/h recorded.
- Resources: mineral ore, iron ore, nickel, chromium, copper, gold. Contains oil and gas, ocean species such as krill (a shrimp-like creature), and penguins.
- Population: no indigenous peoples. There is a temporary population of about 4000 — research scientists, support staff, and tourism-industry staff. The population declines to about 1000 during the severe winter months.
- Ownership: not owned by any country. The 1961 Antarctic Treaty declared that all previous claims to its territory were null and void, and established Antarctica as a location for international co-operation and research. In 2000, there were 44 treaty member countries.
- Economy: scientific research, tourism (13 000 visitors in 2000), and a fishery. In 2000, 120 000 tonnes of fish were caught around Antarctica.

FIGURE 7-18 Antarctic ice

FIGURE 7-18 Antarctic ice

During the winter, Antarctica's surface area doubles in size, to a total of 14 200 000 square kilometres.

weeks; there is a gradual decline in the total amount of ice. In 1995, the massive Larsen A Ice Shelf, measuring 1994 square kilometres, completely disintegrated. The Pine Island Glacier on the West Antarctic Ice Sheet melted by 1.6 metres per year between 1992 and 1999. The Larsen B Ice Shelf — which was about the size of Rhode Island — collapsed into the Weddell Sea in March, 2002.

These enormous changes have also affected the local ecosystems. For example, there have been significant declines in the penguin populations as their habitat has changed.

For a first-hand account of the effects of warming temperatures in a polar region and the potential effects on the rest of the world, consider the following article, written by journalist David Helvarg following his visit to Antarctica.

For the past 30 years, climatologists have predicted that global warming would occur most rapidly at the poles, a fact now confirmed by scientists in Alaska, Canada, and Greenland, at the North Pole and on the Antarctic Peninsula. The peninsula is a rocky kite tail 1126 kilometres long, curving out from the coldest, driest, highest continent on earth. The peninsula is also, as I discovered, a wildlife-rich habitat undergoing a frighteningly rapid change.

At Palmer Station, one of three Antarctic bases administered by the National Science Foundation, I spoke with the chief scientist, Bill Frasier, who has been studying the Antarctic climate since 1974.

FIGURE 7-19 Leopard seals, whose diet consists of fish and penguins, are high on the food chain, and are thus extremely vulnerable to a decline in krill.

"When I was a graduate student, we were told that climate change occurs, but we'd never see the effects in our lifetime," Frasier told me. "But in the last 20 years I've seen tremendous changes. I've seen islands pop out from under glaciers; I've seen species changing places and landscape ecology altered."

While global temperatures have, on average, warmed by about 1 Celsius degree over the last century — parallelling increased industrial output of carbon dioxide and other greenhouse gases — the Antarctic Peninsula has seen a jump of about 3 Celsius degrees in just 50 years, including an incredible 5 degree average warming during its winter months. As a result, huge pieces of the ice shelf have begun calving (dropping icebergs) off its eastern shore.

And scientists are now discussing the possibility that the adjacent Western Antarctic Ice Sheet could experience a sudden meltdown, raising global sea levels by more than 4.5 metres over the next century (instead of 1 metre, as currently predicted).

While most experts believe this melting will occur sometime after the twenty-first century, by the time they know for sure it will probably be too late to do anything about it.

Today's warming poses a more immediate threat to Antarctica's abundant wildlife. And here too there are implications that extend to the rest of the world, researchers told me.

Tiny shrimplike creatures called krill — the most abundant animal on earth in terms of their total biomass — are the broad base of Antarctica's food chain, consumed in vast quantities by penguins, seals, and whales. (A single blue whale eats 3.6 tonnes a day.) Without access to sea ice, krill shrink, lose weight, and are vulnerable to early death.

A decline of krill due to melting of the ice shelf could wreck much of the Antarctic ecosystem that depends on it.

Rising temperatures also increase precipitation — which, in Antarctica, takes the form of snow. Excessive spring snow has disrupted the nesting and breeding of Adelie penguins, leading to the extinction of many of their colonies. At the same time, more adaptable species such as chinstrap penguins, elephant seals, and fur seals are increasing their numbers, threatening to displace ice-dependent sea animals such as Weddell seals, crabeater seals, and leopard seals.

What these changes in the Antarctic Peninsula suggest is that rapid warming could speed up a global chain reaction of extinctions that — thanks to the impact of humans — is already under way.

"Weedlike" species that are highly adaptable to disrupted habitat (pigeons, rats, deer, and elephant seals) will displace more specialized creatures (tigers, monarch butterflies, river dolphins, and Adelie penguins) that depend on unique ecosystems such as tropical rain forests, coral reefs, and the Antarctic ice shelf.

Rising temperatures may kill off certain plant species as well. At Palmer Station, I met Tad Day, a plant biologist who studies Antarctica's only two flowering plants: hairgrass and pearlwort. Hairgrass, which was the dominant species in Antarctica, is now being displaced by pearlwort, a mosslike plant. Day has found that warming improves growth of pearlwort but appears to have a negative impact on hairgrass.

"Global warming," Day told me, "has the capacity to shift the competitive balance of species in ways that, until we get out there and do the research, we don't understand yet, and that could have important consequences on our ability to produce food and fibre."

Increasingly reliable climate models now predict a 1.0 to 3.5 Celsius degree planetary warming in the next century, with regional shifts in agriculture that will favour the industrial north at the expense of the poorer nations of Africa and Latin America. There will also be increases in extreme weather events, coastal storms, and the spread of tropical diseases.

In that light, the work of Antarctic scientists like the ones I met suggests that — for better or worse — environmental change will define much of the politics of the twenty-first century.

A global problem

When physical changes to the land, oceans, and ecosystems occur at both polar regions, we often disregard the news about these changes because these areas are so remote. It does not hurt us directly, so why should we worry about it? Yet, there is a link and many predict that warming at the poles will be catastrophic to large numbers of people, including us.

If vast amounts of freshwater are released from glaciers and ice sheets as predicted, and warming trends continue, this will have a devastating impact on millions of people who live in low-lying coastal regions.

We, as Canadians, are directly involved. Our lifestyle trends are in line with the industrial, consumer-driven lifestyles that are said to be the major cause of global warming. If it is true that human lifestyles and human-related emissions are responsible for global warming, then our actions as Canadians contribute to this problem. When rising seas threaten low-lying islands, we must remember that there is an atmospheric link connecting all regions of the world under the earth's atmospheric blanket.

13. Review the changes observed in both of the polar regions — the Arctic and Antarctica. Which three observations from each region do you believe provide the most impressive evidence that climate change is underway?

14. What concerns scientist Bill Frasier most about his observations on the Antarctic Peninsula?

15. Describe the impact of the changing climate in Antarctica on wildlife.

16. Why does climate warming at the North and South Poles matter to those of us living far away from these regions?

Global Warming — Canadian Impacts

Canada is a significant producer of greenhouse gases. According to Environment Canada, the country contributes only 1.8 percent of all the world's greenhouse emissions, but ranks second in the world in per capita output. Environment Canada attributes this to the fact that Canada is a northern country with severe, cold winters that require a lot of heating in the fall, winter, and spring. As well, Canada's population is dispersed, necessitating much travel. Canada has a relatively high rate of industrial growth. All of this contributes to high levels of greenhouse gas emissions.

The temperature change in Canada over the past half century varies from increases of 2 Celsius degrees to decreases of 1 Celsius degree. Environment Canada believes that weaker warming temperatures (and in some parts of Canada, cooling temperatures), can be attributed to changes in atmospheric circulation over time. Changing patterns of ocean circulation, especially in the North Atlantic Ocean, can also contribute

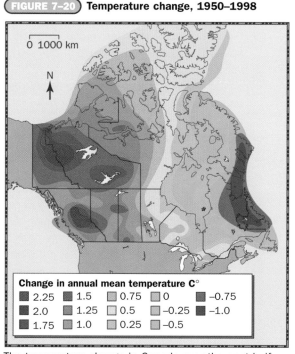

FIGURE 7–20 Temperature change, 1950–1998

0 1000 km

N

Change in annual mean temperature C°

2.25	1.5	0.75	0	–0.75
2.0	1.25	0.5	–0.25	–1.0
1.75	1.0	0.25	–0.5	

The temperature change in Canada over the past half century varies from increases of 2 Celsius degrees in northwestern Canada, to decreases of 1 Celsius degree in eastern Canada.

to changes in temperature within this region. High levels of industrialization, which produced higher sulphate emissions between 1950 and 2000, may also be a factor.

A warmer Canada

Canada is often described as "a winter country." Because of Canada's size, there are obvious regional differences within the country but, for the most part, Canada has longer winter months than many countries and a relatively short summer. In light of all the evidence that the world is warming, some Canadians may wonder why a warmer Canada would be a bad thing.

- Canadian farmers might welcome longer growing seasons (although some would suffer from increased drought).
- The tourism industry might receive a summertime boost, with more Americans possibly fleeing north to spend time away from the increased heat of the southern United States.
- Manufacturing sectors could increase their business through demands for additional cooling and heating processes.
- Camping and golf seasons in southern Ontario and Québec could be extended by 3 to 4 weeks.
- The St. Lawrence Seaway season would be extended, allowing for penetration of goods into the heartland and greater exportation of resources.
- The northern Arctic seaways would remain open throughout the winter.

Environment Canada researchers suggest that we should take advantage of these potentially positive changes in order to counterbalance costly impacts, because not all of the effects of a warmer Canada would be advantageous.

- In Canada's northlands, there is a great deal of permafrost (a layer of subsoil or

---

Issue briefing

Heat waves and pollution — A deadly duo

Climate change scenarios suggest that the average number of days above 30°C in Southern Ontario could increase (from the current 10 to 50 days a year) by the middle of the twenty-first century. Keeping cool will be only half the battle if climate change brings more heat waves. The big concern will be staying healthy. Air pollution, combined with more heat and sunlight, produces additional smog. And smog makes breathing more difficult for children, the elderly, and people with asthma and other respiratory illnesses. Air pollution has already been linked to an increase in hospital visits and 16 000 premature deaths each year in Canada. This number will likely rise if the climate warms up.

According to research funded by Environment Canada, heat-related deaths are most common in large, densely populated cities where air pollution levels are generally higher. A recent study of heat stress in the Toronto-Windsor corridor found that there were significantly more deaths among the elderly on the hottest days (above 32°C). And the link between heat stress and deaths was greatest in Toronto, London, and Hamilton, which have higher population densities than other communities in the region.

The combination of urban sprawl, more vehicles, and longer drives to work contribute to higher levels of air pollution that may worsen the health effects of heat stress in the region. The problem could get even worse as cities grow and the number of elderly persons increases.

rock that remains frozen year-round under a surface layer that freezes and thaws). In a warmer Canada, the region containing permafrost may expand hundreds of kilometres farther north from its present size. Where the permafrost is deep, the stability of the surface layer should not be affected. However, in areas where the ground is not frozen too deeply, roadbeds, bridges, pipes, and even foundations for homes could be unsettled.

- Environment Canada asserts that in southern Canada, the infrastructure (homes, power lines, communication towers, and roads) is designed with current climate and climate extremes in mind. If the climate changes even subtly, the existing infrastructure will not suit the changed conditions.

17. Review the potential effects of global warming presented in the "Issue briefing" article on heat waves and pollution.

   a) With a partner, brainstorm five to ten more possible effects that may result from climate change in Canada.

   b) Assume that you are a government official who has been given the responsibility of creating an action plan for change in response to global warming. Select what you consider to be the five most important changes that you will recommend. Place these in priority from 1 (being the most serious) to 5.

   c) Discuss your list with a partner and arrive at a new list of five changes upon which you both agree. You may have to argue why you want to include some changes and not others. Then, meet in a group of four. Repeat the process and arrive at a final list of the five most important changes.

   d) As a group, brainstorm ways in which Canada should prepare itself for these changes.

   e) Share your group findings with the rest of the class.

Confronting global warming in Canada

The Intergovernmental Panel on Climate Change believes that, in order to keep the greenhouse gas concentrations from increasing beyond a level that could be considered safe, the world population would eventually have to reduce its global emissions of greenhouse gases by 50 percent. How will Canada contribute to the overall reduction?

Canada consumes more energy per capita than any other country on this planet. In order to make the kind of emission cuts needed, Canadians would have to make a significant change in their way of life. There would have to be lifestyle changes made at the individual level, as well as far-reaching decisions made by government.

Some environmental groups suggest that governments in Canada and around the world are reluctant to address this issue because necessary actions would make politicians too unpopular — increased "carbon taxes" on items such as gasoline, heat, lumber purchases, and many manufactured products would be charged to the consumer.

FIGURE 7–21 Smoke billows from the Lakeview Generating Station in Toronto as smog obscures the skyline.

According to the United Nations Environment Programme, the impacts of global warming could cost the world approximately $300 billion per year by 2050.

To date, atmospheric changes have not been large enough to concern the public overmuch. As environmentalists see it, many people appear willing to accept the costs of severe storms, hurricanes, and flooding as the price to pay for maintaining a high-consumption lifestyle.

There are alternatives that allow politicians and policymakers to address the issue in a manner that is politically manageable. Some researchers suggest that attention be initially focussed on the need to reduce soot and ozone-laden smog. They believe that these pollutants are just as responsible for producing global warming as carbon emissions are. Soot and smog are also more directly linked to ill health and respiratory diseases that cause death. Politicians could probably "sell" the idea of reducing smog, soot, and other pollution more easily than the idea of cutting back on industrial emissions of carbon dioxide.

These researchers also believe we have underestimated the contribution of methane as a greenhouse gas, and that methane would be easier to control and reduce than other greenhouse gases. Such ideas have received a good deal of support from economists and industrialists, who fear the political and economic effects of carbon dioxide emission control.

Issue briefing

What can people change in their homes?

Even though industry and commercial sectors of the economy create much more greenhouse gas emissions than we do in our homes, it is important that individuals contribute in any way they can toward the reduction of the emissions. Environment Canada's advice on how to reduce these levels includes the following:

- Insulate your home well to prevent excess use of energy (heating and air conditioning) due to heat or cold escaping.
- Insulate your home to an "R-2000" standard. This represents a standard where insulation and energy efficiency is much higher than for normal building standards. An R-2000 home can use half as much energy as other homes for utilities such as heat, hot water, and light.
- Use a programmable thermostat to lower temperatures at night when colder temperatures are better tolerated.
- Use an energy-efficient furnace. Old furnaces burn much more gas and do not produce heat as efficiently. Ensuring that furnaces are energy-efficient saves overall gas usage, which results in fewer carbon dioxide emissions.
- Use the sun to obtain "passive" energy through windows and skylights. This not only provides extra light, but allows the sun's energy to heat up the home, thereby cutting down on the use of burned energy.
- Use plenty of shade techniques (blinds, plants, trees, and so on) in summer.
- Use a manual lawn mower instead of an electric or gas-powered mower.
- Burn fluorescent and quartz halogen lighting instead of conventional incandescent lighting, as these methods use far less energy.
- Hang clothes out to dry on windy days. Nature is efficient at drying them and saves the energy that would be used by clothes dryers.

18. Why might some politicians be reluctant to act on the issue of global warming?

19. How efficient is your school in terms of the energy that it uses?

    a) Prepare and circulate a survey within your school to assess awareness levels of the global warming issue, and the degree to which people believe that individuals can and should contribute to emission reductions.

    b) Arrange a discussion with school custodians. Ask them for:
       • their opinions on ways in which the school wastes energy
       • any data available on actual energy usage and costs
       • ideas that could be used to make the school environment more energy-efficient

    c) In groups of four to six, analyse the opinions and data you have collected, then design an action plan to make your school more energy-efficient. This could involve many things, such as replacing old light fixtures, fixing air leaks in windows, or implementing a program of recycling/reducing the waste generated by the school. "Think globally, act locally" could be demonstrated in your action plan by suggesting that weekly newsletters be distributed electronically rather than by photocopying them. This example will help to reduce wood harvesting and protect Canada's carbon sinks. You may wish to invite school board officials to help collaborate on ways in which efficient systems can be introduced or proactive action can be taken (for example, planting more trees around the school property).

20. Design a pamphlet giving advice to Canadians on ways to reduce greenhouse gas emissions. Introduce the issue within your pamphlet and then offer some solutions to this problem.

21. Write a letter to your local politicians. Tell them what you believe Canada should do to help lessen global warming and its effects.

Carbon Sinks and the Kyoto Protocol

The international community faced the issue of the enhanced greenhouse effect in 1997 when countries from around the world agreed to sign what became known as the **Kyoto Protocol**. This agreement stated that industrialized countries should reduce their greenhouse gas emissions by a given percentage of those levels emitted in 1990. In Canada's case, this meant a reduction of emissions by 6 percent of its 1990 levels.

Under the Kyoto Protocol, countries can use their resources (such as forests and agriculture) to help limit their promised targets of emission reduction. For example, if a country promises to grow more forests or cut down fewer trees, it may be allowed to exceed its 1990 limit or reduce its promised cuts. In this way, carbon sinks would be used as **carbon credits**. Under the agreement, it is even possible to trade these carbon credits. Australia is already trying out this strategy; the Sydney Futures Exchange has created a carbon credits trading market, where companies and individuals that are carbon emitters can buy carbon credits from forest growers.

Canada's carbon sinks

According to Environment Canada, Canada emits about 150 million tonnes of carbon each year. However, how much can Canada's carbon sinks — forests and agricultural lands — absorb? Experts are unable to agree on a figure. A detailed Canadian Forestry Service model of carbon budgets suggests that within the last decade, Canada's forests have become a net producer of about 50 million tonnes of carbon, probably due mainly to the aging and decaying of the forests. A study by the Canada Centre for Remote Sensing suggests that the forests are in a budget balance.

The country's mature forests provide an advantage in the realm of carbon sinks. With a small population and a large amount of forest

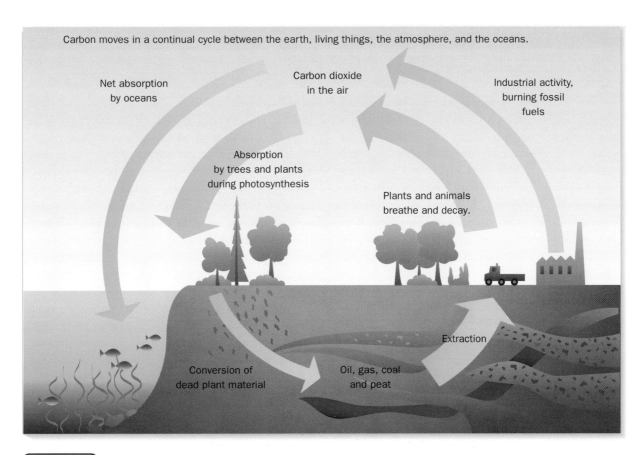

Carbon moves in a continual cycle between the earth, living things, the atmosphere, and the oceans.

Net absorption by oceans

Carbon dioxide in the air

Industrial activity, burning fossil fuels

Absorption by trees and plants during photosynthesis

Plants and animals breathe and decay.

Extraction

Conversion of dead plant material

Oil, gas, coal and peat

FIGURE 7–22 Carbon moves in a continual cycle between the earth, living things, the atmosphere, and the oceans. As trees grow, their leaves absorb carbon dioxide. Young trees are net exporters of carbon; it takes about 20 years before they become carbon sinks. According to the government of New South Wales, Australia, planting 40 000 hectares of forest means absorption of a million tonnes of carbon dioxide per year from the atmosphere.

and agricultural industry, Canada is potentially better off than its neighbours in the United States, who have ten times the population and industrial capacity, but not nearly as much forest cover. This is considered by many environmentalists to be Canada's potential "green advantage." At the moment, Canadian forests are older and decaying more than those in the United States, where trees are generally much younger and are likely to remain a net sink for a long time. However, Canada has large potential to develop new sinks through afforestation programs. Its new trees will take years to become carbon consumers, but should provide the country with a large sink capacity in the future.

22. Make a copy of the carbon cycle in Figure 7–22. In a short paragraph, explain how the carbon cycle works.

23. Define the terms "carbon source" and "carbon sink."

24. How would you respond to someone who suggests that Canada need not worry about carbon emissions because it soaks up more carbon than it emits?

25. Investigate carbon credit trading at the Sydney Futures Exchange online. Identify its strengths and weaknesses. Is this an idea that Canada should adopt? In a one-page report, express your opinion, citing specific information.

Global warming negotiation

Global warming is an important issue facing the global community. It is one that illustrates the tragedy of the commons (discussed in Chapter 1). Every country adds to atmospheric greenhouse gases at apparently no individual cost. There is increasing industrialization around the world, which has a similar effect as putting additional cows on a public meadow or common — eventually, everyone will pay the price. Just as the common grazing land eventually collapses and is unable to feed any livestock, so will our atmosphere and carbon sinks become saturated with greenhouse gases, and the earth will grow too hot. Ecosystems will have to change or collapse.

Annual summit to reduce greenhouse emissions

As a world community of industrialized nations, you and your classmates have decided to meet at global summits annually to pledge action that will lead to reduced global emissions of greenhouse gases. In this activity, you will be assigned a country to represent at the summit meeting. Once you have been assigned a country, you must do some research to learn the following information:

- your country's population and growth rate
- your country's main economic activities and what percentage of your economy is made up of industry

You will meet to discuss the issue of too many greenhouse gas emissions. The meeting is open-ended in that you can set your own agenda and discuss any aspect of this issue. As a group, you may elect a chair to keep things in order.

During the meeting, agreements to commit spending to reducing emissions will be made by individual countries or groups, or even perhaps by the whole summit group. You will be allowed to "spend" up to 5 percent of your gross domestic product (GDP). (More than this would be crippling to your economy.)

Of course, if your country spends a great deal, it will be at an economic disadvantage relative to other countries. It will be each country's goal to encourage other countries to commit to spending on emission reductions, while spending as little as possible itself. Thus, countries will have to find ways to negotiate amounts. One possible basis for negotiation may be found in Figure 7–23, which shows the total amount of forestry within each country. Perhaps the summit group can establish a system of carbon credits based on these figures.

There will be ten summit meetings in the simulation. Each country will give a spending commitment for each summit and keep a running total of its spending. At the end of the simulation, you will calculate how much total spending you have contributed as a country. You will then calculate your contribution as a percentage of your annual gross domestic product, followed by a calculation based on a per capita basis. (To do this, divide the total amount you have spent in the ten-year period by your country's population.) In this way, it will be possible to determine which countries have spent the least and the most toward reducing global greenhouse gases. You will have the opportunity to discuss the implications of these results with other summit representatives.

At the end of each summit meeting, each country will be given a spending commitment sheet on which they will write down the figure they will spend to reduce emissions (each country's annual, per-summit expenditure). Note that countries often promise money for initiatives like this, but never raise it. To your spending commitment sheet, attach a short list of some ways in which your country will live up to its spending commitments.

	Total emissions (million tonnes)	Emissions per capita (tonnes)	Forest area (square kilometres)	GDP (US$billion PPP)
1. United States	1 515	5.6	225 993	9 963
2. China	930	0.5	163 480	4 500
3. Russia	400	2.7	851 392	1 120
4. Japan	388	2.4	22 081	3 150
5. India	252	0.2	64 113	2 200
6. Germany	230	2.8	10 740	1 936
7. Canada	156	4.9	244 571	774
8. United Kingdom	152	2.6	2 794	1 360
9. Italy	121	2.1	10 003	1 273
10. France	109	1.8	15 341	1 448
11. Ukraine	104	2.1	9 584	189
12. Mexico	101	1.0	55 205	915
13. South Africa	99	2.2	8 917	369
14. Australia	94	5.0	154 539	445
15. Brazil	89	0.5	543 905	1 130
16. Poland	85	2.2	9 047	327
17. Spain	82	2.1	14 370	720
18. Netherlands	64	4.1	375	388
19. Belgium	38	3.7	728	259
20. Czech Republic	29	2.8	2 632	132
World totals	**6 143**	**1.0**	**3 869 455**	**43 600**

Summit debriefing

- What strategies did you use to make sure you supported your country's best interests?
- Were people "reneging" on deals they made with one another? Why did this happen?
- Were there countries that put the interests of the world ahead of their own?
- Were the large-emission countries fairly co-operative regarding emission reduction?
- How successful were you as a world community in addressing the problem?
- How does this simulation demonstrate the tragedy of the commons described on pages 14–15 in Chapter 1?

Geopolitics

When you watch the news on television, have you ever noticed which international topics are usually highlighted within the first few minutes of the broadcast? The most common topics include war, conflict, disputes, peacekeepers, and the involvement of international organizations in various countries around the world. What is it about these stories, do you think, that grabs the world's attention?

These fleeting media images and stories are dramatic and engaging, but examining the political, environmental, social, and economic interactions within and among countries — **geopolitics** — in greater depth provides us with a greater understanding of the issues.

FIGURE 8–1 A Canadian peacekeeper in Haiti takes a break to visit a local orphanage. Why do you think a government would decide to involve its people, like this Canadian peacekeeper, in a foreign conflict?

- Analyse geopolitical relationships between selected countries and regions.
- Predict geographic consequences of separation or independence for a region or cultural group that is now part of a larger country.
- Analyse instances of international co-operation and conflict, and identify factors that contribute to each.
- Research and report on the human and ecological cost of global military spending.
- Identify similarities and differences in the economic and political aspirations of selected regional or cultural groups within different countries.

Studying the geopolitics of an issue helps us to understand specific world events; we look at the locale, the key players, and their reasons for involvement. The term "geopolitics" also describes how nations exert their influence over their own people and over other nations in order to achieve greater international power. Often, a nation's political stance is directly related to its geographic situation. Both play a significant role in shaping global events. In other words, as Simon Dalby at Carleton University writes, geopolitics is a term used to refer to "great power rivalries and the geographical dimensions of global political power."

Our geopolitical landscape is constantly changing as a result of innovative communication technologies, high-tech weapons and surveillance devices, international trade agreements, and the emergence of new political and economic structures such as the European Union (EU). These forces of modernization and globalization present new challenges to governments and international organizations, as they address changes through foreign policy initiatives and government decisions. Sometimes these forces of change can lead to conflict within or between states. It is these geopolitical conflicts that often make the news headlines and are worth exploring in more depth; their causes, effects, and possible solutions are very complex.

Find recent news articles (either from a newspaper, news magazine, or the Internet) that feature a geopolitical event. Using evidence from these articles, explain:

a) why this event supports the definition of "geopolitics"

b) who is involved in the event

c) where the event occurred

d) what has caused the event

e) how you think the situation could be solved

Be prepared to share your explanations with fellow students.

Geopolitical conflict

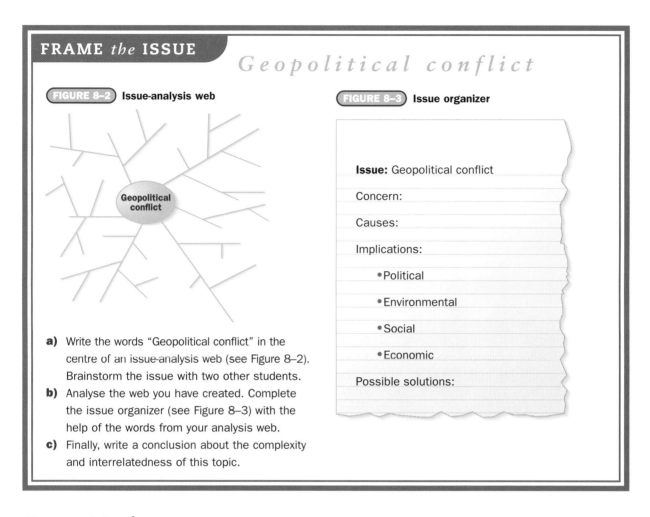

FIGURE 8–2 Issue-analysis web

FIGURE 8–3 Issue organizer

Issue: Geopolitical conflict

Concern:

Causes:

Implications:

- Political
- Environmental
- Social
- Economic

Possible solutions:

a) Write the words "Geopolitical conflict" in the centre of an issue-analysis web (see Figure 8–2). Brainstorm the issue with two other students.

b) Analyse the web you have created. Complete the issue organizer (see Figure 8–3) with the help of the words from your analysis web.

c) Finally, write a conclusion about the complexity and interrelatedness of this topic.

State, Nation, or Nation-State?

Before we examine geopolitical events in greater detail, the concepts of state, nation, and nation-state should be clearly defined. For example, the United Nations (UN) is an organization of states — not nations — as the following description clarifies.

State

A **state** is often referred to as a political entity, institutional structure, or organization. A state must be **sovereign**, which means that it must have the ability to make its own independent decisions and laws, free from external control or influences. The attributes of a state can include:

- a defined territory of land
- a permanent resident population
- an organized economy
- an interconnected system of financial and infrastructure services (for example, banking, transportation, communication, and power services)
- a form of government recognized by the international legal system as the legitimate structure of government for the people within its territory

According to the United States State Department, there are 191 states in the world, as defined by the above criteria.

Nation

If a state is characterized by geographic territory and political legitimacy, then what constitutes a **nation**? The word "nation," derived from the Latin word *natio* (meaning "of birth"), suggests a group of people related by birth. However, as societies become more complex, the term "nation" is used rather to describe a large group of people who are aware of, and share, one or more cultural features such as language, ethnicity, historical experience, identification with a "homeland," customs, values, and religion. For example, nations with a single, dominant language may use their language as a defining feature (for example, the Polish language is a feature of the Polish nation).

Unlike states, nations are not limited by geography. Instead, the members view themselves and each other as belonging to a distinct group, regardless of location. Benedict Anderson of Cornell University considers a nation to be an "imagined political community," since it exists in the minds of its members rather than within a physical setting. For example, the Kurdish people, who are predominantly nomadic and live in Iran, Iraq, Turkey, and Europe might be said to make up the Kurdish nation.

Nation-State

Nations and states evolve and change over time. Recently, there has been an increased movement toward the combination of the nation and the state into the **nation-state**. The progression may sound simple, but is actually very difficult. Imagine trying to "wrap" a state around a nation and ensure that each person within one political boundary shares the same cultural traits.

In order to achieve a sense of unity, nation-states use their government powers to try to create a common culture. For example, Lesotho can be classified as a nation-state — 99.7 percent of its population identifies with the Sotho culture and language, making this the **dominant culture**. (The rest of the population is Zulu.) Often, we tend to interchange the terms "nation-state" and "country." However, according to James John Guy in his book *People, Politics and Government*, attaining a true nation-state is quite difficult, since there are over 1400 nationalities in the world.

The multiethnic and multicultural nature of many countries presents a challenge to forming a

FIGURE 8–4 The separation referendum illustrates the fact that the Québec population has divided itself into two main groups — federalists who wish to remain part of Canada, and sovereigntists who want their own state and sovereignty.

nation-state. The issue of Québec's separation from Canada is a good example of the limitations of the nation-state concept. If the sovereigntists had won the most recent referendum in 1995 by 51 percent, it would have been very difficult for them to create a new nation-state when a large proportion of Québec's population wished to remain in Canada.

Unless an overwhelming majority of the population is willing to "belong" to the dominant culture, the nation-state concept is difficult to implement. The breakup of former **multinational** states (those made up of a number of equally empowered ethnic groups such as the former Yugoslavia) has resulted in the creation of new nation–states but has also increased ethnic tensions, as redrawn boundaries fail to clearly define these various groups.

1. Which of the following would be considered a "state"? Explain why or why not.
   a) Austria
   b) Venezuela
   c) Hong Kong
   d) Bosnia
   e) Falkland Islands

2. Which of the following would be considered a "nation-state"? Explain why or why not.
   a) Japan
   b) United States
   c) Turkey
   d) Canada
   e) Belgium

3. What challenges do some countries and/or regions face in their attempts to form a nation-state?

4. Research the Israeli-Palestinian conflict and write a summary outlining:
   a) the nationalities of the groups involved
   b) the significant events in the Palestinians' quest for a nation-state (since the state of Israel was created in 1948)
   c) the importance of geographic sites to each group's identity
   d) an update of the current status of this conflict

Nationalism

Today, there are more than 190 states in the world, containing many ethnically diverse groups. How do countries like Canada and the United States, with so many varied groups within their boundaries, remain united? To answer this, think back to the last Olympic games. If you watched the opening ceremonies on television, whether or not you are a sports fan, how did you feel when you saw the Canadian flag raised above the medal podium, heard the anthem being

FIGURE 8–5 Comment on the extent to which you think events such as the Olympics stir feelings of nationalism.

played, or watched the athletes waving the flag? You probably felt excited — maybe a smile spread across your face or perhaps even a few tears welled up in your eyes. For many people, these emotions are associated with feelings of patriotism and a sense of belonging to their country, otherwise known as **nationalism**.

Nationalism's emotional appeal can be used by states as a uniting force during times of war, or to inspire economic development. **National cultural integration** is an attempt to bind people together in a shared national identity by means of a common language, history, or customs. In his book *The Role of National Development in Determining the Policy and Structure of Education*, Dr. John

Boswell states that national cultural integration is a process that has been utilized since the 1950s by Western European nations and by the United States. In contrast to Canadian policies, which promote distinctiveness or a **cultural mosaic**, the United States uses **melting pot** (assimilation) strategies to promote unity.

Feelings of nationalism can help to mobilize groups in their attempt to create a state or a nation-state. Nationalistic feelings can also challenge the unity of a state when a **secession** movement (an attempt to withdraw from the state) takes place. The United Nations estimates that only 25 of its member states are free from secessionist disputes.

 **FIGURE 8–6** Union republics in the former USSR

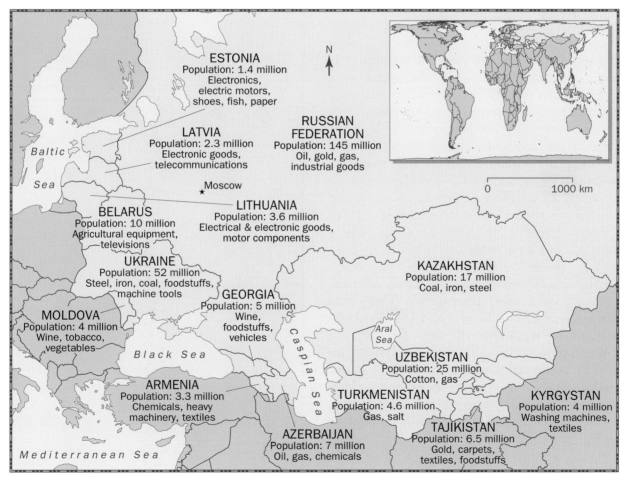

Not all attempts result in conflict. When the Union of Soviet Socialist Republics (USSR) dissolved in the early 1990s, 15 **union republics** (independent states) were peacefully created. However, fearing further breakups and the loss of valuable resources, the present Russian Federation has refused to grant independence to **autonomous regions** (self-governing provinces) such as Chechnya.

Chechnya proclaimed its independence after the demise of the Soviet Union in 1991. Moscow did not acknowledge the independence of this republic, fearing the possibility of other republic independence movements, as well as loss of access to valuable oil deposits and pipelines. A devastating war with the Chechen people resulted. Despite subsequent control by Russian troops in 1999, there are ongoing skirmishes.

Many contemporary geopolitical events are influenced by nationalistic forces and can sometimes result in either non-violent or violent attempts to create new national identities. In some countries like Canada, the sovereigntist movement peacefully challenges national unity through political campaigns and referenda.

However, if nationalism becomes very powerful, it can lead to **irredentism** — the desire to incorporate all areas within the state that were once part of the state, or to absorb those areas occupied by people who belong to the nation but do not reside within state boundaries. For example, in the late 1890s, Taiwan was a province of China. It then came under Japanese rule for the next 50 years, after China's defeat in the first Sino-Japanese war. This political, cultural, and economic separation from China made the return of Taiwan to Chinese rule (at the end of World War II) very difficult. The continuation of Taiwan's capitalist system, the fear of losing rights such as freedom of speech under Chinese rule, and the recent Taiwan election of Chen Shui-bian — a pro-independence leader — illustrate Taiwan's desire to become independent from China. Attempts by China to renew its control over this province have resulted in threats of war.

Extreme nationalism can also result in **chauvinism** (excessive feelings of superiority over other peoples and states). This can lead to an aggressive drive to conquer, which often leads to **imperialism** (one country extending its rule over other countries). Examples of imperialism span history; recent examples include Nazi Germany's occupation of most of Europe during World War II, and the 1990 Gulf War in which Iraq invaded Kuwait.

Chauvinism in Sri Lanka

Located off the southern tip of India, Sri Lanka (formerly Ceylon) — with a population of 18 million — is a multicultural society of many

FIGURE 8–7 Ethnic divisions in Sri Lanka

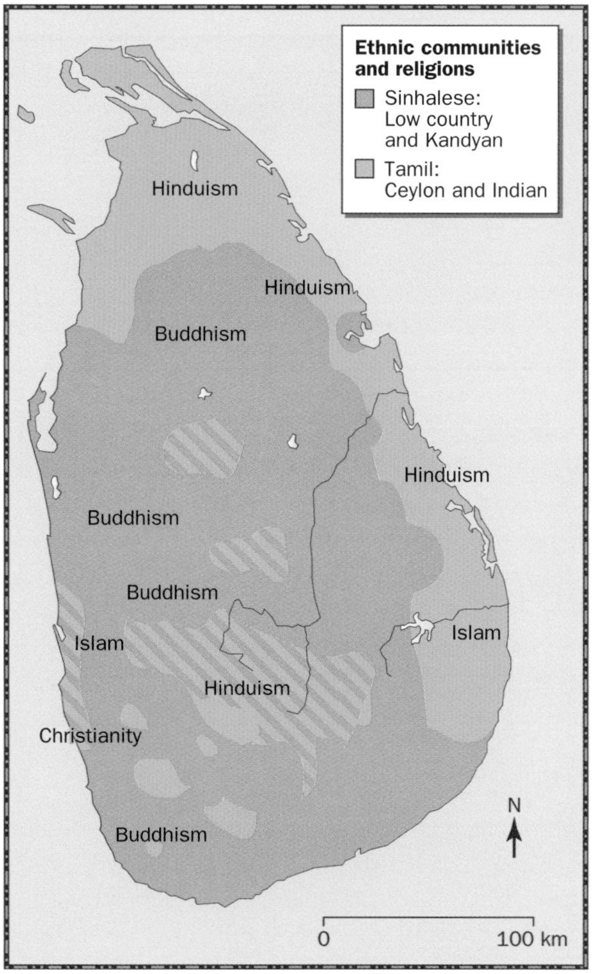

Ethnic communities and religions
- Sinhalese: Low country and Kandyan
- Tamil: Ceylon and Indian

Hinduism
Hinduism
Buddhism
Hinduism
Buddhism
Buddhism
Islam
Islam
Hinduism
Christianity
Buddhism

N

0   100 km

different ethnic groups (Sinhalese, Tamil, Moor, Malay, and Vedda), religions (Buddhist, Hindu, Muslim, and Christian), as well as three main languages (Sinhala, Tamil, and English).

The Sinhalese (74% of the population) and the Tamils (18% of the population) are the two largest ethnic groups.

Even though multiculturalism has led to present-day conflicts in Sri Lanka, these diverse communities did co-exist peacefully, mix socially, and work together to gain independence from British rule. Ethnic tensions surfaced in 1958, when Sinhalese chauvinism became apparent: the government defined Sri Lanka ethnically. It declared Sinhalese the official language, instituted university admission quotas that limited Tamil entrance, and denied opportunities for Tamils to be employed in public administration.

Tamil groups attempted political action through the creation of opposition parties and by signing an accord to create "Eelam" — a separate state — through democratic means. Tamil chauvinism emerged as well: militant Tamil youth groups such as the Liberation Tigers of Tamil Eelam (LTTE) — the "Tamil Tigers" — sought independence outside of the parliamentary system. By 1983, violence broke out between the Sinhalese and the Tamils. Most of the 1990s were dominated by civil war and political instability, resulting in over 75 000 deaths, a large number of refugees, and a cost of US$10 billion. The twenty-first century has witnessed the involvement of Tamil political parties in constitutional change and negotiation, in order to give Tamils a greater opportunity to run their own administration. Short-term ceasefires are being attempted, to advance the peace process.

Nationalism among the Kurds

Nationalism is not always tied to a state. For example, the Kurdish people are a large ethnic group of 36 million who inhabit several states: Turkey, Iran, Iraq, Syria, the former USSR, and parts of Europe. Over one-half of the Kurdish

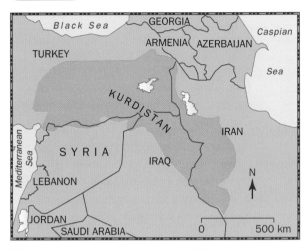

FIGURE 8–8 Possible boundaries of a Kurdistan state

If it ever came into being, the state of Kurdistan would be a considerable political force in terms of its population, geographic size, and oil resources, since two-thirds of Iraq's oil supplies would fall within Kurdish boundaries.

people live in Turkey; the Kurds are the third-largest ethnic group in the Middle East.

The 1920 Treaty of Sevres — an extensive treaty affecting many countries — included provisions for a Kurdish state. However, Turkey subsequently made a formal agreement with Iran and Iraq not to recognize a Kurdish state, and thus did not observe the treaty's provisions. Despite the increasing integration of Kurdish people into urban Turkish lifestyles, Turkey does not recognize the Kurds as a distinct ethnicity. The Kurds believe that this denies them religious and cultural rights.

The Kurdistan Workers Party (Kurdish acronym PKK) was formed in 1984 to promote a Kurdish state. Several factors thwart Kurdish independence: the Kurds' long-standing animosity with Iraq and Iran; the Turkish belief that the PKK is a terrorist group determined to destroy Turkey; the lack of existence of a single Kurdish language; and lower levels of education and income. Despite these obstacles, the Kurds' strong sense of patriotism in terms of their culture and heritage continues to fuel their demands for greater rights and autonomy within their occupied region. They strive for their ultimate goal of an independent state.

5. In your own words, define the term "nationalism." Reflect on your personal experiences for examples.

6. a) What major challenge exists to Canadian national unity?
   b) Do you think that Canada should encourage national cultural integration as used by the United States? Explain.

7. a) How can new states emerge from existing states?
   b) This emergence of new states can either be a peaceful or a violent transition. Explain by using examples for each situation.

8. What can happen if nationalism becomes too extreme? Think of additional geopolitical examples to illustrate this situation.

9. As a lead researcher for the think-tank GeoPol International, you have been asked to deliver a statement, about 3 to 5 minutes long, outlining your prediction of the geographic consequences of independence (or separation) within *one* of the following groups, regions, or countries:
   a) the Québec sovereigntist movement
   b) the Kurds
   c) Sri Lanka
   d) the Basques in Spain
   e) Indonesia/East Timor
   f) Chechnya
   g) Northern Ireland

Ensure that your statement is well researched and concise. Consider various aspects such as altered boundaries, economic and social impacts, and governing concerns.

Boundaries — More Than Just Lines on a Map

Boundaries appear on maps as lines that mark the limit of sovereignty of a state. (A better representation of a boundary would be a vertical plane that cuts through the airspace and the sub-soil of an adjacent state.) The actual marking of the ground limit (a boundary on the physical landscape) is called **demarcation**, but very few boundaries can be seen in this way. The more obvious the boundary, the less likely it is that there will be disputes.

Boundary "administrations" exist in order to maintain boundaries and address any disputes. These administrative bodies can be local, regional, or international in composition. For example, the International Boundary Commission maintains the Canada/United States boundary by inspecting it regularly and fixing (or adding) boundary markers. Three representatives from each of these two countries act as Commissioners. The International Joint Commission (IJC) was established by Canada and the United States to assist them with the management and conservation of boundary waters such as the Great Lakes.

Drawing the boundary line between two friendly nations is advantageous; accurate definition

FIGURE 8–9 The mandate of the Waterton-Glacier International Peace Park, an example of a transboundary, is to protect its shared ecology and co-operatively manage its vegetation and its wildlife, such as grizzly bears and their habitat.

and demarcation is essential for law enforcement. The United Nations International Court of Justice, in accordance with international law, settles disputes submitted by member states. Some of these disputes are boundary-related. Recently, Nicaragua argued that its maritime Caribbean boundary with Honduras had not been determined, and requested the court to demarcate it, in accordance with international law.

Transboundaries (boundaries outlining an area that may cross country boundaries) can be used to protect and promote politically divided ecosystems, while encouraging international collaboration and management. The Waterton-Glacier International Peace Park (IPP), created in 1932 and located on the Alberta/Montana border, is the world's first park legislated by both Canadian and United States governments.

Negotiated boundaries — Canada and Nunavut

On April 1, 1999, Canada's political map changed with the addition of a new territory. Formed from the eastern part of the existing Northwest Territories and stretching over 2 million square kilometres, Nunavut — meaning "our land" in Inuktitut — was created after 20 years of negotiations.

Even though 85 percent of Nunavut's population is Inuit, this group chose a public government structure that would represent the interests of all its residents, not just those of the majority group. Inuit values and beliefs are promoted (by the government department of Culture, Language, Elders, and Youths), and the working language is Inuktitut (Inuit), but other languages such as Inuinnaqtun, English, and French are also used.

This new territory has its own share of challenges: namely, the high costs of goods and services, high unemployment rates, low education and income levels, and a limited number of experienced government personnel. The government of Nunavut hopes that the creation of Nunavut will provide greater opportunities for Aboriginal self-governance to solve these problems.

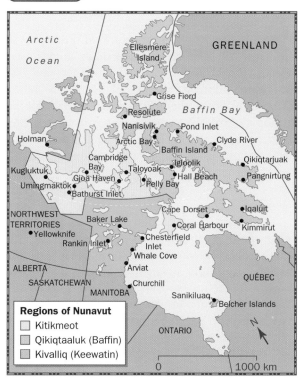

FIGURE 8-10 Nunavut

The 1993 Nunavut Land Claim Agreement — whereby the Inuit received a billion-dollar federal government settlement, substantial control over surface mineral rights, and self-government — laid the foundations for this new territory.

FIGURE 8-11 The flag of Nunavut

The colours are meant to symbolize the riches of the land, sea, and sky. Red is a reference to Canada.

Disputed boundaries — Ethiopia and Eritrea

In 1993, Eritrea — a province of Ethiopia — obtained its independence through an internationally monitored referendum. However, this amicable relationship ended in 1998 when Eritrea took over the border town of Badame, in Ethiopia. Ethiopia claimed that Eritrea was illegally occupying the Yirga triangle in northwestern Ethiopia, as well as other locations along this desert border. Eritrea claimed that this land was theirs and that the Ethiopians had previously been encroaching upon it.

The border established was not demarcated when Eritrea obtained its independence. This border dispute was further complicated by the fact that Ethiopia would not agree to a United Nations ceasefire (so that the UN could demarcate this border) until the Eritreans withdrew their troops to pre-1998 boundaries.

Economics also played a significant role in this dispute, since Eritrea controlled two ports and claimed potential oil reserves in the Red Sea — a resource that Ethiopia wanted to gain via access to the sea.

Evolving boundaries

Boundaries are not static. Have any of the boundaries in your atlas changed since it was published? Can you name a country or region whose boundaries have been altered?

As the forces of nationalism continue, the emergence of new states may result in the establishment of more land and maritime boundaries. Even though states will continue to defend their territory, some boundaries are becoming more "permeable" — information and transactions flow across borders via communication technologies. The function of boundaries may change as the expansion of political and economic blocs shift us closer to the notion of a "borderless" world.

The size and shape of boundaries can also be an influential factor in the stability of a state. Examine a world map. The number of large-sized states is not equal to the number of small-sized states. In fact, there are fewer than ten large states, over 50 **microstates** (independent countries with a total area measuring less than 450 square kilometres) like the Vatican City, Monaco, or the Maldives, and many variations in-between.

Large states that are underpopulated or unevenly populated, such as Australia or Canada, may experience internal political division. At one time, states grew in size to obtain greater power, as in the process of colonialism. Recently, the trend is toward forming smaller states. This raises questions about how to achieve equilibrium, and how much voting power smaller states should have in the international arena.

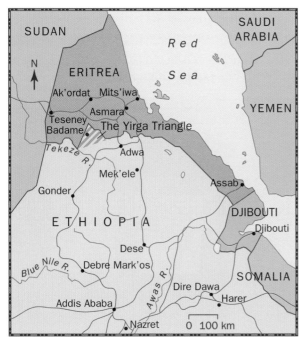

FIGURE 8–12 **Eritrea and Ethiopia**

This map shows Eritrea and Ethiopia, and their disputed border.

10. Write a letter to the editor of a national newspaper explaining why you agree (or disagree) that the formation of Nunavut could act as a global model that demonstrates how boundaries can change to reflect the ethnic composition of an area, peacefully. Use specific examples from the Nunavut and Ethiopia/Eritrea cases, as well as other events, to support your stance.

Changes in the Geopolitical Landscape

Ideologically based conflicts such as "communism versus democracy" or "West versus East" largely ended with the dissolution of the USSR. Today, in the **post-cold war** era, our geopolitical landscape is dominated by regional conflicts: ethnic, civil, revolutionary, interstate (that is, between states), or a combination of these.

The Centre for Systemic Peace — an American organization that researches global conflict and management of societal conflict — views this as a "shift from wars for separation or supremacy to wars for elimination or survival." In response to this shift, intervention tactics and strategies are undergoing change, in attempts to manage the various forces that challenge global stability.

Types of conflict

Armed conflict has been steadily increasing since the 1970s, but recent trends indicate a slight downturn, as shown in Figure 8–13. Contemporary trends of ethnic, revolutionary, and interstate conflict (Figure 8–14) follow a similar pattern to global warfare totals.

From the end of World War II to 1990, the overall warfare trend was increasing, and in partic-

ular revolutionary and ethnic warfare. However, by the early 1990s, diminishing cold war ideologies provided increasingly less support for this type of warfare thus resulting in its decline. At the same time, interstate conflict rose in number as groups attempted to achieve a "social identity" — the desire to have greater political recognition. The steady increase of interstate conflict indicates how persistent this type of conflict is, since it is based on strongly held nationalist sentiments that are less likely to be solved quickly by war or negotiated agreements. The conflicts in the Balkans and sub-Saharan Africa are examples of this trend.

The Centre for Systemic Peace has recently observed the following global conflict trends:

- There are growing concerns that long-standing disputes or rivalries may escalate the conflict into serious fighting.

- There is a growing trend in separatism, as distinct ethnic groups continue to fight for independence from a central power that will not accept separatism and may use force to stop it.

- Rebel groups have increased control over lucrative resources such as diamonds, oil, and drugs, which are used to pay for weapons.

- Regional warfare tends to continue, or even escalate, without resolution.

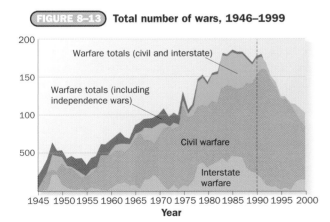

FIGURE 8–13 Total number of wars, 1946–1999

FIGURE 8–14 Trends in violent conflict, 1946–1999

The broken lines on the graphs indicate the ending of the cold war with the breakup of the Soviet Union.

What do the graphs show us about the "shift" from the cold war era to recent times?

Cracks in the Geopolitical Landscape

As the geopolitical landscape shifts, states begin to face new challenges. Just as tectonic forces cause plates (sections of the earth's crust) to move so that cracks emerge on the earth's surface, forces that pose a challenge to global security can also cause "cracks" in our geopolitical landscape. What are the forces that can lead to instability?

Economics

Globalization, with its expansion of **trade blocs** (trade alliances formed among countries in a specific geographic region) and increasing democratization, is a major force that can change economic and political power in the world. The influence of multinational corporations, trade agreements, and organizations such as the International Monetary Fund (IMF) and the World Trade Organization (WTO) create a situation which economist Robert Heilbroner calls **supranational capitalism**. Globalization may force states to alter their political and economic policies while placing additional pressure on them to produce wealth or face opposition. These economic pressures may also contribute in part to the breakup of states such as Czechoslovakia, where resentment grew between Slovakia and the more economically developed Czech Republic.

The ever-increasing gap between "have" and "have not" states is a source of geopolitical instability. Declining incomes in developing countries, expansion of wealth in developed countries, and the **internationalization** of North American culture and consumption patterns has heightened difficulties. Disparity among the world's states has increased the **wealth-poverty polarization**, with the majority of the "have" states in the northern hemisphere and the majority of the "have not" states in the southern hemisphere.

This wealth-poverty polarization is further compounded by the relatively unstable population growth, expanding debts, economic exploitation, and political instability in many developing countries. The situation enables developed nations to continue to control the global economy. The global wealth disparity has also fuelled anti-American feeling in some regions — many view American lifestyles and culture as unattainable ideals. Migration to northern states has increased and in the flurry of activity, has resulted in human smuggling rings, increased border restrictions and, in some cases, backlash against immigrants by residents of host countries.

Global power shift

In the current post-cold war era, the two main poles of influence — the United States and the USSR — have eroded. There has been a diffusion of political, military, and economic power away from these superpowers toward individual states and regions. A new world order is being created, one that has no established parameters. This situation has led to the emergence of a number of economic and political regional power centres (for example, Japan in Asia, Germany in Europe, and the United States in the Americas), as well as opportunities for

FIGURE 8-15 Tokyo, Japan is an example of a major economic and political regional power centre — part of the new world order.

governments — and organizations like the United Nations — to re-define their roles in the global community.

Nevertheless, it is the emergence of rogue states, or states that seek to challenge international norms and order, that are of most concern. The proliferation of weapons of mass destruction (WMD) and conventional weapons have provided these states with the military might to extend their control to other states.

Global terrorism

The attacks on the World Trade Center and the Pentagon in the United States on September 11, 2001 jolted the international community into accepting the significant impact terrorism has on the geopolitical landscape. According to the report "Patterns of Global Terrorism" published by the US State Department's Office for the Co-ordination of Counterterrorism prior to the September 11 attacks, the number of terrorist incidences declined from the mid-1980s until the turn of the century. However, the number of deaths due to acts of terrorism almost doubled to 405 in 2000, and the death toll at the end of 2001 was just under 3000.

Thomas Homer-Dixon, director of the Centre for the Study of Peace and Conflict at the University of Toronto, points to various "root causes" of terrorism:

FIGURE 8–16 The destruction of the World Trade Center in New York City on September 11, 2001 shocked the world. Do you remember where you were when you heard news of this event?

- rising numbers of unemployed young people in urban centres in populous regions such as the Middle East and South Asia
- environmental stress such as droughts and the loss of farmland
- long-standing geopolitical conflicts that remain unresolved
- the existence of international political and economic systems that are more focussed on global economic issues than on human concerns

These conditions can lead to growing discontent and the formation of groups who demand explanations and seek targets upon whom to vent their frustrations.

It was hoped that the post-cold war era, with its push toward greater democracy and market economies, would result in the end of terrorism. In light of these complex root causes and recent attacks, the United States government has concluded that "terrorism continues to pose a clear and present danger to the international community."

Defining terrorism

A major obstacle in dealing with this issue is that global terrorism has no universally accepted definition. The cliché "one person's terrorist is another's freedom fighter" illustrates the wide-ranging interpretations of this term. It is this cliché that is at the centre of the debate as the United Nations General Assembly attempts to define what constitutes terrorism.

As the debate around the definition of terrorism continues, the nature of terrorist attacks is changing. Terrorism was traditionally viewed as a conflict between groups and the state. In some cases, it is **state-sponsored** in that one state fosters and funds terrorism against another state. **Ethnonationalist** or **separatist** groups, like the Basque Fatherland and Liberty (Basque acronym ETA) in Spain, the Irish Republican Army (IRA), the Kurdistan Workers Party (Kurd acronym PKK) in Turkey, or the Tamil Tigers in Sri Lanka, are those that seek to establish their own states. Such groups often use violent tactics such as bombings, kidnappings, hijackings, and assassinations.

While this type of terrorism continues, there has been a rise in terrorism motivated by religion. According to RAND (a contraction of Research and Development) — a non-profit institution and think-tank that helps to improve policy and decision making through research and analysis — **religious terrorists** can be classified by their belief that "violence is first and foremost a sacramental act or divine duty executed in response to a theological demand." For example, Japanese followers of Shoko Asahara, a religious cult, unleashed sarin nerve gas in a Tokyo subway, killing 12 people and wounding almost 4000. It is important to note that this type of terrorism can be domestic or international, and can span various religious beliefs.

It is also important to realize that some groups may have a religious element, but their end goal is mainly political in terms of achieving independence. In contrast, it has been said that religious terrorists do not seek to appeal to any other group apart from their own and see themselves as "outsiders" striving for fundamental changes in the existing social, political, or religious order.

Counterterrorism

The recent increase in terrorist casualties and the growing use of non-conventional weapons have led to rising concerns that future terrorism may become more violent and devastating. There is increasing use of cyberterrorism and non-conventional weapons such as nuclear, chemical, and biological warfare. These weapons of mass destruction allow terrorists to work on a broader international scale, cause a greater loss of life, and make it more difficult for security forces to trace the group's actions after an attack. What should governments and international organizations do in response to this ever-changing issue of global terrorism?

FIGURE 8–17 How is terrorism defined? To some Kurds, the actions of Abdullah Ocalan, in his quest to establish the state of Kurdistan, were that of a "freedom fighter"; others viewed him as a terrorist.

The problem of global terrorism is too complex to be addressed by a single solution. Counterterrorism efforts are varied and complicated: increased airport security measures; greater border and immigration control; the possible use of identity cards; increased dialogue of tolerance; the reduction of anti-Western sentiments through greater economic equality; and attempts to bridge the gap between mainstream and alienated groups within and between societies.

Ethnopolitical movements

Ethnopolitical movements are those in which the political mobilization of minority groups is organized along ethnic lines, or where groups align themselves with political parties or interest groups that promote their ethnicity. This type of movement can also include ethnonationalist interest groups: ethnicity and nationalism are combined. As a new world order takes shape, this growing phenomenon that links cultural, political, and economic ideals plays an important role. Groups striving for independence begin to alter the number and structure of states. Sometimes this can be achieved through peaceful means, such as a referendum. It can lead to conflict, as witnessed with the East Timorese in Indonesia, or the Chechens in Russia.

Resource demands and environmental constraints

When rapid population growth surpasses economic growth and contributes to resource depletion, long-term development becomes difficult to achieve, and political instability can result. Exceeding the world's environmental carrying capacity will affect not only developing countries, but will also impact developed countries, due to their dependence on imported resources. Therefore, conflict may arise over control of strategic resources like oil, minerals, food, and freshwater. Current resource disputes are common in the Middle East, in central Africa (for example, the diamond wars in Angola and Sierra

FIGURE 8–18 A soldier and a land mine victim in the village of Cuito, Angola. What are some of the reasons for Angola's decades-old conflict?

Leone), and in Southeast Asia (where there are territorial disputes over offshore oil reserves). Future conflict may occur in resource-rich, but jointly-claimed regions such as the Antarctic.

11. How has the spatial distribution of political systems changed in our geopolitical landscape since the end of the cold war?

12. Why is the breakup of the superpower structure becoming a concern? Use examples to support your answer.

13. Create your own definition of terrorism. How does the notion of point of view apply to this definition?

14. Briefly explain the causes of terrorism, and outline the main challenges you believe counterterrorism efforts face.

15. Research and compare the human and ecological consequences of military spending in two countries (or regions) currently experiencing conflict.

Case in point — Africa

Although frequent media coverage of war, political coups, and terrorist bombings seem to suggest that all of Africa is in conflict, many parts of the continent are not involved in conflict at all. However, some African countries are presently engaged in conflict because of such factors as resource wealth, ethnicity, or political change. For example, conflicts in the African continent have included wars in Sierra Leone over the control of diamond resources, the border dispute between Ethiopia and Eritrea, and the ethnic civil war in Rwanda and Burundi.

Geopolitical change involving African countries is not new. The exit of colonial rulers often left behind poorly developed governing and economic institutions and infrastructure, thus allowing for another centralized leadership system to emerge, which involved the risks of patronage and corruption.

The cold war era witnessed centralized power, with one leader often dominating a country. However, the cold war also separated countries along an "east-west" (that is, communist and non-communist) divide. Military expenditure and training was conducted by states such as Cuba, China, and the United States, in order to secure ideologically strategic locations for themselves. This military strengthening during the cold war saw the state-to-state transfer of large weaponry such as tanks and aircraft. The arms trade continues today, but is focussed more on smaller weaponry such as rifles and grenade launchers, that are sold through commercial or illegal transactions. The US State Department cites sub-Saharan Africa as one of the world's top regions for importing weapons. In order to achieve peace and stability in conflict-ridden countries like Sierra Leone, the United Nations has imposed arms **embargoes** (restrictions) on the sale and mining of "blood diamonds" (uncut diamonds sold by rebel forces to purchase weapons).

The Organization of African Unity (OAU) was developed in the early 1960s and aimed to "eradicate all forms of colonialism in Africa." In May 2001, the OAU was replaced by a new pan-African organization — the African Union. Its aim is to create a more united Africa by considering the adoption of several common features: currency, foreign policy strategies, and defence and economic programs.

The beginning of the twenty-first century presented a new geopolitical situation. According to the Africa Policy and Economics Department of the British government, by the year 2000, the extent of conflict in Africa was greater than any other region in the world, affecting over half of the countries and 20 percent of the population. In particular, over the past 20 years, sub-Saharan Africa has been more affected by conflict than anywhere else in the world, the Department states.

FIGURE 8–19 **Areas of political instability in Africa**

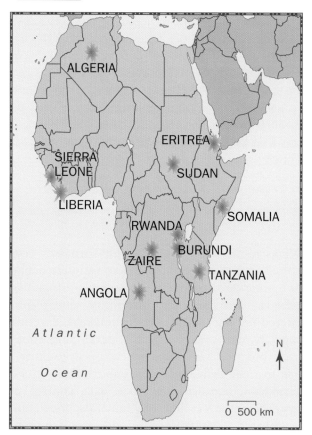

This map outlines the geopolitical situation in Africa in late 2001.

Democratic Republic of the Congo (capital, Kinshasa)
- Independence: from Belgium in 1960 (formerly Zaire)
- Population: 53 624 718 (over 200 ethnic groups — Bantu 45% of the population)
- GDP per capita: PPP US$600
- Main industries: mining (diamonds, copper, zinc), mineral processing, consumer products, cement
- Military expenditure: US$250 million (1997)

Sierra Leone (capital, Freetown)
- Independence: from the United Kingdom in 1961
- Population: 5 426 618 (indigenous African ethnic groups 90%, Creole 10%)
- GDP per capita: PPP US$510
- Main industries: mining (diamonds), petroleum, small-scale manufacturing
- Military expenditure: US$46 million (1996/97)

Ethiopia (capital, Addis Ababa)
- Independence: oldest African independent country at 2000 yrs
- Population: 65 891 874 (Oromo 40%, Amhara and Tigre 32%, other 28%)
- GDP per capita: PPP US$600
- Main industries: food processing, chemicals, metals, beverages, textiles, cement
- Military expenditure: US$138 million (1998/99)

Eritrea (capital, Asmara)
- Independence: from Ethiopia in 1993 (formerly Eritrean Autonomous Region)
- Population: 4 298 269 (Tigrinya 50%, Tigre and Kunama 40%, other 10%)
- GDP per capita: PPP US$710
- Main industries: food processing, textiles, clothing, beverages
- Military expenditure: US$160 million (2000)

South Africa (capitals, Cape Town, Bloemfontein, and Pretoria)
- Independence: from the United Kingdom in 1910
- Population: 43 586 097 (black 75.2%, white 13.6%, people of mixed race 8.6%, Indian 2.6%)
- GDP per capita: PPP — US$8500
- Main industries: mining (world's largest producer of platinum, gold, and chromium), textiles, auto manufacturing, iron and steel, chemicals, fertilizer, foodstuffs
- Military expenditure: US$2 billion (2000/01)

Rwanda (capital, Kigali)
- Independence: from Belgium-administered UN trusteeship in 1962
- Population: 7 312 756 (Hutu 84%, Tutsi 15%, Twa 1%)
- GDP per capita: PPP — US$900
- Main industries: cement, agricultural products, beverages, soap, furniture, shoes, plastic goods, textiles, cigarettes
- Military expenditure: US$58 million (2001)

Nature of conflict in Africa

Unlike previous conflicts against colonial rulers or authoritarian regimes, the nature of conflict throughout African countries has changed recently due to a variety of factors, including collapsing state structures, regionalism, ethnicity, and resources.

Collapsing state structures

Many state structures in Africa are collapsing due to a combination of various political, economic, and territorial forces. Challenges to centralized government controls, combined with economic decline and crippling foreign debt, have left many African countries unable to maintain an infrastructure and provide basic services. This has given rise to independence movements, territorial disputes, and political and military coups. These situations have also created greater political, social, and economic inequality, not just between individuals, but also between groups.

Regionalism

Regionalism leads to a "new" type of conflict in parts of Africa. Where conflicts were once internal, states now find themselves crossing borders and aligning with other states, or ethnic groups, to protect resources, defend territories, or maintain (or overthrow) political control. The war in the Democratic Republic of the Congo has drawn in seven neighbouring states who support either the government or the rebels. Why would an external state interfere in the politics of the Democratic Republic of the Congo? One reason is to demonstrate ideological support for one side or the other by giving political and military assistance. Another reason is that an external state may wish to secure its interests in the Democratic Republic of the Congo's mining, lumber, and billion-dollar diamond industry.

This regional pattern of conflict in Africa is becoming a significant concern as it is spreading to other states such as Sierra Leone, and continues to draw still more states into conflict. In fact, the Africa Policy and Economics Department estimates that, in 2001, there were 14 African countries engaged in only 4 regional conflicts!

Ethnicity

The re-emergence of conflict associated with **genocide** (the systematic attempt to exterminate defined groups of people with different religious or ethnic background) has had devastating effects in countries like the Republic of Rwanda. Rwanda contains two main ethnic groups — the Hutus and the Tutsis. In Rwanda in 1994, three months of genocide left almost 1 million people (Tutsi and any Hutu deemed sympathetic to Tutsis) dead, killed by the Hutu militia. Rwanda has recently experienced some political stability, but a war in the Democratic Republic of the Congo has increased regional tensions between Uganda and Rwanda. Burundi is also familiar with ethnic violence between its own Hutus and Tutsis since its independence from Belgium in 1962.

FIGURE 8–20 Rwandans lay wreaths on a mass grave containing the remains of genocide victims in 1999 — the fifth anniversary of the beginning of the genocide.

Resources

Conflicts over scarce resources such as water and grazing land, as well as conflicts over lucrative resources, have emerged. Countries that are economically dependent on the sale of oil and mineral resources, for example, can experience internal and external struggles to gain control of these resources; military and rebel groups now look to these resources to finance and sustain wars. For example, the Revolutionary United Front (RUF) — a rebel group in Sierra Leone — earns tens of millions of dollars from the country's diamond industry. In Angola, the Union for the Total Independence of Angola (UNITA) uses money earned from illicit diamond mining, as well as from coffee and gold exports, to buy weapons. The government of Angola funds its side of this long-standing war from oil exports.

What are the costs of these conflicts? According to the African Policy and Economics Department of the British government's Department of International Development, some costs include the following:

- By the year 2000, over 14 million people in Africa were either displaced within their own countries or fled their home countries as refugees.
- Conflict in African countries has resulted in greater suffering for civilians, either directly or indirectly, because of famine, disease, or injuries from exploded land mines. It is calculated that over 8 million people in Africa have died over the past 30 years as a consequence of war.
- Conflict has become one of the leading causes of poverty, the destruction of resources and infrastructure, and an overall economic decline in many African countries.
- There are growing incidences of extreme violence in parts of Africa, not only against armed groups, but also toward civilians and entire ethnic groups.
- Military and rebel groups are recruiting children in order to create a separate fighting force. It is estimated that almost two-thirds of the world's "child soldiers" are found in Africa.

Hope for Africa

Although conflict has engulfed many African countries, there are others that have resolved their conflicts. Democracy is spreading throughout the continent, providing some African states with a more accountable and equitable method of governance. For example, South Africa used free and open elections to help bring an end to **apartheid rule**, wherein racial discrimination and separation had been institutionalized by a series of "apartheid laws." Examples of such laws were those prohibiting interracial marriages, outlining "whites-only" jobs, and prescribing where blacks could and could not live. However, a more democratic style of government is not a perfect solution, and the transition from despotic rule to a multiparty system is never easy.

Preventing conflict

Regional and international intervention play an important role in preventing conflict. For example, the African Union works with the United Nations to this end. The International Monetary Fund (IMF), the World Bank, and the European Union (EU) provide training and financial support for post-conflict development.

The United Nations has been involved as a peacekeeper in many African conflicts. However, more recent missions to Sierra Leone and Somalia have hampered the UN's credibility as a peacekeeping force. Specifically, UN peacekeepers were taken hostage in Sierra Leone, and attempts by the UN to organize famine relief were rejected by warlords in Somalia. The UN has also been criticized as slow to respond to the genocide in Rwanda and Burundi. These criticisms have led the UN to re-evaluate its strategies in order to bring about and maintain peace more effectively.

16. Form groups of three or four. As a team of journalists, you have been asked to develop a "behind the scenes" news report on the current geopolitical climate in the African continent. You will need to research your report using a variety of sources and media. The report can be presented orally, visually, or digitally.

    • Your report must contain news briefs on two separate conflicts in Africa, one of which should highlight a country that has either resolved a conflict or has avoided becoming engaged in conflict.

    • Your news briefs should:
      – supply background information about the countries involved
      – highlight where the conflict is taking place
      – outline the reasons for conflict
      – list the groups or individuals involved
      – discuss the human and ecological costs of the conflict
      – describe the actions taken so far to resolve the conflict.

17. Reflecting on the conflicts you examined and those presented by your peers, write a one to two page response to the statement that "conflict in Africa will only continue to spread."

Geopolitical Intervention

As we watch our geopolitical landscape shift via up-to-the-minute satellite images, we can find out what is happening in countries near and far. What should we, as a global community, do when conflict erupts and threatens local, regional, or global security? Any answer to this question involves the important concept of **intervention**. By definition, the word "intervention" means the act of interfering or mediating, especially by one state in the affairs of another. There are two main types of global intervention — military intervention and humanitarian intervention.

Military intervention is the deliberate act of a nation or group of nations to threaten or use military force or coercion to alter an existing conflict where political and civil rights are being violated. This action may be used in conjunction with, but does not directly include, economic intervention tactics such as sanctions against South Africa in response to apartheid or against Iraq following the Gulf War.

Humanitarian intervention is often used in conjunction with military intervention in the internal affairs of a state, in order to protect civilians from human rights violations. It should not be confused with **humanitarian assistance**, which also aims to protect human rights, but usually

FIGURE 8-21 US soldiers in Saudi Arabia during the Gulf War. Under what circumstances do you think it is right for foreign forces to intervene in a country's affairs?

does so through non-government organizations (NGOs) rather than in conjunction with military tactics. Humanitarian intervention can be led by an organization of states, like the North Atlantic Treaty Organization (NATO), or it can be led by one state, as in the intervention by the United States in the Gulf War. Following the invasion of Kuwait by Iraq in 1990, the United States assembled a coalition of traditional allies such as Canada, Britain, and France, as well as Arab states including Saudi Arabia and Egypt. This coalition engaged in the bombing of Iraq — "Operation Desert Storm." After these air and ground attacks, Iraq withdrew from Kuwait and had to abide by the resolutions passed by the UN Security Council.

According to the World Council of Churches, the issue of intervention, and especially humanitarian intervention, faces some important questions, such as:

- Why intervene in some situations and not others?
- Will intervention help resolve the situation and/or protect people's human rights?
- Should the sovereignty of states be upheld by not "crossing borders" or should international laws be rewritten to establish the parameters for intervention?
- How do we determine which rights to protect — human, political, economic, or cultural? Are they all equally weighted?
- Who are we specifically trying to protect (or fight against) in regional conflicts where the identification of the groups involved is not very clear?

- When the global community intervenes, who decides if it is right or wrong — the United Nations, the North Atlantic Treaty Organization (NATO), or the European Union (EU)?
- How long should intervening countries remain involved? Should they assist until the situation is resolved, or until it is stabilized? What if the intervention proves to be ineffective?

The legality of intervention

Global recognition of human rights, and enforcement through the International War Crimes Tribunal — a United Nations special committee to investigate crimes against humanity — makes it more difficult for states who commit such crimes to "hide" behind their boundaries. However, the UN Charter does not currently allow states or nations to attack others based on possible (or even proven) violations of human rights. Article 2(4) of the Charter prohibits the "threat or use of force against" another state. Accordingly, how does one state justify involvement in another's conflict? Because the Charter allows the United Nations Security Council to use force to counter threats to international peace, states have used this argument to justify intervention.

Where does intervention go from here? Bernard Kouchner — a co-founder of Doctors Without Borders — feels that the movement for humanitarian intervention was helped when the United Nations established (in 1988) that humanitarian volunteers like the International Committee of the Red Cross (ICRC) or Médecins Sans Frontières (Doctors Without Borders) should be guaranteed free access to victims, possibly through force. Kouchner also feels that it is now necessary to "take the further step of using the right to intervention as a preventative measure to stop wars before they start and to stop murderers before they kill." He calls for a "decisive evolution in international consciousness," by including developing nations in the decision-making processes of the United Nations, and by extending the right for the "world body" to intervene on behalf of weaker groups.

FIGURE 8–22 Red Cross food aid reaches villagers affected by Serbian-Albanian conflict in Macedonia, in 1999. In 1988, the United Nations established that humanitarian organizations like the Red Cross should be guaranteed access to victims, through force if need be.

International government organizations (IGOs): These are voluntary associations of two or more sovereign states that meet regularly, have full-time staff members, and can be described according to their membership and goals (for example, the United Nations and the North Atlantic Treaty Organization).

United Nations (UN): This IGO was created in 1945 to settle international disputes in order to guarantee world peace, and to enforce its decisions through a system of international laws. Since peacekeeping missions began (in 1948), the UN has launched over 50 missions using troops from 100 countries. The five permanent and ten non-permanent members of its Security Council make intervention decisions. This organization is also responsible for social and economic development programs worldwide.

North Atlantic Treaty Organization (NATO): This organization was formed in 1949 to function as a collective security alliance of "western" states against the threat of communist aggression. Today, it participates in peacekeeping missions in conjunction with the UN.

Non-government organizations (NGOs): These are specialized organizations that work to develop national interests and involvement in world affairs through education programs, support programs, the mobilization of support for global initiatives, and the promotion of international co-operation. Prominent examples include the International Committee of the Red Cross, Amnesty International, and Médecins Sans Frontières.

International Committee of the Red Cross (ICRC): This organization seeks to alleviate the suffering of affected populations by assisting displaced people. It also promotes health by providing people with secure supplies of safe drinking water and medicine.

Amnesty International (AI): This organization was founded in London, England in 1961. It operates as a grassroots activist organization dedicated to freeing prisoners of conscience, gaining fair trials for political prisoners, ending torture of such prisoners, and preventing overall human rights violations.

Médecins Sans Frontières (Doctors Without Borders): This international humanitarian agency, established in 1971, provides emergency medical assistance to populations in danger and in areas that have poor or non-existent basic medical facilities. Médicins Sans Frontières also seeks to raise awareness about crisis situations and the need for greater humanitarian assistance.

The Future of the Geopolitical Landscape

On the one hand, many people speak of the world becoming more and more of a "global village," helped by such factors as feelings of a shared ecological fate and faster, more economical communication and travel. On the other hand, the world continues to fragment along geographic, cultural, ethnic, religious, political, and economic lines, as evidenced by the many examples of geopolitical conflict touched on in this chapter.

The "new code" of intervention is beginning to alter the role that international organizations play in maintaining global security. As a result of all these stresses, strains, and shifts, we are unable to accurately map our future geopolitical landscape. Nevertheless, we can be assured of one thing: that our emerging "new world order" will be subject to frequent change.

18. Why has intervention become such a "hot" global topic?

19. Explain the difference between military intervention and humanitarian intervention.

20. What difficulties does humanitarian intervention encounter in efforts to stop global conflict? Explain.

A KASHMIR NUCLEAR STAND-OFF

The nuclear powers acquired by India and Pakistan have caused their dispute over Kashmir to intensify. India and Pakistan's geographical proximity, intense regional differences, and desire to become the dominant nuclear force in the region increase the threat of a nuclear stand-off.

The former Indian principality of Kashmir was divided between India (predominantly Hindu) and Pakistan (mainly Muslim) when both countries won their independence from Britain in 1947. Under this partition plan, Kashmir was free to accede (formally assent) to becoming part of either India or Pakistan; the ruling prince decided to accede to India. Since 80 percent of Kashmir's population was Muslim, Pakistan was opposed to this decision. This resulted in wars being fought over Kashmir in 1947 to 1949, and again in 1965. Despite the efforts of the United Nations to enforce its 1949 "line of control" (dividing Kashmir into a Pakistani-controlled

area and Indian-controlled area), the conflict continues. The testing of nuclear missiles by India and Pakistan has heightened the Kashmir dispute to one that involves a serious nuclear threat.

As a result of the September 11, 2001 terrorist attacks and subsequent United States military action in Afghanistan, new challenges face this region. How Kashmir will be affected by this situation, if at all, is unclear. On the one hand, greater international attention in the region may either help to increase pressure for a settlement to this decades-long conflict, or it may present new obstacles to a resolution of the dispute.

Achieving stability in Kashmir does not appear to be an easy task. After the December 13, 2001 attack on the Indian Parliament, in which 14 people died, tensions began to escalate. India blamed the attack on what it considered to be Pakistani-sponsored Islamic separatist groups opposed to Indian rule of Kashmir — and charged Pakistan with cross-border terrorism. Pakistan denied these accusations, arguing that India had no proof. By early 2002, the threat of war intensified as India and Pakistan embarked on one of the largest movements of troops in over 15 years, combined with increased gunfire across the disputed border of Kashmir.

The international community is concerned that any further action will lead to devastating conflict between these two nuclear neighbours. China, which controls 20 percent of Kashmir after its violent 1962 border dispute with India and subsequent support of Pakistan's attempts to gain control of Kashmir, is also using a balanced diplomatic approach to urge both sides to decrease the threat of this nuclear stand-off. It is hoped that international diplomatic efforts will diminish tension and pave the way for peace talks concerning Kashmir, and that this will ensure greater regional stability.

FIGURE 8–23 **Kashmir**

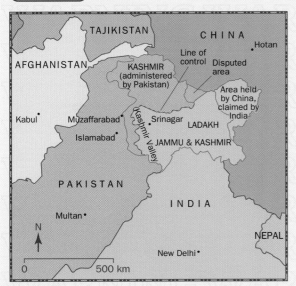

Refer to an atlas. Why is this northern region of India one of the most difficult for India to control?

The political nature of maps

It is possible to use maps for political propaganda (see page 21). Maps can be a very powerful tool in forming people's impressions and opinions about a geopolitical issue: they can play a key role in illustrating borders, conflict, regional inequities, and territorial claims. In his book *How to Lie With Maps*, Dr. Mark Monmonier says, "People trust maps, and intriguing maps attract the eye as well as connote authority. Naive citizens willingly accept maps based on a biassed and sometimes fraudulent selection of facts." Over the years, many governments have deliberately added, removed, or modified features on their maps in order to manipulate or mislead either their citizens or foreign populations. How can cartography be used to misinform?

The essence of cartography

Cartography primarily concerns the concept of mapmaking (*carta* is Latin for map, or chart). The creation of maps is both a science and an art. The science of cartography involves a set of rules that is followed in order to best represent the information. The art of cartography concerns the emotion created by the image produced. Like a painting, a map has the capacity to reach out to the viewer. By manipulating the rules of cartography and complementing this with the right visual and emotional appeal, a map can effectively slant a story or even, in some cases, tell a story that is untrue.

Bias in maps

Perhaps the simplest way to illustrate bias in cartographic information is through the use of colour. Colours have different meanings for different people and these meanings are often culturally defined. Scientifically, red is a very exciting colour, as it grabs one's attention immediately. Artistically, however, in North American culture, the meaning of the colour red is far more complicated — it can mean love, anger, blood, danger, urgency, or heat. In a choropleth map, red draws the eye — and one's attention — even when it colours a relatively small area.

Powerful devices like this can be used to influence a reader's understanding of a map.

Choropleth maps are one of the most popular forms of maps and are frequently misused. In this type of map, specific area divisions such as provinces, countries, or states, are shaded according to specific variables. For example, a map of Ontario might be shaded according to political affiliation: the area in which the majority voted for one party would have a certain colour, while an area in which the majority voted for another party would have a different colour. This mapping technique is often used to show regions (like provinces or countries) in different colours, to distinguish one from another. Using the same colour for different regions is a misuse of the choropleth mapping technique — it allows a cartographer to make a country or province appear as though it is part of a greater whole, even when boundaries are under dispute. A classic example of this is that of China and Taiwan: Chinese maps often depict Taiwan in the same colour as China. The implications are clear.

The positioning of labels on a map is another way in which information may be misrepresented. We usually associate textual information with the object to which it is closest. By adjusting a label so that its position is ambiguous, inappropriate associations can be created.

FIGURE 8–24 Two choropleth maps using identical data

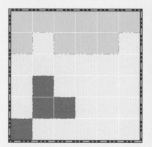
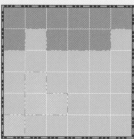

These two maps appear to be different from each other because of the colour scheme used. What might they be used to describe?

There are several ways in which maps can be used to misrepresent spatial information, but none is so bold as simply omitting disputed boundaries, so that the area appears to be undivided. The official map of India and the official map of Pakistan both show Kashmir as being entirely under their respective control. This, of course, is not so — Kashmir is disputed territory that has been divided between India, China, and Pakistan. None of these countries is about to admit that it does not have complete control of Kashmir and therefore, as a statement of national pride, it remains in their control on each of their maps.

Higher-tech manipulation

In wealthier countries — where the technology exists — the use of three-dimensional (3-D) maps is becoming increasingly popular. It is very easy for a 3-D map to be given an exaggerated elevation to make mountains look larger than they really are. Such manipulation has its advantage in discouraging invasion or attack from neighbouring countries or reducing the anxiety of a country's citizens about the likelihood of such an attack. The 3-D map of Kashmir (Figure 8–25) was created by WorldSat International, a Canadian company that specializes in highly accurate imagery.

Now that computers are often used in the process of mapmaking, some additional issues have arisen. Today, anyone can create a professional-looking map, but few people have an appreciation of the power that maps wield. When people with no cartographic training create computerized maps, they can easily make mistakes. Often, a software package will randomly assign colours, label positions, textures, and other cartographic elements inappropriately. If maps are to be respected as forms of communication, then it is important to realize the responsibility that is attached to their creation and use.

FIGURE 8–25 A 3-D map of Kashmir

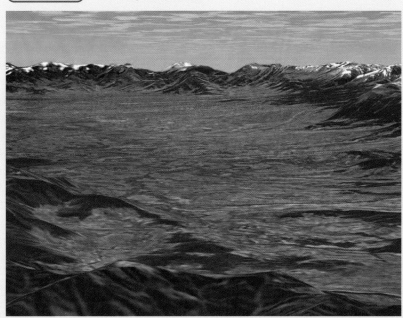

This 3-D image showing the Vale of Kashmir with the Himalayas in the background is accurate. How could it be manipulated to mislead the viewer?

a) Using the Internet, research ten general rules of cartography. Share them with a friend. See how many of them your friend has never heard of.

b) Develop a critical eye for the quality of maps by examining maps that appear in newspapers, magazines, and on television. What is the story that these maps are trying to tell you? How do you know whether or not they are accurate? Select one example. What inferences are being made? What are the implications?

c) Research and examine maps of countries that have disputed boundaries. Are there any examples similar to that of Kashmir, where two countries have claimed the disputed territory? How can mapmakers treat such a dispute without hurting anyone's national pride?

Check out www.gagelearning.com/onthethreshold for an activity on effective cartography.

Case in Point — Afghanistan

In the days following September 11, 2001, the world's attention focussed intensely on Afghanistan. Via television, people watched as an American-led coalition conducted air raids and, along with ground support from the Afghani Northern Alliance, overthrew the ruling Taliban government. Why this foreign intervention in Afghanistan?

The United States viewed the "war on terrorism" as a consequence of the Taliban's refusal to hand over Osama bin Laden and the other members of his group, Al-Qaeda, suspected of planning the attacks on the World Trade Center and the Pentagon on September 11. Along with the United Nations, numerous international organizations have provided humanitarian assistance in Afghanistan.

Governmental and non-governmental intervention is not a new occurrence in the landlocked south Asian nation. Afghanistan has been plagued by decades of conflict, internal hostilities, poverty, earthquakes, and drought.

FIGURE 8–26 **Afghanistan and its neighbours**

Chronology of conflicts

From 1933 to 1973, Afghanistan experienced a time of relative stability under King Mohammed Zahir Shah. King Zahir aimed to modernize and "westernize" the country through development programs and attempts to reform Afghanistan's government into a parliament, with open elections and the establishment of political parties. However, the traditional religious leaders of Afghanistan, led by Zahir's cousin, Muhammad Daoud, opposed these reforms. Daoud staged a coup in 1973 and became the new leader, but his reign was short-lived — he was assassinated in 1978 — and a pro-Communist government came into power.

Afghanistan faced conflict throughout the years 1979 to 1996, beginning with the Afghan-Soviet war. The country became a key battleground during the cold war era when Soviet troops intervened to support the government's fight against the **mujahidin** (various groups of Islamic fighters who had joined forces in a Holy War against the communists). The mujahidin, covertly supported by the United States with over US$2 billion in weapons and money (according to the Center for Defense Information), drove the Soviets out of power by 1989.

However, peace was not achieved. Civil war continued in Afghanistan as mujahidin factions fought against the new Afghan government. By 1993, an Islamic government was established, but the different ethnic factions (Tajiks, Uzbeks, and Pashtuns) failed to unite, and a power struggle among the factions resulted. Further fragmentation of Afghanistan along ethnic lines then occurred, when warlords took control of each region, making it more difficult for a centralized government to maintain control.

Long-standing animosities and acts of discrimination within Afghanistan's multi-ethnic society have contributed to the political instability. For example, Pashtuns of southern and eastern Afghanistan, who are generally Sunni Muslim, are the largest ethnic and linguistic group in the area and have had significant control over Afghanistan for some time. The Tajiks of northeastern Afghanistan and the predominantly Shia Muslim Hazara located in central Afghanistan have attempted to protect what is left of their ethnic role and political influence. Religious tensions have escalated between the dominant Sunni Muslims and minority Shia Muslims. The Uzbeks of the north are often regarded by other ethnic groups as former communists, since many Soviet troops in the Afghan-Soviet war came from Uzbekistan.

The Taliban

The lack of centralized control, ethnically driven civil wars, and widespread poverty enabled a new group to emerge in Afghanistan. By 1995, the Taliban movement — a militia of Islamic fundamentalist students from southern Afghanistan led by Mullah Mohammed Omar, a Pashtun — gathered strength. The group appealed to the Afghan people at a time of great political instability (both ethnic and religious), and promised an end to the civil war, a revival of the economy, and a refusal to deal with regional warlords.

In 1996, the Taliban captured Kabul and declared themselves a legitimate government — one not recognized by many countries worldwide. As a strict Sunni sect, the Taliban implemented their interpretation of Islamic law in an attempt to turn Afghanistan into an Islamic state. Some of the regulations imposed on women included ordering them to quit most occupations and to wear traditional *burqas* (which covered their entire bodies), as well as prohibiting them from seeking education or medical attention.

Regulations were also imposed on men. They were ordered to grow beards and to stay away

At a glance — *Afghanistan*

- Population: 26 813 057
- Total land area: 647 500 km²
- Climate and terrain: arid to semi-arid with cold winters and hot summers; mostly rugged mountains with plains in the north and southwest
- Total fertility rate: 5.79 children born/female
- Infant mortality rate: 147.02 deaths/1000 live births
- Life expectancy: 46.24 years (males 46.97 and females 45.47 years)
- Literacy: total population 31.5% (47.2% males, 15% females)
- Ethnic groups: Pashtun 38%, Tajik 25%, Hazara 19%, minor ethnic groups (Aimaks, Turkmen, Baloch, and others) 12%, Uzbek 6%
- Religions: Sunni Muslim 84%, Shia Muslim 15%, other 1%
- GDP per capita: PPP US$800
- Labour force by occupation: agriculture 70%, industry 15%, services 15%

FIGURE 8–27 A young girl peers out from a group of Afghan women in Kabul, Afghanistan, in 1996.

from women in public places, and were forbidden to approach a woman unless a male family member accompanied her. Taliban leaders argued that these regulations were necessary, as they were based on readings from the Koran. However, the international community considered these regulations to be oppressive and criticized the Taliban for violating basic human rights.

By 1999, the Taliban controlled 90 percent of Afghanistan. Nevertheless, this control was subject not only to international scrutiny, but also to strong opposition from anti-Taliban ethnic factions, namely the United National and Islamic Front for the Salvation of Afghanistan (UNIFSA). This group, more commonly known as the Northern Alliance, contains diverse ethnic and religious groups — Tajik, Uzbek, and Hazara — united by their desire to remove the Taliban.

The end of 2001 witnessed significant geopolitical change in Afghanistan, as the Northern Alliance, supported by a United States-led military coalition, escalated their fight against the Taliban. The United States air raids helped push the Taliban out of all of the cities it once held.

Pondering Afghanistan's future

By late 2001, the Taliban was no longer in power in Afghanistan. A United Nations-sponsored conference was held in Bonn to outline the parameters for an interim government. This conference involved intense negotiations among differing factions within the Northern Alliance,

FIGURE 8–28 Areas occupied by Taliban and Northern Alliance prior to US-led intervention

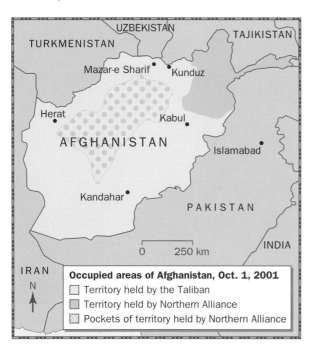

Occupied areas of Afghanistan, Oct. 1, 2001
- ☐ Territory held by the Taliban
- ☐ Territory held by Northern Alliance
- ☒ Pockets of territory held by Northern Alliance

FIGURE 8–29 The International Security Assistance Force commenced in January 2002 under British command with a total of 5000 ground troops from various countries, but is not considered a traditional peacekeeping force, since it can defend itself if fired upon.

FIGURE 8-30 A bag of wheat is unloaded from a truck at a World Food Programme distribution centre in Kabul in December, 2001.

women, and exiles loyal to the former king, Zahir. The Bonn Agreement, signed on December 5, 2001, resulted in the creation of a 24-member interim administration (the Interim Afghan Authority) to govern for six months. Thereafter, a transitional administration established by the Loya Jirga (a council where leading elders from different factions and ethnic groups make decisions) is intended to lead Afghanistan toward a fully representative and elected government.

There is much uncertainty as to whether this "power-sharing" administration will be able to bring stability to a country faced with economic collapse, widespread hunger, ethnic tensions, fighting among warlords, and factional opposition to the interim government.

In order to assist the Interim Afghan Authority in Kabul and its governance in surrounding areas, the United Nations Security Council authorized the establishment of an International Security Assistance Force (ISAF). The Security Council authorized this group to use force and "take all necessary measures" in order to carry out their duties.

Humanitarian intervention

Along with military intervention, the importance of humanitarian assistance to the people of Afghanistan is illustrated by the numerous international organizations that continue to provide services throughout turbulent and often dangerous conditions. Many organizations such as the United Nations World Food Programme have encountered various obstacles, ranging from poor or non-existent infrastructure for the shipment of supplies and food warehouses being taken over by the Taliban, to air and land attacks during the anti-Taliban conflict.

The United Nations warned in late 2001 that "Afghanistan is suffering the world's worst humanitarian crisis." According to the New Internationalist, it is feared that almost one third of the Afghan population could face starvation as a result of food-aid routes and supply depots being cut off, combined with four years of drought. These extreme conditions forced millions of Afghans to flee their homes and seek shelter and assistance in displaced persons' camps within Afghanistan, or in refugee camps in neighbouring countries such as Pakistan.

In response to this critical situation in Afghanistan and to the Bonn Agreement's official request that the United Nations and the international community help in Afghanistan's recovery, many organizations have become involved:

- Médecins Sans Frontières (Doctors Without Borders) has been providing basic medical services in Afghanistan since 1979, and has increased its efforts.

- The World Food Programme is working to replace dwindling food supplies, and the United Nations Children's Fund (UNICEF) and the International Committee of the Red Cross (ICRC) have also been delivering emergency food and medical supplies to Afghanistan, in particular to the rural and central mountain regions.

- Along with distributing food and medical supplies, and reconstructing water and sanitation systems, Oxfam International is assisting with the clearance of what the group estimates to be 7 to 10 million land mines in Afghanistan.

- Since the anti-Taliban conflict, the Canadian International Development Agency (CIDA) has contributed US$16 million in humanitarian aid to Afghanistan, and the Canadian government has pledged additional funds for humanitarian assistance and reconstruction projects in Afghanistan.

21. Create a a timeline to highlight the significant conflicts that have occurred in Afghanistan since 1979. On your timeline, record the dates, the individuals or groups involved, and the outcome of each event.

22. Referring to the ethnic division map (Figure 8–26) and a political map of Afghanistan, explain the influence that geography has on the location of various ethnic groups within Afghanistan.

23. Using evidence from Afghanistan's numerous conflicts, describe how the country's ethnic divisions have contributed to its political instability.

24. What roles are the Bonn Agreement and the International Security Assistance Force intended to play in helping Afghanistan attempt to achieve political stability?

25. As a reporter for a Canadian newspaper, your editor has asked you to write a report outlining Canada's involvement in Afghanistan. Your article should highlight Canada's past and present intervention, both military and humanitarian. (You may wish to consult the Canadian Department of Defence or Foreign Affairs for information.) Remember to give your article an appropriate headline.

26. The United Nations has commissioned you and your team of geopolitical advisors to draft and present a minimum of five key guidelines to help Afghanistan achieve and maintain greater political and social stability. Your guidelines should be clearly explained and should take the following into account:
- current social and economic conditions in Afghanistan
- ethnic and religious divisions
- equitable representation of ethnic groups, in terms of their governing decisions
- role of international military forces
- role of international humanitarian organizations

Once your guidelines have been developed, rank them in order, starting with the guideline that you feel is the most important. Be prepared to justify your ranking. The use of maps, data, and presentation aids is encouraged.

Newland — The boundary challenge

As a member of a specialized group of geopolitical strategists, the United Nations (UN) has commissioned you to outline where the boundary lines should be drawn for the state of Newland.

Newland — located midlatitude on the earth, with a total population of 10 million — has recently been granted independence from a distant colonizing nation called Strassa. Due to diverse ethnic groups within Newland, the United Nations has stressed that the boundaries your team creates must minimize the chance of conflicts arising among the groups, and between Newland and its neighbours. You will make your suggestions to the special envoy of the United Nations Secretary General, who will govern Newland throughout its transition to an independent state.

You may either suggest adding district boundaries within the existing colonial boundary of Newland, or moving the colonial boundary itself in places, or both. Your team will submit a strategy proposal (one to two pages long) explaining:

- why you drew your boundary lines where you did
- your recommendations for helping guide future United Nations intervention in Newland
- any other social or political initiatives you think should be introduced by the envoy of the United Nations Secretary General to encourage a peaceful transition in Newland.

You will also demarcate a map of Newland, showing the boundaries you describe in your strategy proposal. Use the map and the information on Newland to develop your recommendations.

Major ethnic groups in Newland

NEPS (35 PERCENT OF THE POPULATION)

- The Neps were the first settlers in Newland and are the most populous group within this territory.

- They feel that the capital of independent Newland should be named after them and should be located on the Basolt River.
- They are mostly farmers and cattle raisers, but are interested in expanding their control of nearby oil and gold deposits.
- They are considering challenging the old colonial boundary with Flanland to include the Neps who reside within Flanland.

MINS (10 PERCENT OF THE POPULATION)

- The Mins are mostly farmers who feel that it is unjust that some of the more powerful Neps have claimed the better-quality farmland along the coastal plain.
- They are concerned about their livelihood and want to ensure that the Bins do not take over the remaining farmland.

BINS (10 PERCENT OF THE POPULATION)

- The Bins are also mostly farmers, but want to expand their fishing industry by securing coastal areas and the waterways between the mainland and the outer islands.
- They feel strongly that they should have full control over their land to prevent the Mins from taking over their farmland, especially on the outer islands, which contain ancient Bin burial grounds.

MOBOLS (10 PERCENT OF THE POPULATION)

- The Mobols are concentrated along the coast and are predominantly fishermen.
- They believe strongly that the outer islands of Newland should belong to them because these are valuable fishing grounds and provide the Mobols with their livelihood.
- They also want to secure waterways around the outer islands, especially to the coral reefs, in order to expand their lucrative fishing industry.

SOARES (5 PERCENT OF THE POPULATION)

- The Soares are a sparsely populated group who live within the rain forest area.
- They are very environmentally conscious people who are trying to prevent the neighbouring state of Tropia from cutting down the shared tropical rain forests for lumber exports. The Newland Soares rely on the Tropian Soares to protest the Tropia government's decision to allow more logging.
- They are also concerned that major flooding will occur if the Butes proceed with plans to construct hydro-electric dams along the tributaries of the Butaine River, thus destroying the habitat for hundreds of rare plant and animal species.

BUTES (25 PERCENT OF THE POPULATION)

- The Butes are the second-largest, but most wealthy group and are spread throughout Newland.
- They will go to any lengths — including the use of military action — to secure their resource wealth (gold, oil, diamonds, and hydro-electric power).
- They strongly believe that these resources belong solely to them since they occupied the resource areas at the time of independence.

STANDIES (5 PERCENT OF THE POPULATION)

- The Standies are a small group of nomadic herders scattered throughout the interior.
- They were the first group to occupy any part of Newland and view this area to be their sacred homeland.
- They cannot afford to develop oil resources within this area, but are fearful that the more powerful Neps or Butes will take control. They are tired of being "pushed around" by the Neps and Butes and want a land agreement to protect their ancestral roots.

Neighbouring states

FLANLAND

Flanland is politically stable, but is worried that the ethnic mobilization of the more powerful Neps in Newland will spread across the border. The Neps make up a significant proportion of Flanland's population and the group frequently crosses the border to move their cattle to prime grazing areas. Flanland is also worried that the Newland Neps will demand that their borders be redrawn, since these grazing lands once belonged to them.

TROPIA

Tropia, also politically stable, plans to begin cutting down its rain forests for lumber exports in order to boost the economy. Since the boundary between Tropia and Newland is not clearly marked in the rain forest area, lumber companies pay little attention to where they cut down trees and take some from Newland.

BIGLAND

Geographically, Bigland is large, but lacks essential resources for its population and for sustaining its economy. Bigland's predominant group, the Biggles, are in desperate need of freshwater and are looking north to Lake Iris for help. They are also interested in the gold deposits near the Newland/Bigland border. Due to a shared cultural heritage, the Butes are inclined to help the Biggles. However, in return for resources, the Butes want the Biggles to join them in defending their claim to resources and to engage in military action if resources are threatened. The government of Bigland is concerned that an alliance with the Butes will escalate an already unstable situation in Newland. It is not comfortable with this arrangement, but feels it has no other choice if it wants to obtain crucial resources.

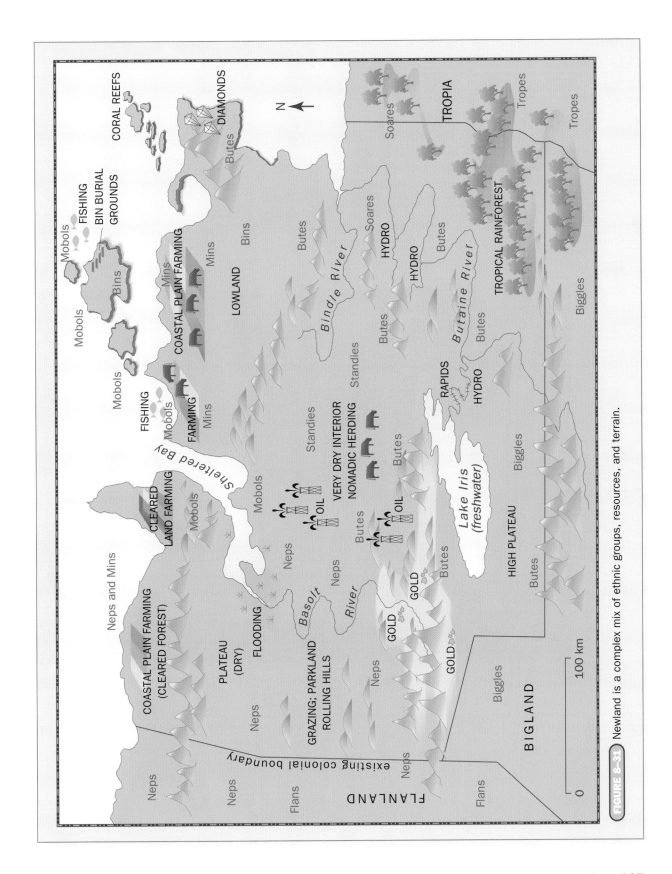

FIGURE 8–31 Newland is a complex mix of ethnic groups, resources, and terrain.

Geopolitics **237**

CHAPTER 9

Economic Globalization

FIGURE 9–1 What is the basis for this angry confrontation? Use the evidence in this photo to answer this question.

- Demonstrate an understanding of the interdependence of countries within the global economy.
- Analyse the economic and environmental consequences for selected countries of colonialism in the past and economic colonialism in the present.
- Demonstrate an understanding of how quality of life and employment prospects are related to the global economy.

- Describe the structure, membership, and activities of an international economic alliance.
- Evaluate the performance of a selected transnational corporation with respect to the promotion of environmental sustainability and human rights.
- Explain how new technology affects employment and resource management.

Rapid change has become part of everyday life. When Roberta Bondar was growing up in Sault Ste. Marie, Ontario, she dreamed that one day she would look down on earth from space. As a result of fast-paced technological advances, her dream became reality when, in 1992, she flew on the space shuttle *Discovery* and became Canada's first female astronaut. Dr. Bondar, a medical specialist in neurology, became a national hero and a role model for countless young Canadians. Today, not only specialists are able to fly into space; anyone with the financial means can book a trip on board a space shuttle for the trip of a lifetime.

Perhaps the most significant change that has occurred recently is the way in which people view the world. The prevalence of rapid, economical communication and travel makes it seem as if the planet is "shrinking." The cell phone — which was an unusual item in the 1990s — is now a common possession, almost like a watch or a wallet. Likewise, the Internet — which is now offered as a standard utility in many homes — has become a gateway to the world, utilized by more and more global citizens. Words like "globalization" and "global village" have entered our language, as people increasingly see the planet as one big, shared community.

FIGURE 9–2 Dr. Roberta Bondar — a Canadian hero — prepares to board the *Discovery*.

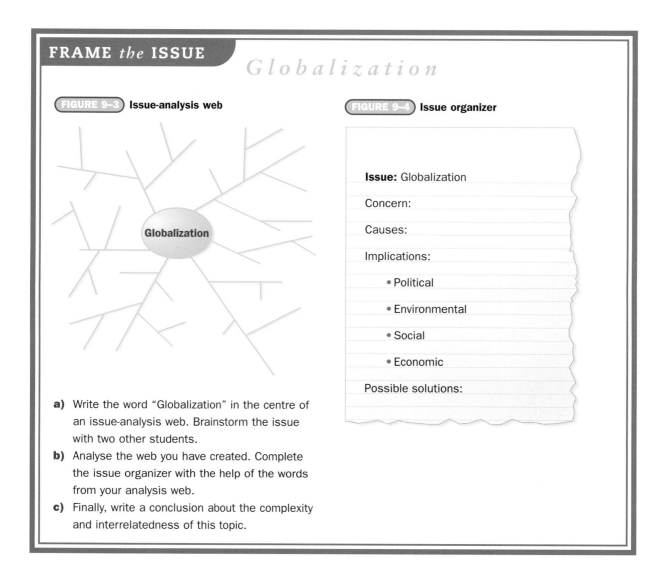

FIGURE 9–3 Issue-analysis web

Globalization

FIGURE 9–4 Issue organizer

Issue: Globalization

Concern:

Causes:

Implications:

- Political

- Environmental

- Social

- Economic

Possible solutions:

a) Write the word "Globalization" in the centre of an issue-analysis web. Brainstorm the issue with two other students.

b) Analyse the web you have created. Complete the issue organizer with the help of the words from your analysis web.

c) Finally, write a conclusion about the complexity and interrelatedness of this topic.

Globalization — Our Shrinking World

The Internet connects people around the world and provides an unprecedented forum for the **dissemination** (dispersal) of knowledge and information. Nua, an Ireland-based Internet statistics source, predicts that over 1 billion people will be online within the next five years.

With new wireless connections imminent, the communications revolution is gaining speed. Wireless communications will allow countries like China and India, which have weaker landline infrastructures, to support rapid communication development. As usage increases, the costs of wireless technologies and communications will decrease, making them accessible to more people. Technologies that are currently available only in richer, developed countries will quickly spread. Computers will process information at increasingly greater speeds.

The communications revolution will continue to have many impacts on how we live and relate to one another. Telecommunications have already made a lot of travel unnecessary — rather than travelling to meet business associates in person, many businesspeople choose to hold teleconferences.

In the future, personalized devices may be created using computer chips that automatically decode languages and make global communication truly integrated. Political boundaries may become obsolete, as information and economic transactions move across them. The world may have to rethink the complex nature of politics and boundaries, and of having separate countries and laws. New international orders and laws will emerge. Already, large-scale mergers of businesses, and trading alliances and agreements among countries, are becoming more common.

We know that the world cannot actually shrink, but we can certainly travel around it much faster and send information to far-off destinations at incredible speed. Business can operate on a global (rather than on a local or regional) basis, which vastly expands a company's pool of potential customers. As the planet seems to shrink, opportunities to share knowledge and innovate increase. These changes have led to some interesting trends, including what has become known as **globalization**.

Globalization, as defined by the International Labour Organization (ILO), is a process of growing interdependence between all people on the planet. Trade, investments, and governance link people together economically and socially; market liberalization, faster communication, and better transportation technologies speed the process.

Globalization is a world issue, however, because it is controversial. Many people and interest groups see it as a threat to the world's poor, and as a conspiracy between multinational corporations and the rich to exploit the poorer markets of the world. These critics worry that the proponents of globalization have no regard for protecting the world's environment or saving its diminishing resources. Meanwhile, supporters of globalization see it as a way in which true equality and prosperity will reach all corners of the world, bringing with it international peace and co-operation.

FIGURE 9–5 In 1967, Marshall McLuhan, a Canadian communications theorist, wrote that the developments in communication (telecommunications, advances in transportation technology, and the use and power of computers) had caused the world to become a "global village" — a phrase that has been widely adopted.

1. In what four ways have technologies made you more "globally connected" or more of a "global citizen"?

2. Research one example of cutting-edge technology. Present a "technological snapshot" to the class, explaining the new technology and outlining the ways in which it will add to the increasing globalization (interconnectedness) of the planet.

3. Globalization refers to the growing interdependence of the world's people and regions. Reflect on what you have learned so far in this course about how people and regions on the planet are becoming more dependent on each other. State five ways in which the world is becoming more interdependent.

The History of Trade

Countries can either consume what they produce in goods and services, or they can sell their products on the international market. Every country in the world imports the things it needs from other countries. In this regard, we have long been an interdependent world.

- European countries began assembling shipping fleets in the seventeenth and eighteenth centuries, so that they could enrich themselves with resources found in distant lands; *colonies were established* to bring these lands (and their resources and people) under European control.

- Exploitation of colonies continued well into the last century, until the colonies gained independence. *Trade that had essentially been a one-way flow was gradually replaced by the reciprocal (two-way) movement of goods, services, and people.* Trading reached a peak during the first half of the twentieth century which, to a limited extent, was the first age of globalization. World trade was still dominated by the rich, industrialized countries and still followed the predominant pattern of bringing resources from the developing world to developed countries.

- During the 1950s, a new phenomenon emerged: *countries started building trade barriers.* In order to guard their internal industries and jobs, countries began to introduce **tariffs** (trade taxes) to ensure that local products were cheaper than the products of foreign merchants. This led to tariff wars, ignited by feelings of national pride and **protectionism** (policies that encourage the consumption of local goods rather than imported ones). Also, during the cold war era between 1945 and the late 1980s, western democracies and eastern communist regimes established political empires and placed limitations on political and economic contact. Nationalism and political ideologies became more important than open contact and trade. Many people in China and the (former) Soviet Union were deliberately isolated from global contact, and the financing of weapons and armies became a priority for many governments.

- It was not until the end of the last century that countries once more began to co-operate and expand both their political and economic alliances. This *movement toward an international community* received a huge boost through the creation and development of such organizations as the United Nations (UN). The movement gained strength in 1948 when 23 countries signed the General Agreement on Tariffs and Trade (GATT). The member countries agreed to meet regularly and discuss ways to expand trade, and to settle trade disputes.

FIGURE 9–6 The Chinese Trade Minister signs the document that makes China part of the World Trade Organization.

This organization evolved to become the World Trade Organization (WTO) with more than 140 member countries, 100 of which are developing countries. The World Trade Organization oversees 90 percent of all world trade. As an organization, it has seen worldwide tariffs reduced to about one-tenth of what they were when the General Agreement on Tariffs and Trade was first established.

Whereas political organizations have ensured that democracy is the dominant global trend, trade organizations — along with giant multinational corporations — have become important vehicles through which countries communicate, and have become the dominant force in globalization. As such, they are also the target of criticism from groups angered by what they see as a lack of attention to such things as fair labour practice, tough environmental policies, and plans to combat poverty.

Expanding world trade

Global trade continues to flourish. According to the World Bank, between 1987 and 2000 the value of a country's trade relative to its gross domestic product rose from 27 percent to 40 percent in developed countries, and from 10 percent to 18 percent in developing countries.

Technology is making the world seem a smaller place; our increasing financial interdependence also greatly motivates the process of globalization. Today, money flows around the world electronically at an extraordinary pace and in large amounts, due to three main factors:

- growth in the amount and scope of international trade
- flow of money as an investment from one country to another, known as **foreign direct investment**
- movement of money from one international investment market to another, known as **international capital flow**

Companies make foreign direct investments for many reasons. For example, there may be lower costs for labour and materials in another country. Or perhaps, by opening a branch plant, companies can be closer to a new or growing market for their product. The World Bank states that between 1988 and 2000, the total amount of foreign direct investment tripled from US$192 billion to over US$620 billion. Usually, the majority of this investment flows from one developed country to another: for example, a German company may set up an operation in Canada. Only 25 percent of all foreign direct investment takes place in developing countries.

Banking and investment services are the perfect example of how technology has supported the process of globalization. Individuals and organizations can shift capital, stocks, and bonds from one country to another at any time of the day or night through Internet connections. A vast amount of capital flows around the globe on a daily basis, seeking the best opportunities for economic growth. This is a source of concern. Some economists believe that because of these flows, confidence in a country or region can quickly grow or evaporate, perhaps based solely on rumour and momentum. According to Corpwatch, a non-government organization (NGO) that critically monitors the work and role of international corporations, about US$1.8 trillion is traded each day on foreign exchange markets, 95 percent of which is in short-term investments — investors seeking a quick profit.

4. Review the International Labour Organization's definition of globalization on page 241. Suggest three ways in which the world is interconnected both socially and economically.

5. Develop a timeline on which you annotate trends and developments in global trade over time to the present day.

6. Describe the similarities and differences between the former General Agreement on Tariffs and Trade and the present World Trade Organization.

	1970	1975	1980	1985	1990	1995	2000	2002
GDP (PPP)	4399.6	7449.8	12889	19130.8	26820.5	33996.4	44548.8	50612.4
Exports of goods and services	393.4	1061.1	2400.9	2344	4267.2	6263	7707.2	8683.4
Imports of goods and services	−394.2	−1069.8	−2407.1	−2357.9	−4297.2	−6165.9	−7717.4	−8812.7

7. Define the term "foreign direct investment." What motivates corporations to participate in this type of investment?

8. a) For each of the three categories in Figure 9–7, calculate the percentage growth between each five-year period from 1970 until 2000.

   b) Between 1970 and 2000, when was there the most growth in each of the three categories? How would you explain this pattern?

Free Trade and Protectionism

There are a number of advantages in opening up and freeing the world's economy. Organizations such as the World Bank believe that this freedom allows a greater number of countries to participate in trade, which should then lead to economic development, which should then reduce the gap between "have" and "have not" countries. However, critics of this view believe that this in fact does not happen, and that those countries already dominating world trade will continue to do so. Opening up other markets allows dominant countries to control an even larger proportion of trade, while the poorest countries remain excluded or are exploited. For many poor countries, crippling debt repayments need to be made before they can engage in any real development or expanded trade.

At one extreme, a country may believe that trade should be open to anyone, and that products and services should flow between countries without the restriction of tariffs or quotas. Such a country is not concerned about job losses within domestic industries. It believes that foreign competition encourages its own industries to strive for higher-quality products at a lower cost; as a result, the consumer gets a better deal. These are the ideals of **free trade**. To facilitate the trading process, some countries enter a **free trade agreement** that spells out which goods and services are (or are not) exempt from tariffs and **import quotas** (limits on the quantity of imports allowed).

At the other extreme, a country can decide that it does not need to trade much with other countries. For example, it may want to protect its own industries from the risk of cheaper products flooding its market, or it may want to control the type and quality of imports. In such a case, the country would adopt a policy of **isolationism**. It would introduce high tariffs and complex regulations to deter foreign producers and competitors from entering its economy. A country that adopts such an absolute protectionism policy (the opposite of free trade) would be practising **autarky**.

Trade agreements

Few countries could fit either of the extremes of total free trade or total autarky. North Korea and Cuba come close to practising autarky; although they still trade internationally, their trade partners were chosen for their ideology and support of state socialism.

Free trade areas

There are even fewer examples of completely free trade. The European Union (EU) has been slowly moving toward this ideal. Canada, the United States, and Mexico institutionalized free trade with the **North American Free Trade Agreement** (NAFTA), which came into effect on January 1, 1994. This pact calls for the gradual removal of tariffs and other trade barriers on goods produced and sold in North America.

Exactly how free are these free trade areas? Many products that flow between countries are subject to tariffs and quotas, both within the European Union and under the North American Free Trade Agreement. For example, softwood lumber exports from Canada to the United States were long considered a "subsidized" product by the Americans. If a product receives grants, soft tax-law treatment, or direct subsidies, it can be argued that it is not competing fairly with similar products within a free market.

In retaliation for this so-called "subsidization," the United States added a 19 percent import tariff on Canadian softwood lumber imports in 2001. Soon after the introduction of this tariff, Canadian loggers began losing jobs — evidence that protectionism is still alive and well, even between partners in a "free trade" area.

FIGURE 9–8 Companies logging in Canada pay a stumpage (licence to cut trees on government-owned land). This fee is considered too low by many Americans in the logging industry, and is therefore viewed as a subsidy to Canadian logging companies. Canadians counter that logging companies in the United States have higher costs only because there is greater competition for forests in the United States, which are mostly on privately owned land.

Frame of reference

Tariff: This is a tax or duty placed on imported products or services. It is an extra cost that is added to an imported item, thus making domestic products cheaper for consumers. Tariffs therefore protect domestic businesses and their workers' jobs from foreign competition.

Quota: This is a fixed limit on the quantity of goods that a country is allowed to sell to another country. Quotas often accompany tariffs. A tariff may be set for a portion of a quota, and this tariff may then rise or fall for the remaining amount of goods within the quota.

Free trade: This is a form of trade between countries where there is an absence of tariffs and import quotas on goods and services. Countries and groups of countries sometimes enter a "free trade agreement." This agreement spells out which goods and services are or are not exempt from tariffs and import quotas.

Autarky: This is practised when a country strives to be self-sufficient and isolated from other countries. Countries that practise autarky want to "go it alone" in order to achieve economic independence.

Protectionism: This occurs when countries take action to protect their domestic industries and employment by placing restrictions, quotas, or tariffs on goods and services that could be imported from other countries. As with autarky, policies of protectionism are the opposite of free trade.

Trade blocs

Many countries enter into trade blocs with other countries. This allows them to create larger regional markets for themselves, and share and solve local trading problems. These blocs are often based on regional geography, where countries have a number of things in common. For example, five Southeast Asian countries (Indonesia, Singapore, Malaysia, the Philippines, and Thailand) formed the Association of Southeast Asian Nations (ASEAN) in 1967. This organization was formed to allow economic co-operation and development in the hope that it would bring peace and prosperity to the region, which at that point was badly divided ideologically and politically. Since its formation, other countries have joined the organization: Brunei, Vietnam, Laos, Myanmar, and Cambodia.

Multilateral agreements

A controversial aspect of many trade agreements is the use of a clause called a **Multilateral Agreement on Investment (MIA)**, which is an agreement designed to allow capital and investment to flow more freely between countries. The agreement restricts laws within a country that could prevent or hinder foreign investments being made. It is currently found in the North American Free Trade Agreement, and the Organization for Economic Co-operation and Development (OECD) hopes to expand this clause to all its member countries. Critics suggest that the clause would allow companies to sue governments if they felt that their trading powers had been compromised, and that it would remove power from a sovereign country and give it to large, international corporations instead.

9. Write a memo from the World Trade Organization to the finance minister of a country that is being accused of practising protectionist trade policies. This country has put a 20 percent tariff on banana imports. The only exception to this tariff are two small countries, former colonies that still have close economic ties to the protectionist country, and whose major export is tropical fruit. In your memo, explain why open free trade is better than protectionism.

10. In addition to the North American Free Trade Agreement, select two other trade blocs from the top ten (see Figure 9–10), including one from Asia. Make a comparison chart for the three trade blocs using the following criteria: a brief history; a list of member countries; major exports; major imports; and future expansion plans. Research the trade blocs using Internet search engines. Each of these organizations has its own Web site.

11. Develop a graph that shows the level of trade for the top 20 countries from Figure 9–11. Each country should have two bars — one for exports and another for imports. Write a summary of the patterns reflected in the completed graph.

12. Develop a graph based on the data in Figure 9–11 that illustrates regional trade patterns, for example, Europe, Asia, and so on. Write a summary about these trade patterns.

FIGURE 9–9 The total population of the Association of Southeast Asian Nations region is more than 500 million people, stretched over 4.5 million square kilometres. The total gross national product of this trade region is US$685 billion and these ten countries have a combined trade of over US$720 billion. Their regional, combined market contains 100 million people more than North America. This allows them to produce products on a scale that enables them to compete with other giant trading regions such as North America or Europe.

FIGURE 9–10 Top ten trade blocs by size of exports (US$ billions)

Rank	Trade bloc	1970	1980	1990	1990
1	Asian Pacific Economic Co-operation (APEC)	58	357	901	1904
2	European Union (EU)	76	456	981	1376
3	East Asian Economic Caucus (EAEC)	9	98	282	621
4	North American Free Trade Agreement (NAFTA)	22	102	226	581
5	Association of Southeast Asian Nations (ASEAN)	1	13	28	81
6	Latin American Integration Association (LAIA)	1	10	12	35
7	Bangkok Agreement	0.1	1	4	15
8	Southern Cone Common Market (MERCOSUR)	0.4	3	4	15
9	Central European Free Trade Agreement (CEFTA)	1	7	4	13
10	Gulf Co-operation Council (GCC)	0.1	4	6	7

FIGURE 9–11 Top 20 leading exporters and importers in merchandise trade, 2000

Rank	Exporters	Value (US$ billions)	Rank	Importers	Value (US$ billions)
1	United States	781.1	1	United States	1257.6
2	Germany	551.5	2	Germany	502.8
3	Japan	479.2	3	Japan	379.5
4	France	298.1	4	United Kingdom	337.0
5	United Kingdom	284.1	5	France	305.4
6	Canada	276.6	6	Canada	244.8
7	China	249.3	7	Italy	236.5
8	Italy	237.8	8	China	225.1
9	Netherlands	212.5	9	Hong Kong, China	214.2
10	Hong Kong, China	202.4	10	Netherlands	198.0
11	Belgium	186.1	11	Mexico	182.6
12	South Korea	172.3	12	Belgium	173.0
13	Mexico	166.4	13	South Korea	160.5
14	Taiwan	148.3	14	Spain	153.5
15	Singapore	137.9	15	Taiwan	140.0
16	Spain	113.7	16	Singapore	134.5
17	Russia	105.2	17	Switzerland	83.6
18	Malaysia	98.2	18	Malaysia	82.2
19	Sweden	86.9	19	Sweden	72.8
20	Saudi Arabia	84.1	20	Australia	71.5

Multinational Corporations

Trade statistics usually consist of import and export data for countries. When people look at these figures, they naturally assume that the countries themselves are the backbone of global trade, but this is not the case. Trade takes place between companies, not countries. The companies that dominate international trade generally have two things in common — they are international in nature and are extremely large.

These international companies — **multinational corporations** — have a tremendous impact on the global economy and on the lives of the millions of people who are influenced by their decisions. A multinational corporation (called a "transnational corporation" in Europe) is a company that has operations in more than one country. For example, the oil company Royal Dutch Shell refines its oil in 34 countries and sells petroleum in over 100 countries; the giant grain company, Cargill, markets and distributes grain and grain products in 54 countries; and Nortel, Canada's multinational giant, operates and sells its telecommunications products in more than 150 countries.

As of 2001, there were 63 000 multinational corporations in the world, operating a further

FIGURE 9–12 In a year, Wal-Mart receives more in revenues than the government of Turkey.

690 000 smaller affiliate companies. Most multinational corporations run relatively small operations in a few countries; other multinationals, such as Wal-Mart, are gigantic. Decisions made by multinational corporations are often viewed as being just as important as those made by governments, because the impacts of these decisions can be far-reaching for many countries. Their power therefore extends beyond international boundaries.

Issue briefing

Global economics

- Of the world's top 100 "economies," 51 are corporations.
- Of the 100 largest multinational corporations, 99 are from industrialized countries.
- North America, Japan, and Western Europe provide the home base for nearly all of the multinational corporations.
- The wealthiest 20 percent of companies today earns 74 times as much as the poorest 20 percent, as opposed to only 30 times more in 1960.

- The richest 20 percent of the world's population produces 86 percent of the world's domestic product. The poorest 20 percent of the world's population produces only 1 percent of the world's domestic product.
- Of the top 50 firms (in terms of revenue), 24 are located in the United States, 9 are in Japan, and 6 are in Germany.
- The top 10 corporations hold a global market share of 86 percent of telecommunications, 85 percent of pesticides, and 70 percent of computers.
- The top 5 automobile manufacturers produce 60 percent of all automobiles.

Anatomy of a multinational company

There is some debate about what makes a company multinational. Some say that a company becomes multinational only when groups from two or more countries own a company. For example, Shell is an oil company owned by both Dutch and British interests. Others believe that a company becomes multinational when its parent company has branches of its operation in other countries. For example, the Nestlé Corporation is centred in Geneva in Switzerland. However, it operates 509 factories in 83 countries. Nestlé's annual revenue is approaching US$50 billion, which is an astonishing amount for a privately owned company.

Once a company becomes multinational, it generally follows one of two paths — it either forms a geocentric company or a polycentric company. A **geocentric company** targets the world as its open market — the products it makes are designed for universal world consumption. For example, McDonald's Corporation is a geocentric company that prides itself on the uniform nature of its food. A **polycentric company** focusses more on manufacturing products designed for local markets and needs. In both cases, control and decision making within a multinational corporation usually occur at its international headquarters.

Benefits of becoming multinational

What makes a company decide to become multinational in the first place? It has to have sound business reasons before it commits itself to foreign direct investment. Expanding sales into foreign countries may be difficult because of protectionist tariffs and set quotas. To circumvent these sorts of problems, a company may decide to open branch plants in other countries. This allows them to avoid the trade laws, tariffs, or quotas that would have been applied to their imports because their products will not be imported — they will be manufactured domestically. When companies in the United States found it difficult to penetrate the European Community (now the European Union), they built branch plants in many European countries. Similarly, Japanese car manufacturers have built assembly plants in Canada (Honda at Alliston, Ontario, and Toyota at Cambridge, Ontario).

What are the main benefits of becoming multinational?

- The *market for products is expanded*. Once a company experiences success in a domestic market, its management — in a push to increase sales — may look for markets in other countries, to increase the number of potential customers.

- *Lower costs may be available* for such things as materials, land, or labour, especially in developing countries. For example, branch companies may be in closer proximity to many raw materials that previously had to be shipped back to their manufacturing centres — they can manufacture goods locally.

FIGURE 9–13 McDonald's, a prime example of a geocentric multinational, also offers some regional variations — beer in Europe, the McLobster sandwich in Nova Scotia, and non-beef burgers in India.

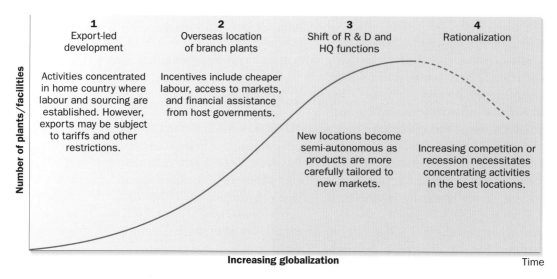

FIGURE 9–14 Multinational growth patterns

1 Export-led development

Activities concentrated in home country where labour and sourcing are established. However, exports may be subject to tariffs and other restrictions.

2 Overseas location of branch plants

Incentives include cheaper labour, access to markets, and financial assistance from host governments.

3 Shift of R & D and HQ functions

New locations become semi-autonomous as products are more carefully tailored to new markets.

4 Rationalization

Increasing competition or recession necessitates concentrating activities in the best locations.

Number of plants/facilities

Increasing globalization

Time

Typical growth patterns of multinationals follow the sequence shown here.

- Strict business and environmental *regulations may not apply in different countries*, so companies may not have to spend huge amounts of money for "environmentally friendly" manufacturing processes.

- It may be *easier to acquire or merge with competitive companies that operate in other countries*, rather than to compete with them. The merger between Daimler (Germany) and Chrysler (United States) means that these two companies are no longer competing with one another in Europe and North America.

- The governments in some countries may be pleased to help foreign companies open local operations because of the employment opportunities this will bring. Help and encouragement may take the form of *incentives and grants*.

- *Borrowing money may be less expensive* and easier to do in foreign economies.

FIGURE 9–15 Foreign-owned corporations in Canada*

Ownership region	Number	Percent
United States	6 819	53.6
European Union (EU)	3 387	26.6
Pacific Rim	1 350	10.6
South America	27	0.2
Mexico	20	0.2
Other	1 122	8.8
Total foreign-owned	**12 725**	

* Corporations with gross revenue of at least US$15 million or assets over US$10 million

Eventually, companies located in foreign countries may become so successful that parts of their headquarters' functions — such as the research and development department, for example — are splintered off and relocated. According to Statistics Canada (StatsCan), nearly 13 000 companies in Canada are foreign-owned, which makes them **branch plants**. Because of this, it has often been said that Canada has a **branch-plant economy**. Figure 9–15 shows the ownership pattern of these foreign-owned companies.

FIGURE 9–16 Top ten companies in the world by revenue, 2000

Company/Country	Revenues (US$ millions)
Exxon Mobil	210 392
Switzerland	207 000
Austria	203 000
Bangladesh	203 000
Sweden	197 000
Wal-Mart Stores	193 295
Ukraine	189 400
General Motors	184 632
Ford Motor Company	180 598
Portugal	159 000
Vietnam	154 400
Chile	153 100
DaimlerChrysler	150 070
Royal Dutch/Shell Group	149 146
British Petroleum (BP)	148 062
Venezuela	146 200
Denmark	136 200
Romania	132 500
Czech Republic	132 400
General Electric	129 853
Mitsubishi	126 579
Norway	124 100
Peru	123 000
Toyota Motor	121 416

The gross national incomes of selected countries have been entered in this table, for comparison.

A multinational may have to "shrink" due to circumstances such as competition, local recessions, and/or changes in technology. When this occurs, the parent company has tough decisions to make. It must attempt to **rationalize** itself into a more streamlined operation, cutting back on those parts of its operations that are less profitable.

The non-government organization Corpwatch has noted how quickly some of these companies pass through stages of growth. As recently as 1990, there were five companies that were not listed in the top ten largest companies, but which are now among the world's leaders: Microsoft, Cisco Systems, Lucent Technologies, Intel, and the fastest grower of them all — Wal-Mart Stores, Inc.

Multinational giants

Some multinational corporations are immensely wealthy. In 2000, the world's top four revenue earners (Exxon Mobil Corp., Wal-Mart Stores Inc., General Motors Corp., and the Ford Motor Company) all had revenues greater than the gross national income of Portugal, Vietnam, or Chile. (See Figure 9–16.) Canada's gross national income of US$614 billion is only about 3 times the revenue of Wal-Mart Stores Inc.

13. Define the term "multinational corporation."

14. Explain the difference between "geocentric" and "polycentric" trade patterns.

15. Explain the normal growth pattern of multinational corporations.

16. Suggest three advantages and three disadvantages of Canada having a "branch-plant economy."

17. You are the marketing manager for a Canadian company producing a computer software package. Write a short speech that you will give at a shareholders' meeting, in which you explain the advantages of your company "going global" in its marketing strategy.

18. Why might someone argue that decisions made by multinational companies are as important, and have as much impact, as those made by individual countries?

19. Research and report on a multinational company and evaluate:
    a) its performance in protecting the quality of the local environment in which it operates
    b) its employment practices, with regard to human rights

E-communication

Our success as a family, a town, a nation, and a global village is dependent on communication. Increasingly, both local and international communication have been facilitated by a powerful tool — the Internet.

Behind the Internet

The Internet is an international network of computers. Remarkably, the Internet is non-proprietary — it is not owned by any person, country, or organization. An organization may own part of the network, but eventually it is connected to hardware outside their building, country, and control. The Internet makes it possible to share information between individuals or organizations on the opposite side of the planet as quickly as it would take to make a phone call to a friend living nearby.

No other technology has had such a tremendous impact on the connections people have with each other. According to Optistreams (an Internet research company), it took 38 years for 30 percent of people worldwide to own a telephone and 17 years for 30 percent to own a television set. It took only 7 years for 30 percent of people worldwide to make regular use of the Internet.

The power of the Internet for individuals

Reasons for using the Internet vary depending on whether the user is an individual, a corporation, a government, or a non-government organization (NGO). The main reasons, however, are that it provides greater accessibility to information, and better communication with other people.

From an individual's standpoint, the Internet can mean access to information about investments or banking, researching a recipe, or simply keeping in touch with a friend who has moved to Australia.

The Internet also facilitates knowledge sharing and employment. Many universities, colleges, and even high schools provide access to courses online. Students meet with their instructor and colleagues via e-mail and chat rooms, and do their entire course online. Canada is a leader in this area, providing several virtual universities (such as Athabasca University), which have no physical campuses at all. Most Canadian universities offer online courses, or plan to do so in the near future.

The power of the Internet for business

For corporations, the Internet is primarily a key productivity tool. E-commerce (electronic commerce) is a way to reach customers anywhere in the world and provide them with access to a wide variety of products and services. According to the International Data Corporation, Internet sales were worth US$120 billion in the year 2000. Business (especially in North America or Europe) depends on the Internet to assist in all processes of a product, from its research to its delivery.

Increasingly, companies are allowing their employees to work from home. Such employees are often called telecommuters. A company that supports telecommuting can realize significant financial benefits — it needs less physical space for employees and would see a drop in almost all related costs. It has also been suggested that telecommuting reduces the amount of traffic accidents and improves air quality. Furthermore, the concept of telecommuting transcends country boundaries. It is possible to own and run a company in a country that you have never seen, by using the Internet.

Information technology (IT)

Along with the boom in the number of Internet users, a boom has also occurred in the related information technology field. There is a worldwide shortage of information technologists (a group of careers including positions such as systems analysts and computer engineers). The United States Department of Commerce estimates that the demand for information technology specialists will more than double by the year 2006.

Mapping Internet usage

Geographers are able to map patterns of Internet usage. Figure 9–17 shows that the Internet has tremendous reach and potential. However, the patterns of usage are a concern for some.

a) Do you think that the uneven global distribution of access to the Internet has economic implications? If so, is the solution simply to ensure equal Internet access for everyone?

b) In North America, instead of embracing telecommuting, many companies have been restraining employees from working from home. They cite a variety of reasons for believing that telecommuting will not help their company. Brainstorm some of these reasons and share them with your classmates.

c) If one has access to the Internet, one has access to information. In the early days of the Internet, there were people who argued that too much information could be a bad thing. What are some of the concerns of having broad and unrestricted access to information?

d) Can all information on the Internet be trusted? Explain your answer.

Check out www.gagelearning.com/onthethreshold for links to Web sites related to the impact of the Internet.

FIGURE 9–17 Regional Internet traffic around the world

This map uses curved lines to show the level of Internet traffic flowing from one country to another. The lines that are the highest and brightest indicate the most traffic.

The Great Debate — Globalization

There is no question that the process of globalization is a reality in our economic world. Our information technology has developed to the point where we can monitor international trade, corporate ventures, and government economic policies on a daily basis. The world is more interconnected — we *are* more global.

Individuals, interest groups, and many organizations have expressed conflicting feelings about this process of globalization. (It is a great irony that organizations that have mounted protests and demonstrations against conferences on globalization have done so internationally, via the Internet and telecommunications technology.) What are the supporters, and the critics, saying?

FIGURE 9–18 The Tokyo Stock Exchange (above) operates in the same way as the New York Stock Exchange and the Toronto Stock Exchange. Proponents of globalization believe that the competitive nature of a global marketplace benefits all, through more jobs, better wages, and better products.

The positives

The arguments supporting the move toward globalization centre on the free movement of people, ideas, goods, and services around the world.

- Globalization is advantageous for all of the world's economies — *it promotes economic activity* and therefore creates jobs.

- Providing global competition is good for consumers. To compete in the world marketplace, companies will have to be innovative and ensure that their products are of the high quality that consumers desire. The pricing of an end product or service will also have to be competitive. *High-quality, low-priced products* will win a larger share of the market.

- Globalization is good for employees. Companies that are in competition with one another will also have to be competitive in terms of *increased wages for employees.*

- When companies invest in weaker economies, those economies benefit from the infusion of money and jobs. The technologies and skills brought to these growing economies may also have "spinoff" effects on other industries. In 1990, the total amount of private financing entering poor countries was US$44 billion. According to the World Investment Report, this amount has increased to US$300 billion.

- As economies prosper, there will be greater demands for freedoms and democracy. Companies are not likely to invest vast sums of money in a politically unstable country. *Improved economies will allow governments to address social conditions and improve health care, education, and social security.* The World Bank and United Nations believe that economic investment improves social conditions. They point to the fact that in South Asia and sub-Saharan Africa, where there are few multinational corporations and international corporate investment is at a low level, severe poverty rates remain high.

- Some critics have argued that direct investment by multinational corporations harms domestic investment, both by interfering with it and lessening it. However, the 1999 World Investment Report, sponsored by the United Nations, discussed two studies carried out in 69 developing countries. These studies found that *every additional dollar of foreign direct investment in a country increases that country's domestic investment* by 150 to 230 percent.

- Many critics of globalization believe that it encourages the exploitation of labour, especially child labour. However, the 2001 United Nations Development Report shows that during the past 20 years, *the percentage of working children between 10 and 14 years of age has dropped* from 20 percent to 13 percent. (In East Asia, which has considerable multinational investment, the drop was from 27 to 10 percent; and in regions with small multinational investments, such as South Asia and sub-Saharan Africa, the rates dropped from 23 to 16 percent, and from 35 to 30 percent, respectively.)

- Critics have suggested that multinational corporations invest in regions where environmental regulations are lax, so that little expense or attention is required on the company's part to ensure that environmentally friendly practices are employed. However, according to the United Nations 1999 World Investment Report, *foreign companies usually implement higher environmental standards than local companies.*

- At the heart of globalization is the *liberalization of trade policies and regulations around the world.* When countries impose tariffs, quotas, exchange rate controls, bureaucratic regulations on importers or exporters, or other types of trade restraints, they increase transaction costs and reduce the gains from exchange. Of course, import restrictions may expand employment in industries shielded by the restraints, but this does not mean that they expand total employment. Exports provide the purchasing power for imports.

A Canadian perspective

Supporters of globalization argue that when Canadians erect tariffs, quotas, and other barriers limiting the ability of foreigners to sell in Canada, they are simultaneously limiting the ability of foreigners to buy goods produced in Canada. If foreigners are unable to sell as much to Canadians, they will have fewer of the Canadian dollars required to buy from Canadians. Thus, import restrictions will indirectly reduce exports; employment in export industries will decline, offsetting any "jobs saved" in the protected industries. What follows is a paraphrase of an article produced for the Fraser Institute (a think-tank formed to examine the role that markets play in the social and economic lives of Canadians).

> Protective tariffs are as much applications of force as are blockading squadrons, and their objective is the same — to prevent trade. The difference between the two is that blockading squadrons are a means whereby nations seek to prevent their enemies from trading; protective tariffs are a means whereby nations attempt to prevent their own people from trading.
>
> Henry George, 1886

The relaxation of trade restrictions will not endanger Canadian business by encouraging the import of goods produced by cheap labour. High-wage countries tend to import things that are relatively cheap abroad and export goods that are relatively cheap at home. Therefore, high wage countries like Canada import labour-intensive goods, such as wigs, rugs, toys, handicrafts, and fine glass. On the other hand, they export goods like grains, petro-chemicals, leading-edge computers, aircraft, and scientific instruments. Such exports are produced by fertile farm land, resources that are relatively abundant, and high-skilled labour.

Supporters of globalization also argue that if the "job savers" and proponents of trade restraints think their policies are a good idea, why don't they favour tariffs and quotas limiting trade among the provinces of Canada? Jobs are lost when, for example, Ontario "imports" lumber and apples from British Columbia, wheat from Saskatchewan, and fish from Nova Scotia. All of these products could be produced in Ontario. However, the residents of Ontario generally find it cheaper to "import" these commodities rather than produce them locally. Ontario gains by using its resources to produce and "export" automobiles. In turn, these auto sales generate the purchasing power that makes it possible for people from Ontario to "import" goods that would be expensive for them to produce locally. Most people recognize that free trade among the provinces is a major source of prosperity for each province. If free trade among provinces promotes prosperity, so too will free trade among nations.

If trade restraints retard economic prosperity, why do so many countries adopt them? The answer is straightforward: the political power of special interests. Trade restrictions benefit producers (and resource suppliers) at the expense of consumers. In general, the former group (investors and workers in a specific industry) are well organized and highly visible, while consumers are generally poorly organized and their gains are more widely dispersed. Predictably, the organized interest group will have more political clout — more votes and more campaign funds. Thus, politicians will often cater to their views. In the case of trade restrictions, sound economics often conflicts with a winning political strategy.

FIGURE 9–19 Trade between two countries like Canada and the United States, which have similar endowments of resources, tends to be intra-industry trade: cars for cars, beer for beer, cheese for cheese, and softwood lumber for hardwood lumber.

The negatives

Those who are opposed to the concept of a global marketplace believe multinational corporations to be instruments of rich, global capitalists. The main targets of this criticism are the World Trade Organization, the World Bank, and the International Monetary Fund (IMF). These organizations are often linked to corporate interests in that they pursue policies of liberalization, enabling corporations to make vast, globally produced profits. Criticisms of the way in which some of these corporations do business are widespread.

- Many multinationals are accused of *unfair labour practices*. They are said to have little regard for a fair working environment because they invest in regions where they can pay the lowest possible labour costs. They are often accused of exploiting children and demanding long work hours. According to the International Labour Organization, multinational corporations employ 19 million workers in developing countries, and are indirectly connected to a further 100 million jobs. Improving working expectations and conditions would impact a huge labour market.

- Multinational corporations have also been accused of participating in a "race to the bottom," where *they seek to operate in countries where environmental standards and requirements are low or non-existent.* For example, many critics of free trade accuse Canadian companies of relocating to Mexico because of that country's less stringent environmental laws.

- Another criticism of large corporate interests is that *they mismanage natural resources.* Short-term profits are said to carry more weight with shareholders than long-term resource management. This rush to exploit resources such as minerals and forests is said to have caused ecological damage to places such as the Brazilian rain forest and the western Canadian old-growth temperate forests.

- Agribusinesses that use monocropping techniques to maximize crop production are accused of using *too many chemicals for fertilizer, pesticides, insecticides, and herbicides.*

- The push toward bioengineering and genetically modified foods has brought forward the argument that maximizing profits often takes precedence over consideration for *the adverse long-term effects that these genetically modified foods have* on the humans and animals who consume them.

- Globalization is said to be *a cultural threat* to countries such as Canada. For example, the Council of Canadians (a citizens' watchdog group with over 100 000 members across Canada) is extremely concerned about Canadians being saturated with the media of American culture. This group questions whether government controls such as the Canadian Radio and Television Council (CRTC) can stop the growing American cultural influence from entering Canada via media programs. The Canadian Radio and Television Council has set aside a minimum number of broadcasting hours that should contain Canadian content, in order to control the influence of American culture.

Current trends in globalization

Trends toward more companies, bigger companies, more employees, and larger markets indicate that the process of globalization is continually growing. Corpwatch estimates that nearly US$1.7 trillion is spent annually on mergers and acquisitions of companies. When Daimler Benz bought Chrysler, the cost was US$43 billion; when MCI WorldCom bought Sprint Corp, it cost them US$115 billion.

The New Internationalist calculates that nearly 75 percent of all foreign direct investment in 2000 was made in countries that are already developed. The income gap between the 20 percent of people living in the richest countries in the world and the 20 percent living in the poorest jumped from 30:1 in 1960 to 74:1 in 1997. It seems that this investment and expansion is taking place within the arena of wealth, at the exclusion of the poorer parts of the world.

FIGURE 9–20 Many people worry that the global nature of communication will lead to global cultural immersion and global assimilation, with fewer and fewer regional differences existing across the globe. Some would argue that the popularity of baseball in Japan is an example of such cultural assimilation.

Globalization Mainly Benefits One-Fifth of World

by Joe Lauria

United Nations, 13 July 1999 — Globalization has been a boom for the top 20 percent of the world's population and a bust for just about everyone else, says a UN report on human development released Monday.

"The collapse of space, time, and borders may be creating a global village, but not everyone can be a citizen," the 10th annual UN Development Programme's Human Development Report says. "The global, professional elite now faces low borders, but billions of others find borders as high as ever."

Globalization has meant the enrichment of the biggest transnational corporations, often at the expense of an increasingly impoverished developing world. General Motors, Ford Motors, Mitsubishi, Royal Dutch/Shell, Exxon, Toyota Motor, and Wal-Mart Stores all had greater sales in 1997 than the gross domestic products of Malaysia, Israel, Colombia, Venezuela, or the Philippines.

Compounding the problem has been the privatization of research and development. "In defining the research agenda, money talks louder than need — cosmetic drugs and slow-ripening tomatoes come higher on the list than a vaccine against malaria or drought-resistant crops," says the report. "For poor people, technological progress remains far out of reach."

Whereas wealth was once measured by owning land or factories, today it is information. "Writing computer programs and revealing genetic codes have replaced the search for gold, the conquest of land, and the command of machinery as the path to economic power," says the report.

And information technology and cultural production is overwhelmingly controlled by the richest countries. "For the United States, the largest single export industry is not aircraft, computers, or automobiles — it is entertainment, in films and television programs," the report says.

Access to the Internet, which is playing an increasingly important role in the world economy and culture, is almost exclusively restricted to the top 20 percent of the population, which controls 74 percent of all telephone lines, the report says. The US has more computers than the rest of the world combined.

"The UN needs to play a major role in creating some global checks and balances on corporations and for greater accountability," said John Cavanagh, director of the Institute for Policy Studies in Washington.

The report predicts that "ultimately, people and nations will reject global integration and global interdependence if they do not gain from it. Pressures will mount to retreat to isolationism in economic policy, culture, and in political priorities."

Globalization alternatives

Globalization of the world's economy is a controversial issue. On the one hand, it prompts visions of open, expanded markets, with integrated economies. On the other, it is seen as an oppressive way in which those who control the capital wealth of the world seek to exploit resources and people. Those who oppose globalization believe that it threatens the world's resources and its environment; they suggest the following alternative actions.

- Where foreign-owned companies exist, a considerable amount of local money "leaks out" of the local economy. The *creation of local credit unions and small banks* would help prevent this happening. Investing in large, multinational finance corporations may mean that one's money is damaging an environment in a country with weaker environmental legislation.

FIGURE 9–21 In Britain, 1.5 million people belong to local consumer initiatives such as Community Shops and Pubs, Community Energy, Managed Workspace, and Eco-villages. These initiatives are similar to those set up in local villages across Kerala, India (see Chapter 4).

- There needs to be a *shift in emphasis toward local sustainability* in order to protect the larger global economic and environmental systems. The Green Party (an international social, economic, and environmental watchdog group) suggests that countries, and regions within countries, should resume control over economies that have been lost to multinational decision makers. For example, buying items from local suppliers would help the economy; shopping locally would create local jobs. It is estimated that for every US$80 000 spent in a local store, the spinoffs to suppliers and local producers create one new job. Obtaining items from farther distances should be a last resort, according to these organizations.

- In order to help with local priorities, *countries must practise more protectionism* through the use of trade barriers and tariffs. One of the essential requirements for a policy of protectionism to work is access to local capital for local investment. Therefore, movement toward larger banking and financing institutions should be stopped. Instead, smaller banks should be created through **de-merging** (the breaking up of bank conglomerates) that believe in "bank-here-to-sell-here" policies.

If organizations and individuals opposed to globalization were to achieve these goals, what would happen to the multinational corporations and the power they hold? As a result of altered taxation, trade regulations, and anti-trust laws, the multinationals would be broken up into smaller companies. Also, a limit — almost like a business licence — would be placed on how far away they could do business; information, research, and development would be shared within a local network of companies.

20. You are about to take part in a debate regarding the globalization of the world's economy. You will be given a position to support — either one in favour of more globalization, or one against the process of globalization. Once you have been assigned a position, you should review the necessary information presented in this chapter; then you should research other sources of information on the Internet. As you review the information, make notes on important points you may wish to bring up in a discussion about the topic.

a) Share your points with two other students who have been assigned to the same position in the debate as you. As a team, you should prepare an opening statement; a body of evidence to support your position; and a closing statement or summary of your position.

b) Your group of three will then enter into a debate with three students from the opposite position. You will debate the statement that "Globalization is more beneficial than harmful." Each side will make an opening statement; present a body of facts and statements to support their position (ensuring that they include information about the effects of free trade agreements on the natural environment); ask questions of the other side; and make a closing statement, taking into account any new information received during the discussion.

c) After the debate, write a one-page editorial for a global newspaper containing your personal reflection on the debate.

Case in point — Canada, Ukraine, and Ghana

Canada, Ukraine, and Ghana are examples of three different economic situations.

Canada is often voted by the annual United Nations Development Report as being the most desirable place in the world in which to live. It has a modern industrialized economy, with a well-developed infrastructure of education, training, and communication. It has vast resources, a well-developed trade network, and a stable political situation.

Ukraine is an emerging economy. As the rest of the world developed an interdependence and moved toward globalization, Ukraine continued to support a protectionist ideology around its communist, centrally planned economic beliefs. Its economic development only began to take off in 1991, when communist rule came to an end in central and eastern Europe. It now finds itself in a world of fierce competition and lacks capital investment and democratic trading experience.

Ghana is typical of a poorer developing country, in which political colonialism has been replaced by a new **economic colonialism**. Here, the World Bank and the International Monetary Fund (IMF) finance and control the economy. It is a country where resource exploitation still follows the pattern of supplying richer economies with low-cost produce, against a backdrop of crippling debt repayment.

Economic profiles

Canada

- Canada is typical of a modern, advanced, high-tech economy.

- Primary resources are important in Canada, a country that has vast energy, mineral, and agricultural output and potential: it is the world's largest supplier of zinc, uranium, and nickel, and is also a significant supplier of potash, gypsum lead, and asbestos.

FIGURE 9-22 The Canadian Prairies produce approximately 25 million tonnes of wheat annually, which is exported to more than 60 countries.

- Canada also has extensive agricultural regions, and supplies a significant amount of the world's wheat. Its vast forests have made Canada globally important in lumber, and in the pulp and paper industries.

- The sophisticated manufacturing and service sectors in its heartland, stretching from Windsor to Québec City, drives the Canadian economy. Its main imports and exports centre on the automobile industry; it is also the world's leader in telecommunication industries.

- Canada has a high trading volume. Its main trading partnership is with the United States, under the North American Free Trade Agreement (NAFTA), with less reliance on Japan or European partners.

- Canada's workforce is highly skilled and educated. The country has a large public debt that is being addressed by budget surpluses.

Who Owns Canada?
Foreign Ownership Is on the Rise

by Mark MacKinnon

It sounds as Canadian as a company can be: Beaver Fuels Management Ltd. National symbols. Natural resources. But it isn't owned by Canadians. The Alberta-based gas retailer is a subsidiary of Calgary-based Shell Canada Ltd., which is owned by Royal Dutch Petroleum Co. of the Netherlands.

Beaver Fuels, one of 12 725 corporations in Canada owned by foreigners, is in a growing category.

Foreign-owned companies accounted for 31.5 percent of the nearly CDN$1.3 trillion in corporate revenue generated in Canada in 1996 (excluding the financial sector). That share has been slowly rising from a low of 26.9 percent in 1988, just before the signing of the bilateral Canada-US Free Trade Agreement.

"There is no other major developed nation in the world that has the degree of foreign ownership that we do in Canada, not by a long shot," said Mel Hurtig, founder of the Council of Canadians.

Jacek Warda, a researcher with the Conference Board of Canada, pointed out that while long-term foreign direct investment in Canada has more than tripled since 1980 (to CDN$15.6 billion annually in 1997 from CDN$4.1 billion), Canada's share of total foreign direct investment globally has fallen off considerably. Less than 5 percent of all foreign direct investment ended up in Canada in 1997, down from 11 percent in 1980. Mr. Warda said that Canadian personal and corporate taxes are not competitive with other regions of the world, so the country is missing out on potential investment dollars. He believes those who see foreign investment as a bad thing are simply relying on dated ideologies.

Mr. Hurtig says the media, when reporting the quantity of foreign direct investment in Canada, overlook the fact that almost all foreign investment in the country is used for acquisitions, which don't necessarily create new jobs.

According to Industry Canada, foreigners spent CDN$50.5 billion on business ventures in Canada in 1998, of which 98.5 percent was used for takeovers, and only a tiny 1.5 percent represented new business investment.

Nationalists argue that numbers like those mean that Canada is fast on its way to becoming the branch-plant economy that governments once fought so hard to avoid. "In the 1970s, [foreign ownership] was the topic. Now it's vanished," Mr. Hurtig said. "Not one politician has been making it an issue."

Ukraine

- Ukraine is especially suited to agriculture, with fertile, black soil — much like the best parts of the Canadian prairies — that covers 60 percent of the country. It produces large amounts of meat, milk, vegetables, and grains.

- It has important coal and metal mining operations, and is the world's largest supplier of manganese.

- Its industries (in central Ukraine) form one of the densest industrial regions in the world. However, these industries, which produce machinery, chemicals, and fertilizers, are in need of new capital investment.

- Ukraine imports most of its energy needs.

- The United States has also provided the country with an average of US$250 million each year since its independence in 1991. Ukraine is the third-largest recipient of foreign financial assistance from the United States.

- There is no giant, multinational corporation based in Ukraine. (This is typical of all the eastern European countries.) Although its main trading partners are Russia, Belarus, Turkmenistan, and China, Ukraine has applied to become a member of the European Union (EU).

- The International Monetary Fund (IMF), which has invested 2.6 billion in Ukraine, is putting pressure on the country to reform its industries faster and to create more privatization. The World Bank has loaned Ukraine US$260 million to modernize its financial and banking industry.

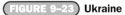

FIGURE 9–23 Ukraine

Nevertheless, the international community has been reluctant to invest in the country because many feel that there has been too much corruption and crime within many of Ukraine's banking and government institutions. Due to these concerns, only US$3.6 billion of international money has been invested in Ukraine since its independence in 1991, although foreign investments are rising. Ukraine received US$437 million from abroad in 1999, US$583 million in 2000, and an estimated US$900 million by the end of 2001.

World Bank Mission Visited Ukraine for New Loan Discussions

A World Bank mission headed by Mr. Luca Barbone, Country Director for Ukraine and Belarus, concluded an eight-day visit to Ukraine to continue the preparation of the Programmatic Adjustment Loan (PAL) for the country.

The PAL — one of the cornerstones of the Bank Country Assistance Strategy (CAS)* — is expected to consist of three separate loans, each of US$250 million, to be disbursed depending on the pace of implementation of reforms envisioned in the government's economic program.

FIGURE 9–24 Ukraine's Magnitogorsk Steel Works (above) is the largest steel mill in the world.

"We believe that the successful implementation of the government's economic program supported by the PAL will help Ukraine make significant progress improving the financial system and the legal environment necessary for business activities. At the same time, the PAL will support the Government's efforts to strengthen public institutions that not only foster economic growth but that will deliver effective social services to the people of Ukraine," stressed Mr. Barbone.

Separately, the Bank team also conducted the eleventh semi-annual portfolio review, assessing the preparation and implementation of 25 projects in Ukraine, putting special emphasis on operations addressing agriculture, the public sector, and the power and coal sectors.

The portfolio review revealed a number of projects in an advanced stage of preparation, such as the Sevastopol Heat Supply Improvement Project (US$28 million), Lviv Water Project (US$24 million), and Coal Sector Social Mitigation Project (US$100 million).

Mr. Barbone also announced the release of US$60 million as the third and final tranche [portion] of the Financial Sector Adjustment Loan (FSAL) to Ukraine. The release was triggered by the fulfilment of the conditions of the loan, including the adoption of a law to regulate banking activities.

*The Country Assistance Strategy (CAS) is the document that outlines the Bank's business plan for Ukraine, describing the level and type of assistance to be provided in the next three years based on an assessment of priorities in the country. It was prepared by the Ukrainian government, in consultation with representatives of Ukrainian civil society and approved by the World Bank's Board of Directors on September 12, 2000.

At a glance — *Canada, Ukraine, and Ghana*

Demographics	Canada (developed economy)	Ukraine (emerging economy)	Ghana (developing economy)
Population	31 592 805	48 760 474	19 894 014
Total fertility rate	1.6 children	1.29 children	3.82 children
0–14 age group %	19%	17.3%	41.18%
Life expectancy	79.56 years	66.15 years	57.24 years
GDP (US$)	$774.7 billion	$189.4 billion	$37.4 billion
GDP per capita (PPP US$)	$24 800	$3 850	$1 900
Industries	agriculture 3% industry 23% services 74%	agriculture 12% industry 26% services 62%	agriculture 36% industry 25% services 39%
Debt (US$)	$1.9 billion	$10.3 billion	$7 billion
Unemployment	6.8%	4.3%*	20%
Exports (US$)	$272.3 billion **Commodities**: motor vehicles and parts, newsprint, wood pulp, timber, crude petroleum, machinery, natural gas, aluminum, telecommunications equipment, electricity **Partners**: US, Japan, UK, Germany, South Korea, Netherlands, China	$14.6 billion **Commodities**: ferrous and non-ferrous metals, fuel and petroleum products, machinery and transport equipment, food products **Partners**: Russia, EU, US	$1.6 billion **Commodities**: gold, cocoa, timber, tuna, bauxite, aluminum, manganese ore, diamonds **Partners**: Togo, UK, Italy, Netherlands, Germany, US, France
Imports (US$)	$238.2 billion **Commodities**: machinery and equipment, crude oil, chemicals, motor vehicles and parts, durable consumer goods, electricity **Partners**: US, Japan, UK, Germany, France, Mexico, Taiwan, South Korea	$15 billion **Commodities**: energy, machinery and parts, transportation equipment, chemicals **Partners**: Russia, EU, US	$2.2 billion **Commodities**: capital equipment, petroleum, foodstuffs **Partners**: UK, Nigeria, US, Germany, Italy, Spain
Foreign aid (annual, US$)	$1.3 billion, donor	$637.7 million, recipient IMF extended funds facility US$2.2 billion	$477.3 million, recipient

*4.3% officially registered; large number of unregistered or unemployed workers

Ghana

- Ghana, in West Africa, still has many characteristics of a colonially ruled country. Its economy is centred on its resources, which are highly valued and exploited by the developed world.

- Ghana's main trading products are timber, gold, and particularly, cocoa. Primary materials — especially cash crops — therefore dominate the economy, but its main cash crop, cocoa, has declined in importance since the 1970s. Bananas, coffee, and rice are also grown for export.

- Subsistence agriculture contributes 40 percent of the gross domestic product and employs about 60 percent of all workers in the country.

- Ghana also produces industrial-grade diamonds, bauxite, and manganese. Although Ghana makes aluminum, its main income is obtained from exporting its primary resources.

- Ghana's main trading partners are the United Kingdom, the United States, Japan, and Germany.

- Ghana is heavily indebted to western countries and banks. The International Monetary Fund imposed a **structural adjustment program (SAP)** on Ghana in 1995. (Structural adjustment programs are economic policies imposed on a country so that they can qualify to receive financial help from international agencies such as the World Bank or the International Monetary Fund.) The policies generally encourage government spending in areas such as health care, education, and social services, and often require the removal of government subsidies; they also encourage exports in order to acquire money for repayment purposes. The World Bank and the International Monetary Fund often suggest policies that include opening trade legislation and regulations (creating

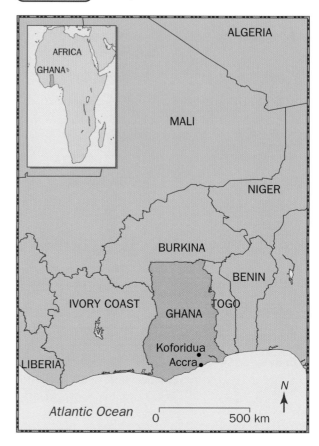

FIGURE 9–25 Ghana, West Africa

opportunities for a more open trade environment), as well as privatization of government services and infrastructure (for example, energy and transportation). In 2000, the World Bank instructed Ghana to follow the International Monetary Fund program more carefully, as it had suffered because of collapsing world prices for cocoa and gold in 2000. This involved more privatization of power supply, water supply, and railway operations. Its Tema Oil Refinery, once government-owned and run, was put up for private sale. Ghana was also to have fewer export restrictions in its cocoa market.

- The World Bank and the International Monetary Fund also required Ghana to improve its educational standards. According to the Structural Adjustment Participatory Review International Network (SAPRIN) — a global organization that monitors the effects of structural adjustment programs and which is financed mostly by trade unions from around the world — results have been mixed. Of the US$400 million loaned to Ghana by the World Bank, most help went to basic literacy and education. Both came with some degree of user fee. Soon after the implementation of these user fees, there was a 40 percent dropout rate from primary school, which is a much higher percentage than previous dropout levels. Some experts worry that as a result, Ghana's population will be mostly illiterate by the year 2020.

■ However, the University of Ghana, centred in Accra, has teamed up with the African Virtual University, headquartered in Nairobi, Kenya. The African Virtual University offers online, interactive courses to students in 17 different African countries, including Ghana. This "university without walls" began as a World Bank Project in 1997 and is now an independent organization, using the latest communications technology to provide professional training and access to an online digital library. The Virtual University's teachers and technicians are experts in technology and are helping sub-Saharan Africa to leapfrog into the hi-tech world.

■ The introduction of user fees in hospitals led to a 33 percent reduction in the number of outpatients. However, increased inoculation programs have led to a significant decrease in diseases such as leprosy and polio. Critics of the structural adjustment program suggest that the World Health Organization (WHO) and the United Nations Children's Fund (UNICEF) should be given credit for improvements in health care, even though there were fewer direct users of the health care facilities.

■ Food supplies are considered shaky. Most farmers in Ghana are subsistence farmers, and an increased emphasis on cash crops for export has led to a reduction in crops for food. Foreign aid in the form of financial contributions to farmers has been reduced, resulting in more malnutrition. This money is now being directed toward more efficient cash cropping.

■ The mining industry has been deregulated and there has been more privatization of state-owned gold mines. The Structural Adjustment Participatory Review International Network believes that this has brought poorer working conditions and lower wages for miners. This situation has worsened because of a devaluation of the currency, which has made locally produced goods more expensive, and because there has been a flood of imports, threatening local suppliers.

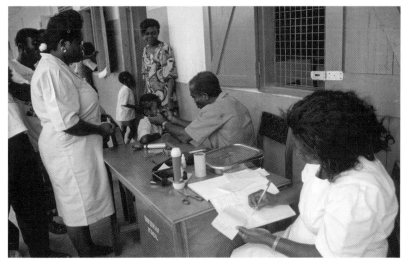

FIGURE 9–26 Health care workers in Koforidua, Ghana. Has health care in Ghana been both helped and hindered by recent reforms? How?

Water for the People — Ghanaians Protest Privatization

by Katharine Ainger

"Water is part of life. It is part of our cultural celebration. It is part of our attachment to the earth and to the moon." Charles Abugre, of the Ghanaian organization Isodec, explains why incipient water privatization is sparking popular resistance in the country's capital, Accra. "This issue has a popular resonance. People realize there is a division between rich and poor, and this even affects whether you can access something as integral to life itself as water."

Ghana qualifies as a Heavily Indebted Poor Country (HIPC), due for partial debt relief under a World Bank initiative to ease the debt burden of the world's poorest countries. The World Bank attaches conditions to this debt relief. In this case, private-sector participation in water provision must be promoted or else the Ghanaian government will not be allowed to access loans.

The World Bank is lending US$100 million for the rehabilitation of water facilities prior to privatization. Abugre says, "There is a lot at stake. The government is broke and US$l00 million is a lot of money. It just picked up the privatization process and decided to fast-track it even though there was no major debate about this."

When the World Bank came and told us we were a Heavily Indebted Poor Country, Ghanaians were offended," says Abugre. "In our culture, that concept means you are unable to do anything for yourself.

"People are now making conscious links between our country's debt, the World Bank, the IMF [International Monetary Fund], globalization, and the privatization going on in many sectors. And resistance to the privatization of water has become a symbol of resistance against externally imposed agendas."

A huge mobilization is building. Local radio stations buzz with daily phone-ins. Trade unions are getting involved. The Church has taken up the cause as a moral and ethical issue. A vigorous four-day debate in Accra led to the creation of the Ghana National Coalition Against the Privatization of Water. Thousands of urban poor turned up to the public meeting, which ended with singing and dancing in the streets. Abugre concludes: "Right now we are looking at a legal injunction against privatization. But we will also have to take this to the streets."

Charles Abugre says the popular feeling is this: "The idea that a foreign company will decide whether I get water or whether I don't get water, when they are pumping that water from my rivers and my streams and turning it into something that I don't have access to when I can't pay — it's outrageous. What right does this company have to do that?

"Privatization is going too far. When they cross that line, they incur the resistance of the people."

21. Review the information on the economy of each country. Write a summary, describing the economic condition in each of the three countries.

22. In your own words, describe the meaning of a structural adjustment program. How successful has the structural adjustment program been in Ghana?

23. Each of these countries — Canada, Ukraine, and Ghana — operates with a great deal of foreign financial involvement. Some would argue that these examples demonstrate a replacement of an old form of control by powerful states in colonial empires with a new form of economic colonialism. Assume that you are a leading correspondent for a magazine called the *New Global Economy*. Write an editorial in which you express your opinion on this issue, using the economies of Canada, Ukraine, and Ghana as examples.

Economic report

You are to prepare an economic report for Flex Corporation. Your task is to review the economic information for three countries — Canada, Ghana, and Ukraine — to determine which country would be the best locale for a new manufacturing plant.

Why have these three alternatives been chosen?

- Canada has been chosen because it is located in the North American market, which your company would like to exploit.
- Ghana has been short-listed because one of the technicians working at the African Virtual University has significant knowledge in the wireless technology your company manufactures. It is also believed that research grants will be available in Ghana, due to World Bank funding.
- Ukraine has been chosen because of its access to eastern European, Russian, and even Chinese markets and technology.

Where will you build your new plant and why?

Background on Flex Corporation

Your company is located near Leeds in northern England. It is a manufacturer of digitized organizers, which are small pocket-sized instruments that have the wireless capability to access e-mail and online banking. Your planning team expects this product to be sold worldwide over the next two to six years.

a) Write an economic report for each of the three countries (Canada, Ukraine, and Ghana). Consider the data and articles provided in this chapter. You may also wish to do more research using the CIA World Factbook, which can be found online.

b) Organize your report using the following headings:
  - Demographic background
  - Finance (gross domestic product and debt)
  - Trade
  - Financial help
  - Quality of life

c) Research trade blocs of which each country is a member.

d) Describe the economic issues facing each country.

e) Develop a list of criteria, as well as a ranking system you will use to determine the site of your new operation. For example, you may wish to rate each country according to their proximity to suitable markets for the product. There are many such variables you may consider.

f) Assess each of the locations according to your list of criteria and/or your ranking system.

g) Write a summary of your recommendations.

Change and Challenge

Boom Towns Changing Farmers' Lifestyle

Some 10 million farmers in China's Zhejiang Province have left behind the lifestyle of their ancestors and started urban life in boom towns that have prospered in tandem with the rapid development of township enterprises.

The boom towns are just like any other big cities in China, with tall buildings, supermarkets, green fields, brightly-lit stores, restaurants, and entertainment centres.

But for the former farmers, the changes are taking place not just within the surroundings, but also in their own lifestyle.

Most people, either business owners or workers, have given up their local dialects and speak *Putonghua*, the standard Mandarin, in a bid to get an easy access to city life.

Unlike their ancestors who used to go to bed after sunset, the townsfolk now enjoy a colourful night life, shopping, and going to theatres and disco bars.

The younger generation, like all their peers, like to surf the Internet to find out more about the outside world. Computers and pianos have become new favourites in these boom towns now that most families have air conditioners and colour TVs.

To seek sustained development, the townsfolk have attached great importance to their children's education. More kindergartens and primary and secondary schools have been set up and well equipped to provide quality training to the younger generation, intellectually and morally.

a) The article suggests that millions of people are migrating from rural areas to the towns and cities of Zhejiang Province. What forces are at work that cause this shift from a rural to an urban lifestyle?

b) What roles have education and modern technology played in these people's desire to live in modern cities with changed lifestyles?

c) Traditionally, the male heads of families and businesses have dominated farming in China. What changes in traditional gender roles may this type of migration cause?

d) What might some negative consequences be of this rural-urban migration, for either the rural or urban regions in Zhejiang Province?

- Analyse the impact of urbanization and urban growth on natural and human systems.
- Demonstrate an understanding of the roles and status of men and women in different parts of the world.
- Demonstrate an understanding of the possibility of a number of alternative solutions to any geographic problem or issue.
- Evaluate the effectiveness of techniques used to predict the future.
- Use a variety of methods and technologies to communicate the results of geographic inquiry and analysis effectively.
- Analyse how the media influence public opinion on geographic issues.

We are on the threshold of an exciting era of innovation and are gaining a better understanding of the limits of our planet. One of the most dramatic challenges facing us may be the speed at which our own life experiences change. Science and technology are leaping ahead so quickly that we barely have time to adjust our lifestyles before we need to readjust them to meet new challenges.

In this chapter, we will look at key changes that challenge many of us on a daily basis. Two issues are profiled — one involving physical change, and the other involving social change. The first affects an ever-increasing number of people around the world — those living in growing towns and cities. The remarkable amount of movement of people to urban environments places enormous pressure on those environments, as well as on the surrounding landscape, in both richer and poorer countries.

A second significant challenge facing a world community that is striving toward greater equality and mutual respect is **gender inequality** (an unequal power relationship between males and females).

As cultures and societies around the world adapt to great technological and scientific advancements, these fundamental issues must be resolved so that we can achieve the ecological and social balance we seek.

FIGURE 10–1 Women in New Delhi (left) attend a march on International Women's Day 2001 to call attention to the abuse of women and the need for social change. A busy street in Hanoi, Vietnam (right) is a result of rapid urbanization, a trend that demands many related lifestyle changes.

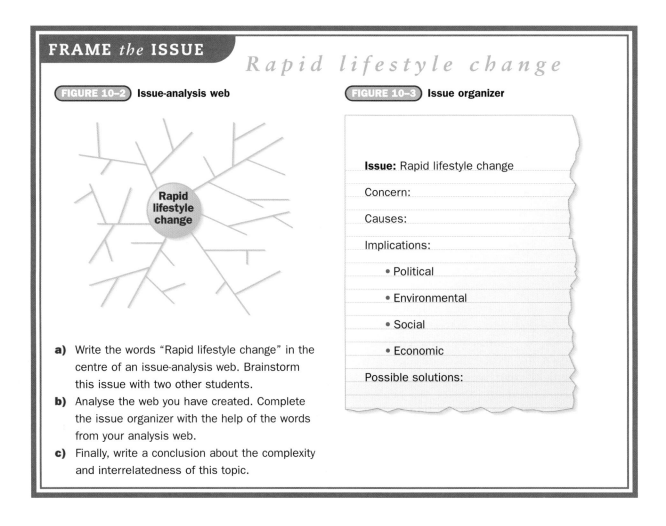

FRAME the ISSUE

Rapid lifestyle change

FIGURE 10–2 Issue-analysis web

Rapid lifestyle change

FIGURE 10–3 Issue organizer

Issue: Rapid lifestyle change

Concern:

Causes:

Implications:

- Political

- Environmental

- Social

- Economic

Possible solutions:

a) Write the words "Rapid lifestyle change" in the centre of an issue-analysis web. Brainstorm this issue with two other students.

b) Analyse the web you have created. Complete the issue organizer with the help of the words from your analysis web.

c) Finally, write a conclusion about the complexity and interrelatedness of this topic.

Urban Lifestyles on the Rise

One of the most significant trends in global population relates to where people choose to live and work. The world is becoming increasingly **urban**. For the first time in human history, the number of people living in towns and cities is about to surpass those living in what are considered rural environments. Such things as an urban habitat, rapid transportation, crowds of people, mass media, consumerism, industrialization, and a faster pace of life are gradually dominating the lifestyle and culture of the world's population. Urbanization (the movement toward living in cities) is one of the most profound forces shaping our lives today and for the future. Only 100 years ago, the population of the planet was 86 percent rural. In 2005 it will be 50 percent urban.

The move toward urban environments

Why has there been a gradual increase in people living in towns and cities over time? Only 2.5 percent of the world's population lived in urban environments in the year 1800. But urban communities have always been centres for providing services or products. The growth of cities occurred most rapidly during the Industrial Revolution (1750–1850) when manufacturing first became mechanized.

FIGURE 10-4 Growth of urban population

	Level of urbanization (%)		
	2000	**2015**	**2030**
Africa	37.9	46.5	54.5
Asia	36.7	44.7	53.4
Europe	74.8	78.6	82.6
Latin America	75.3	79.9	83.2
North America	77.2	80.9	84.4
Oceania	70.2	71.2	74.4
Developing world	39.9	48.0	56.2
Developed world	76.0	79.7	83.5
World total	47.0	53.4	60.3

FIGURE 10-5 World urban and rural population, 1950–2030

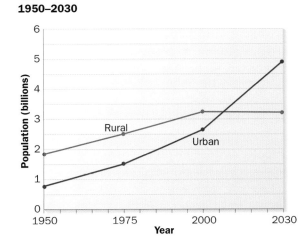

Industrial processes require large numbers of workers. Many people were tempted to leave the low financial security of living in the countryside in order to gain the higher financial rewards offered by the factories. As people moved into the cities, there was a concentration of labour — workers clustered together. New businesses and industries were developed to serve the needs of this growing population. For example, a lot of growth occurred within the European coalfields, to provide a plentiful supply of energy for steam power. As more local people consumed products, more local businesses were needed — and more employees — creating what is called an **urban inertia**.

Improved transportation and communication technology allowed people greater access both within, and between, urban communities. Cities became the centres of a large flow of resources, capital, finished products, and people. These cities — "economic engines" — increased the prosperity of the people living in them. It is little wonder that cities became, and still are, population magnets.

These economic urban forces continued into the twentieth century, but still affected the developed world much more than they impacted the developing world. By 1900, according to the Population Reference Bureau (a non-government organization that collects population data), the number of urban dwellers worldwide was 14 percent. In the year 2000, this number had

swelled to 47 percent. The developed countries of Europe and North America, as well as Australia and Japan, were 76 percent urban in 2000. In the same year, the world's less developed countries lagged behind at only 40 percent.

Within a few years, most of the world's population will live in cities. By 2030, the United Nations (UN) predicts that 60 percent of the world's population (about 4.8 billion) will be urbanized.

1. Develop a timeline from 1800 to 2030 and label appropriate dates with details concerning the world growth in urbanization.

2. Refer to Figure 10–4. Summarize the trends revealed in the predicted levels of urbanization between 2000 and 2030.

Urban migration in developing regions

One of the challenges we will face in the future is dealing with the growth of towns and cities. Soon, the majority of the world's population will live in urban environments.

The fastest rate of urbanization is taking place (and is predicted to continue to take place) in the countries of the developing world, where the majority of the world's population lives.

By 2015, the population of Lagos, Nigeria is expected to grow by 10 million to reach 23 million, while that of Dhaka, Bangladesh will grow from 12.3 million to more than 21 million. Of the predicted global total of 4.8 billion people living in cities by 2030, 4 billion will be in the cities of the developing world. The cities of richer countries will see little growth, or even stagnation. Tokyo, Japan — the world's most populated metropolis at 26.4 million — is not expected to see any growth for the next 15 years.

There are two forces at work causing this explosive growth to occur in the developing world — **economic dependence** and **economic integration**. In the 1960s, economist Andre Gunder Frank explained the developing world's growing economic dependence on the developed world in his **Dependency Theory**.

The theory explains how communities in poorer countries developed to help shift local resources via a network of increasingly larger communities to a final port destination. These resources were then shipped to the manufacturing belts of the developed world in Europe and North America. A reduction in the demand for products and resources would have a devastating effect on the success and growth of the cities in poorer countries. In this way, these poorer cities became dependent on the economic well-being of the developed world. Frank's theory suggested that this was a means of perpetuating poverty in the developing world. In this regard, his theory is similar to the ideas of Immanual Wallerstein, who defined the world in terms of core and periphery regions (see pages 59–61).

The rise of the great colonial cities — Rio de Janerio, Accra, Bombay, Jakarta — is due partly to their roles as **transhipment** points, through which local goods passed for shipment abroad. Through this movement of goods and resources, these cities gathered wealth, thus improving their local economies.

Many countries that were previously part of colonial empires have become integrated into the new global economy, ruled by the giant multinational corporations. These corporations have concentrated their capital and investments in urban centres through branch plant economies, or regional trade headquarters, which protect the interests of the company in the emerging markets of the developing world. The infrastructure and buildings of multinational branch offices in cities such as Hong Kong, Singapore, Kuala Lumpur, and Buenos Aires stand like towers of economic strength to local economies.

As outlined in Chapter 9 (pages 249–251), there are many factors that attract international investment to developing nations. These factors include expanded markets, proximity to raw materials, and often, cheap labour. Banking and finance centres in regions of the developing world — such as Hong Kong, Singapore, and Taiwan — increase the ability of multinational companies to do business abroad.

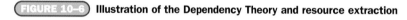

FIGURE 10-6 Illustration of the Dependency Theory and resource extraction

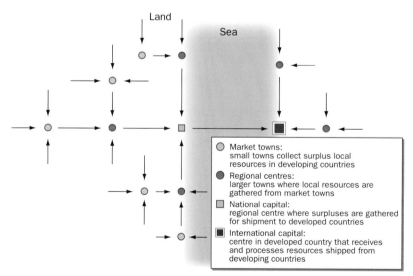

○ Market towns:
small towns collect surplus local resources in developing countries

● Regional centres:
larger towns where local resources are gathered from market towns

□ National capital:
regional centre where surpluses are gathered for shipment to developed countries

■ International capital:
centre in developed country that receives and processes resources shipped from developing countries

Local populations are drawn to the commercial centres. The factors that draw people into an area are called **pull factors**: more job opportunities, higher wages, and better access to social services such as health care and education. **Push factors** (those factors that drive people away) such as deteriorating farmland, or conflict, also contribute to the movement from rural areas to urban areas.

3. Explain the two forces that are considered to be responsible for more rapid urbanization taking place in the developing world.

4. In what ways are the ideas of Andre Gunder Frank and Immanuel Wallerstein similar?

5. a) Give five examples of push factors, and five examples of pull factors, that may influence a person in the developing world to move from a rural area into a city.
   b) Give three examples of push factors, and three examples of pull factors, that may influence a person in the developed world to move from a rural area into a city.

6. Refer to Figures 10–7 and 10–8. What is predicted to occur to average annual urban growth rates by the year 2025?

Megagrowth

In the future, an increasing number of global citizens will live in cities with populations greater than that of many countries. Urban living is hectic; imagine what an urban lifestyle would entail in a city two or three times larger than our largest cities are today. Within the developing world, some cities attract particularly large amounts of growth. For example, during the 1990s the population of Bangladesh grew by 2.1 percent per year. However, during the same period, its capital — Dhaka — grew by 7 percent per year.

This growth has created a phenomenon called the **megacity** — one with population in excess of 10 million. According to the Population Council (a non-profit research organization), there were only 5 megacities worldwide in 1975; by 2015 there will be 23. The Population Council also predicts that by 2015 there will be 564 cities that will contain more than 1 million people, and that 425 of these (that is, 75 percent) will be in developing countries.

Impacts of urbanization

What are the issues that arise as a result of this growth of cities and towns, especially in the developing world? The United Nations states that in 2001, an estimated 600 million people found it difficult to meet their needs for adequate shelter and drinkable water.

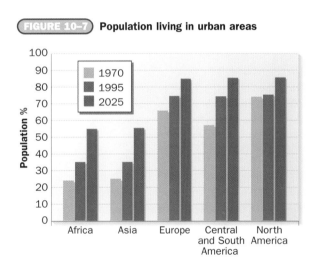

FIGURE 10–7 Population living in urban areas

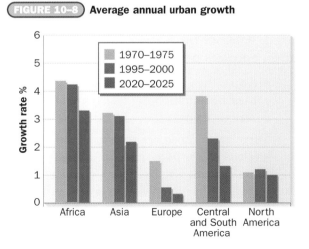

FIGURE 10–8 Average annual urban growth

FIGURE 10–9 Population growth in cities

		2000	2015
		(population in millions)	
1	Tokyo, Japan*	26.4	26.4
2	Bombay, India	18.1	26.1
3	Lagos, Nigeria	13.4	23.2
4	Dhaka, Bangladesh	12.3	21.1
5	São Paulo, Brazil	17.8	20.4
6	Karachi, Pakistan	11.8	19.2
7	Mexico City, Mexico	18.1	19.2
8	Jakarta, Indonesia	11.0	17.3
9	Calcutta, India	12.9	17.3
10	New York, United States*	16.6	17.4
11	Delhi, India	11.7	16.8
12	Manila, Philippines	10.9	14.8
13	Shanghai, China	17.0	19.1
14	Buenos Aires, Argentina	12.6	14.1
15	Los Angeles, United States*	13.1	14.1

*denotes developed country

Toronto, Canada's largest city, had a population of 4 651 000 in 2000, and is predicted to have a population of 5 283 000 by 2015. Compare Toronto with the top 15 cities (ranked by projected population in 2015).

Basic infrastructure is not provided in peripheral areas of cities, where poor migrants are often situated. Some of the lifestyle problems faced by urban populations include the following:

- *Pollution* has increased. This is mainly caused by automobiles, which are large contributors of carbon dioxide emissions.

- There are more *water shortages* and higher levels of *water pollution*. According to the World Health Organization (WHO), the majority of people living in cities in the developing world do not live in sanitary conditions.

- It is difficult to meet the consumer demands of the population, including obtaining *sufficient food* from surrounding land. The Worldwatch Institute reports that London, England, requires 58 times its ecological footprint (land area) to provide an adequate amount of food to its citizens.

- *Energy requirements exceed the supply.* A study by New York-based Allied Business Intelligence suggests that half a million new commercial buildings are constructed every year in the United States. Energy demands from these companies will be difficult to meet.

- The *high volume of vehicles on the roads* makes it difficult for drivers to move both within and around cities.

- Increasing numbers of *unnecessary deaths* occur due to urban conditions. The World Health Organization believes that 700 000 deaths each year are caused by the amounts of carbon monoxide and lead in our urban atmosphere. As well, about 885 000 people are killed each year as a result of auto accidents in cities.

- Communities find it increasingly difficult to find places to dump urban waste.

7. a) Refer to Figure 10–9. Calculate the percentage increase in population for each city, between 2000 and 2015.
   b) Using your calculations, predict the size of the population in 2030 for each of these cities.
   c) Calculate the average increase for the cities in developed countries and in developing countries.
   d) What trends do you see for those cities in developed countries, as opposed to those in developing countries? Write a conclusion based on your calculations.

8. Considering the growth of megacities, what do you feel are the three most serious problems they may experience? For each problem, suggest a step that may help to overcome it.

Case in point — Kenya

The following is adapted from an article by Jane Weru, Director of Pamoja Trust, a non-government organization working with slum dwellers in Kenya.

In Kenya's capital city of Nairobi, there are over 100 slums that are home to 2 million people. The residents of these "informal settlements" constitute 55 percent of the city's total population, yet they are crowded onto only 1.5 percent of the total land area in the city. And even that land is not theirs. The residents of the informal settlements live in constant fear that their homes will be demolished or destroyed in a forced eviction.

The root of this crisis is a government policy that refuses to recognize the urban informal settlements as inhabited areas. The government views the public land on which the poor reside as vacant land that can be transferred at any time to political elites and private individuals for commercial development. In the last decade, Kenya has witnessed much privatization of public land as a means of rewarding political loyalty. Those who occupy this land are simply thrown off it. The result is that a large number of Kenyans are living as refugees in their own country. They have been rendered homeless, and denied their basic human rights and dignity.

FIGURE 10–10 Kenya

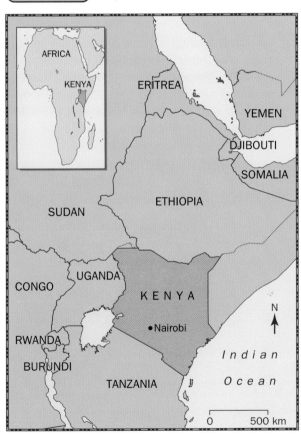

At a glance — Nairobi

- Capital and administrative centre of Kenya, named after local Maasai term *Uaso Nyirobi* (the place of sweet waters)
- Population: 2.5 million. One of the fastest-growing cities in Africa.
- Economy: Manufacturing (textiles, clothing, processed food, construction materials, and communications and transportation equipment). Tourism is an important activity.
- Area: 689 km², including 120 km² of the Nairobi Game Park
- Climate: one of the best of any city in the world — almost on the tropical equator, but at 1660 m of elevation, it has a moderate climate all year long. Average high temperature of 24–29°C almost every day of the year. Constant 12 hours of daylight almost every day.

At the beginning of the nineteenth century, the British government declared vast tracts of land in the colony (including land occupied by indigenous Africans) to be Crown Land, property of the British monarch. It also created "native reserves" in which indigenous Africans were forced to live in order that the best arable land could be taken over and farmed by white settlers. As European settlers continued to expropriate more and more land during the second half of the nineteenth century, colonialists rapidly displaced the vast majority of native Kenyans from their homes.

The post-colonial government failed to address the land issue and millions of Kenyans who had been kept on reserves remained landless squatters. Moreover, due to poverty in the rural areas coupled with a dramatic population growth, a large influx of these landless people migrated to urban areas in search of jobs. Since the state did not (and still does not) provide housing for the poor, this population has been forced to build shacks on vacant government land. Building materials ranging from plastic and cardboard to mud and wattle (interwoven sticks) are their only means of shelter.

The informal settlements in Nairobi (and other Kenyan cities like Mombasa and Nakuru) are severely overcrowded, insecure, and unsanitary; urban infrastructural services are virtually non-existent:

- An average of five to six people live in a room that has an average size of 3 to 6 square metres.

- One-room shanties are sandwiched together so that the density averages 250 housing units per hectare (versus 25 units in middle-class areas and 10 units in high-income areas).

- The only walkways are narrow dirt paths that frequently flood and are impassable during the rainy seasons.

- Residents have no access to electricity.

- Potable water must be purchased from vendors at prices up to ten times higher than the rate charged by local authorities.

- Over 95 percent of the residents do not have access to proper sanitation — people either pay to use a pit latrine shared by approximately 50 people per toilet, or use open areas.

- The city has long since stopped collecting refuse, so garbage lies permanently in stinking heaps, often blocking the drainage channels.

- The lack of sanitary facilities to dispose of human waste and garbage has led to serious environmental and health hazards, including a higher incidence of diseases like typhoid, cholera, and tuberculosis.

- Corruption is rampant. The vast majority of people living in this sector are forced to pay exorbitant rents to local chiefs and wealthy absentee landlords. In some cases, residents are forced to pay a bribe of 3000 Kenyan shillings (about US$40) in order to get permission to repair a leaking roof.

FIGURE 10–11 Residents of Kibera, one of Nairobi's largest informal settlements, take part in the first area-wide clean-up in July 2001.

As a result of this crisis in the informal settlements, the slum dwellers of Nairobi and Mombasa have organized themselves into federations called the *Muungano wa Wanavijiji* (Federation of Slum Dwellers) and the Ilishe Trust, respectively. Their aim is to organize and unite all slum dwellers so that they can resist forced evictions and land grabbing. In addition, these federations are engaged in informing the poor about land rights so that this sector can advocate land law reform.

Land grabbing and forced evictions

On July 1, 2000, the *Muungano* launched an urban land rights campaign in order to highlight the plight of slum dwellers in Kenya — a country that boasts one of the highest disparities of wealth in the world. In that manifesto, the federation demanded:

- a moratorium on demolitions and evictions, to be implemented with the full protection of the law
- official recognition of the right to the land on which the urban poor live
- secure and permanent tenure to the residents of the informal settlements

The *Muungano* is working to unite not only the slum dwellers, but all sectors of society, to press for land law reform. It has received public support from the leaders of the major religious denominations, and the professional associations. This movement is particularly important at this time in Kenya's history because the government, under pressure from the people, has reluctantly agreed to review the constitution. The *Muungano* wants an opportunity to dialogue with the government, and hopes to help revise property and land rights so that all Kenyans can enjoy the full benefit of land in this country.

9. What is meant by the term "informal urban settlements"?

10. How have historical experiences helped to create the problem of landless people in Kenya?

11. What economic conditions have helped to bring about these slum settlements in Nairobi?

12. Describe the work of the *Muungano wa Wanavijiji* in its effort to provide slum dwellers with better security and social conditions. Do you believe that this federation is on the right track toward solving the issue?

Sprawl

Rapid urbanization is a significant current issue facing developing nations; for developed nations, the increase in **sprawl** (the expansion of urban areas, usually along their edges) is the comparable challenge. When towns and cities grow in population, there are two options for accommodating additional people: either the density of population living within the city must increase, or the city must expand outward from its edges. Sprawl is usually an issue of the developed world because it is generally caused by extending roads into outlying areas. In the developing world, however, high-growth cities tend to have higher population densities because such road networks are expensive to build and maintain.

Because people in developed nations depend on the automobile, city planners have built roads and highways connecting commercial areas of cities to the outlying edges, or suburbs. This road network makes it easy for people to live in the outskirts of a city and work in the commerical centres.

There are four types of sprawl (see Figure 10–12):

- **Normal sprawl** usually takes place along the **urban fringe** (edge) of a town or city. This consumes valuable surrounding land at a gradual pace.
- **Leapfrogging** is the development of land at some distance from the urban fringe. This is done to attract buyers of homes on what should be less expensive land.
- **Linear sprawl** stretches outward from a city along major highways. (People like the convenience of being accessible to a highway that connects them to a city.)
- Both leapfrogging and linear sprawl eventually encourage **infilling sprawl**, as developers take advantage of infrastructure and services that have already been provided.

Sprawl profoundly influences most cities in the developed world:

- When cities sprawl into surrounding land, they consume the foodland that surrounds the cities.

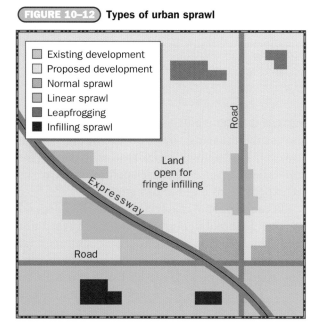

FIGURE 10–12 **Types of urban sprawl**

- Sprawl destroys fragile ecosystems such as wetlands and forests.
- By destroying the sponge effect of natural ground, sprawl contributes to flooding. The paving on roads and parking lots quickly channels water into artificial drains. In extremely heavy rains, these drains often cannot cope and this results in flash floods.
- Sprawl accommodates the personal automobile to the disadvantage of public transportation. If it is easy for people to drive to the centre of town, they will not opt to use the more environmentally friendly bus or subway. In this regard, investments in commuter highways have heavily subsidized the private automobile.
- Sprawl is expensive to service. Stretching out infrastructure such as water pipelines for low densities of people in suburbs is inefficient; providing these areas with police and fire protection is less cost-effective in low-density areas. The result is higher municipal taxes.

There are also social costs involved in sprawl:

- Sprawling suburbs are said to lead to a lack of community identity and a sense of place. Suburbs are often homogenous, with little individual character: chain stores such as Wal-Mart, and franchises such as McDonald's, are repeatedly found in these areas.
- Sprawl consumes time. The average North American is said to spend over 450 hours a year driving to and from work. Over 80 percent of Canada's population currently resides in urban areas, and of these residents, over 50 percent live in the suburbs.

FIGURE 10–13 What are some of the advantages and disadvantages of sprawl?

13. Define and describe the meaning of "urban sprawl."

14. What are the causes of sprawl in developed world cities?

15. Give two examples of the impact of urban sprawl for each of the following headings: Political, Environmental, Social, Economic.

FIGURE 10–14 Rush-hour commutes around Toronto

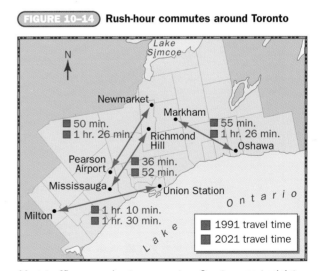

More traffic means longer commutes. One transport ministry study estimated that a trip from Newmarket to Pearson International Airport — which took 50 minutes ten years ago — will take one hour and 26 minutes by the year 2021.

TORONTO'S SPRAWL

A classic case of sprawl is taking place around Canada's largest city. To accommodate the yearly growth in population, Toronto has started to expand outward into its neighbouring municipalities. Most of the development will be in the form of single-family homes (that is, low population density). Toronto will eventually look like most other North American cities — masses of single-family homes dotted with shopping malls.

FIGURE 10–15 Population projections for the GTA (millions)

	1996	2001	2011	2021	2031
GTA	4.781	5.284	6.260	6.975	7.450
Toronto	2.463	2.594	2.855	2.915	3.000
Peel	0.882	1.000	1.185	1.350	1.400
York	0.612	0.760	1.010	1.200	1.360
Durham	0.474	0.530	0.710	0.900	1.000
Halton	0.350	0.400	0.500	0.610	0.690

There are serious consequences of the sprawl that is expanding around Toronto:

- Sprawl will erode the surrounding farmland. This region, which has some of the best soil in Canada, will be lost beneath buildings and highways.

- Housing development will damage the Oak Ridges Moraine — an old glacial deposit of sand and gravel — which is a vital filter and supplier of groundwater for much of the Greater Toronto Area (see Figure 10–16).

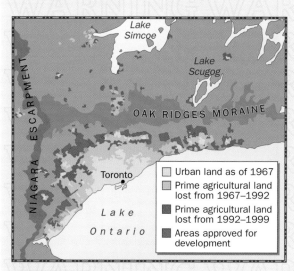

FIGURE 10–16 In 1967, 62 percent of the GTA was prime farm land. This figure is 44 percent today.

Developers have already earmarked this sensitive area for development; environmentalists are trying to save the moraine.

- The larger population will mean that there will be a further 1 million cars on the local roads. A new superhighway — Highway 407 — was recently constructed. This highway runs through the central part of the Greater Toronto Area (GTA) to facilitate better movement of cross-city traffic. Extensions to the northward-flowing 404 highway are also planned. These new highways will add further pressure to the push for development in outlying suburbs.

- The roads in and around Toronto are expected to become more clogged and to reach their maximum capacity by the year 2021. This will add a great deal of time to journeys made across the Greater Toronto Area, and add to the frustration of road users.

What is the answer to this inevitable sprawl? If the problem is seen as purely one of transportation, then the answer could be simple — we need to improve our roads in order to move people and materials around the built-up region more efficiently. However, the problem may not be that simple.

The time-space convergence model (Figure 10–17) demonstrates the dangers of implementing the "wrong" solution. When travel times are seen as intolerably slow, there is a public outcry. Local politicians turn to specialists such as traffic planners to sort out the problem. These planners may suggest adding further roads, or increasing road width, to overcome such problems. As travel time and the frustration of commuting from the edges of cities becomes less, people are temporarily decreasing what geographers call the "friction of distance." This improves the situation for a while, as people can travel greater distances in smaller amounts of time. This is described as **time-space convergence**. However, these improved roads become popular and attract more traffic volume, which in turn contributes to increased traffic jams and travelling time. This is described as **time-space divergence**.

Once more, this leads to an outcry for action, and the cycle begins again.

a) Calculate the percentage growth in population for Toronto and the combined total population for the surrounding municipal regions, between 2001 and 2031.

b) Summarize what is happening to the population growth of:
  • Toronto
  • the surrounding regions

c) How does this data demonstrate that urban sprawl is affecting the Greater Toronto Area?

d) The problem of sprawl affects many global cities. Research the problem of sprawl in two other cities. Compare the amount of sprawl they are experiencing, the causes for the sprawl, and what these cities are doing to overcome the problem.

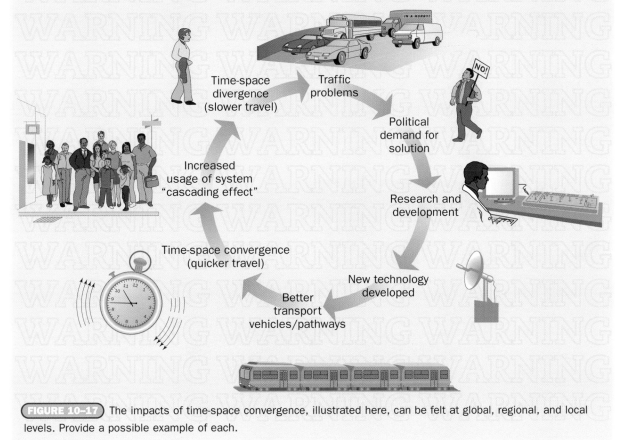

Time-space divergence (slower travel)

Traffic problems

Political demand for solution

Research and development

New technology developed

Better transport vehicles/pathways

Time-space convergence (quicker travel)

Increased usage of system "cascading effect"

FIGURE 10–17 The impacts of time-space convergence, illustrated here, can be felt at global, regional, and local levels. Provide a possible example of each.

Profiling: A technical and statistical technique

Every day, we make decisions based on a large number of factors. Given certain conditions, we try to create a picture in our minds about what the most likely outcome will be. This is called "profiling."

Profiling can be used in almost any field where a decision has to be made and where there are many factors to consider. For example, if there is an infestation of pests in a farmer's field, a profile of the pest is required. Variables must be considered: What type of bug is it? When does it attack? What damage will it do? What might be the best way to neutralize the pest? This type of analysis can be complex and often requires the use of advanced statistical techniques such as factor analysis.

To create a profile, it is necessary to determine what factors will have the greatest and most direct impact on the result. For example, it is possible to identify numerous variables that could cause a car accident. These variables could include the emotional state of the driver; the type of car; the speed of the car; the behaviour of other drivers; the time of day; and the road conditions. However, if the driver had consumed alcohol before getting into the car, this might be the most sig-

nificant factor. Factor analysis is simply a way of distilling a huge number of variables into the few variables that have the most significant impact. In this way, it becomes easier to identify a likely result based on any set of variables. In today's technological world, most of these types of analyses are performed using computer technology.

Transportation and traffic profiling

In most cities, especially wealthy ones, the automobile is the preferred method of travel. As cities expand, the distance people routinely travel gets longer, due to urban sprawl. The Province of Ontario's Ministry of Transportation uses some very sophisticated technology to monitor traffic on its major provincial highways. The Queen Elizabeth Way (QEW) and parts of Highway 401 through Toronto have a system called COMPASS for highway traffic maintenance. This system uses a series of cameras, digital message boards situated on the highway, computers and related network components, road and ramp sensors, and a traffic operations centre to determine what traffic conditions are like at any time.

FIGURE 10–18 Here is one component in the COMPASS traffic monitoring system. The system saves commuters many hours every day by warning them of problem areas along the highway.

The system is designed to increase safety and optimize the flow of traffic by monitoring road conditions:

- Sensors buried within the road's surface determine the number of vehicles that are passing over them, vehicle speed, and a myriad of other characteristics.
- The sensors relay information to computers that analyse the characteristics of the traffic flow and create a profile of what the conditions on the road are like.
- The profile is sent to the traffic operations centre.
- An operator examines the profile and places a message on the digital message board. This message could be a statement that traffic is flowing well, or a warning of an accident ahead with a suggested alternate route.

Anti-ice technology

A system that has been tested by the Ministry of Transportation in Ontario is the Fixed Automated Spray Technology (FAST). This is a system for reducing ice on highways and bridges by spraying a liquid de-icing chemical to *prevent* the formation of ice. Although FAST is not widely used in the province, field testing has shown that it could be highly effective in reducing highway ice and its related hazards.

- Remote sensors detect the potential formation of ice and frost. A complete road weather information system (RWIS) is used to determine air temperature, wind speed and direction, precipitation, relative humidity, dew point (100 percent saturation of the air with moisture), and a variety of other variables.
- All of the information is compiled by computers into a profile of the potential for ice formation on the road. The Fixed Automated Spray Technology system monitors critical factors such as pavement temperature, moisture, and ice/snow/frost conditions.
- As conditions alter, adjustments can be made to the concentrations of various anti-icing chemicals. When certain variables are at critical thresholds, the system activates small nozzles in the road that spray the optimal chemical "cocktail" onto the road. This prevents a buildup of potentially deadly ice on the road surface.

a) Summarize the advantages and disadvantages of using profiling to determine the most likely result of a situation. Can profiles always be trusted?

b) If a profile is used to determine the most likely result of a situation and something goes wrong, who should be held responsible for that error? For example, if the Fixed Automated Spray Technology system sprays to de-ice an area of highway but someone still has a car accident, who should be responsible?

c) The automotive insurance industry uses profiles all the time. Insurance rates for teenage boys are many times higher than that of teenage girls. Is this fair, or a case of discrimination? Discuss this with your classmates.

Check out www.gagelearning.com/onthethreshold for links to Web sites related to a range of topics, including geographical information systems (GIS) activities related to transportation.

FIGURE 10–19 The FAST system is designed to help prevent ice-related accidents like this one.

Solutions to Urban Sprawl

There have been many suggestions for overcoming the growth of urban sprawl. Some of these involve radical thinking concerning transportation systems. Others involve the redesigning of communities to make them more intimate and to create a sense of place and identity.

Mass transit

Perhaps we should de-emphasize the automobile as the preferred method of transportation, as systems of mass transit are more efficient. However, because mass transit requires a large number of commuters to make it profitable, it is thought to be feasible only in places where living densities are high.

Some cities — such as Baltimore, Maryland — have attempted to improve the efficiency of their transport systems, but without much success. This is because they tried to impose new solutions for commuting on an old system of housing sprawl; low-density housing is expensive to service due to the relatively large distance between houses. San Francisco has also tried to introduce radical transportation plans, including small taxi-like systems, special express buses, timed-transfer arrangements (buses timed to meet others so that passengers could transfer without waiting), and special bus routes. None of these has worked well.

On the other hand, the city of Curitiba in southeast Brazil has had some success. As an alternative to allowing sprawl to spread outward in an ever-increasing circle, planners designed five radial roads that led to the centre of the city. These roads were designed for high-speed bus transit: two lanes along the median strip (a strip of land down the centre of a road, for aesthetic or safety purposes) were reserved for express buses. The number of passengers equalled that usually experienced by expensive rail systems. Suburban development was designed around these arterial access routes.

Perhaps sprawl is not a transit problem after all, but one of urban planning and the effective design of land use.

FIGURE 10–20 In North America, people try to design solutions for high-speed commuting using old roads and concentric, low-density sprawl (for example, putting a new "express" bus on an existing road).

Land use

What can be done to slow down outward urban expansion?

■ Developers are in the business of making a profit. Municipalities could *discourage outward growth* by adding heavy taxes on development in fringe areas, where schools and sewer lines are expensive to build and maintain.

■ Greater focus could be placed on legislation to *increase population densities within existing towns and cities*. In the mid-1980s, the city council in Portland, Oregon — worried about sprawl — drew a line around the city and prevented growth beyond that line. This was highly successful, but critics have recently suggested that property values within the boundary are now rising too fast for middle-class people to afford.

One of the strongest developments in overcoming sprawl is new urbanism, also called "neo-traditional urban planning" by many professionals because it reminds them of the early urban designs of European communities. In 2001, there were some 375 such developments either built, under construction, or planned within the United States. In Canada, the best-known examples are the Cornell development in Markham (which will eventually contain 10 360 housing units) and the East Riverside development in Windsor.

Not everyone agrees that new urbanism is the answer to sprawl. Some criticisms include:

■ People continue to rely on cars for work, shopping, and recreation, partially because of poorly expanded public transportation systems.

FIGURE 10–21 Critics believe that new urbanism keeps people out of city centres, except to work.

■ New urbanism encourages lifestyles that avoid city centres by providing cheaper land, sewage systems, and transportation systems on the edges of cities.

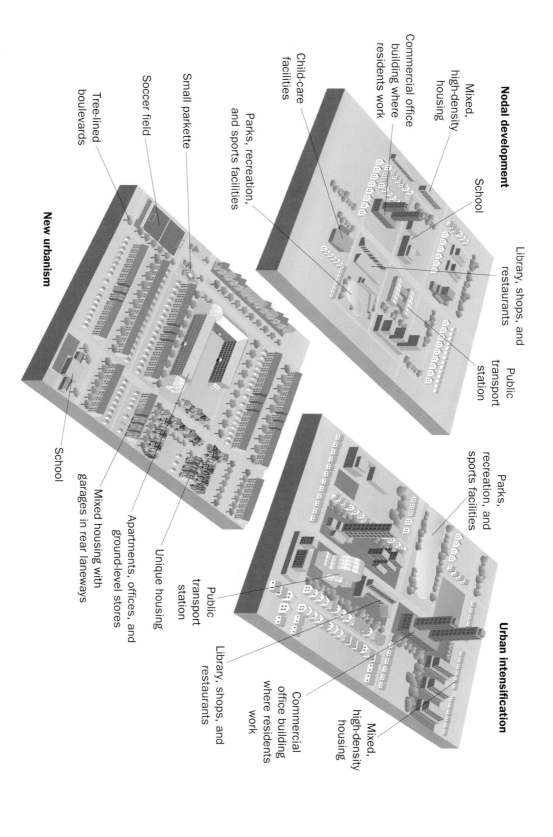

Nodal development

Mixed, high-density housing

Commercial office building where residents work

School

Child-care facilities

Parks, recreation, and sports facilities

Small parkette

Soccer field

Tree-lined boulevards

Library, shops, and restaurants

Public transport station

New urbanism

School

Mixed housing with garages in rear laneways

Apartments, offices, and ground-level stores

Unique housing

Public transport station

Library, shops, and restaurants

Urban intensification

Parks, recreation, and sports facilities

Commercial office building where residents work

Mixed, high-density housing

FIGURE 10-22 Three models — nodal development, urban intensification, and new urbanism — suggest different approaches to coping with, or preventing, sprawl.

FIGURE 10-23 Models for coping with sprawl

	Nodal development	Urban intensification	New urbanism
Residents per hectare	375–625	500–1000	100
Location	Modified, older community or new community in fringe of city.	Old industrial areas or rail land within city.	Usually on the outer edges of the city development.
Travel needs	50 percent of residents will commute out of area to work or school by public transportation.	Many work locally or take streetcar, subway, or bus to work. If work is outside of city, driving is against the flow.	Both home-based telecommuting and travel to downtown. Cars are discouraged. Concept is of a "main street" where people work and shop within their own community rather than driving to malls and workplaces.
Type of buildings	Mixed: towers, condominiums, low- and medium-rise rental apartments, townhouses, detached and semi-detached homes. Some underground parking. Small, if any, yards.	Condominiums, office towers, highrise apartments, townhouses. Underground parking. Few single family homes.	Narrow, tall townhouses; some duplex, semi-detached, and detached. Houses close to street (no front yard). Small back yards. Parking in lanes behind streets.
Facilities	Libraries, schools, parks, and shops within walking distance from homes. Retail and office space at street level.	Close to downtown facilities (jobs, entertainment, and parks). Schools, parks, and shops within walking distance of homes.	Small parkettes in each block. Shops and schools within walking distance. Some office space. Sidewalks, tree-lined medians, and narrower streets to encourage walking and to slow down traffic.

FIGURE 10-24 When a transit system breaks down, commuters suffer long waits. Which of the three models for coping with sprawl could best cope with a breakdown, such as this one, which was due to a snowstorm?

Welcome town planners!

Now it's your turn to work with the problem of sprawl. There is no better way to do this than to design a community that will reflect the values of current lifestyles, yet still overcome the negative effects of sprawl.

As one of the few planning teams selected by the town of Greenfield, you and your three team members have been requested to submit designs for a new suburban community. This community will be situated on 1000 hectares located approximately 40 kilometres east of Urbanville — a sprawling metropolis of 1.8 million people. Officials are concerned about the rapid and uncontrolled population growth of Greenfield, as well as its inefficient land use. This former farming town is looking for an alternative approach to the traditional suburban communities that have been developed in neighbouring townships. The new community will need to accommodate 25 000 people over the next 15 to 20 years. A map of the area has been supplied. The town has suggested the following procedure and criteria for planning designs:

a) Planning teams should review the following criteria, as well as the map of the area for proposed development. Brainstorm a list of factors to be considered when selecting a site for your community.

b) Using your list of factors, discuss and select the site for your community. The site should cover an area of approximately 8 to 10 square kilometres. Outline the general shape of the proposed site on the small copy of the map. Title this map "rough copy."

c) As part of your official plan, specifically describe your design goals for *each* of the following points. A rough draft is recommended.
- target market(s)
- lot style (for example, long and narrow or wide and shallow)
- density (for example, number of people per hectare; number of houses per hectare; number of people per house/lot. (Note: 1 hectare = 10 000 square metres)
- housing types and styles (relating to density), transportation services, and road networks
- shopping and recreational facilities
- future location of businesses
- preservation of the environment and "green space"

d) On your rough map, outline where the various types of land uses for your community will be located. Use the table in Figure 10–25, which outlines the colour codes and specifications for land use, to guide your design. Also include the main street, collector streets (streets that take traffic from local streets and move it to arterial roads), and major arterial roads. (Note: A five-minute walk is equal to approximately 400 to 500 metres. You may wish to divide your overall community into four or five smaller communities to ensure that a sense of place and proximity is created.)

FIGURE 10–25 Land use chart

Land use	Colour code	% of land use
Residential (various types of housing)	yellow	60%
Commercial (stores, shops, services)	red	5%
Industrial (businesses)	blue	5%
Institutional (1 high school, 3 elementary schools, 2 community centres, 1 hospital)	grey	5%
Open space and recreation (green spaces, environmentally sensitive areas, and parks): also include a green space 10 m wide, as a "buffer zone" between buildings and environmentally sensitive areas	green	25%

e) Transfer the information from your rough map onto an enlarged map of the proposed site *or* redraw it onto chart paper, remembering to include the scale. Give this new map the title "master plan" and include a detailed legend.

f) Draw a detailed site plan for one neighbourhood in your community. Indicate where this neighbourhood is located on your master plan. The site plan needs to include:
- 30 to 50 lots
- community centres
- routes of streets and lanes
- commercial facilities
- a segment of the main street
- schools (200 metres in length)
- lot shapes
- detailed legend (use topographic symbols)
- open spaces, parks, green spaces
- street names

g) Using as much detail as possible, on three sheets of 8.5 × 11 paper, accurately sketch the designs of:
- three different styles of homes (exterior) in your sample neighbourhood, drawn from eye level
- the location of these homes on their lots from a bird's-eye view (remembering to include lanes and garages)
- a shopping facility *or* a recreational facility, drawn from eye level

h) In your official plan, add a section titled "Responses." In this section, explain in detail how the following situations would affect the design/planning of your community:
- Environmental groups express their concerns about the impact of your community on the wetlands in the area and are very vocal about your construction practices.
- Halfway through the construction of your first neighbourhood, a lumber strike occurs and you need to consider alternative building materials.
- A major company in Urbanville lays off thousands of employees at all income-earning levels.
- The town requests that your community be able to hold another 15 000 residents within the next 20 years.

i) Create a suitable name *and* an eye-catching logo for your new community.

j) Professionally organize and display your maps (master plan and site map), community name, logo, and sketches. Include your typed official plan with your display. Be prepared to give a presentation (about 10 to 15 minutes) that describes and explains the choices you have made for your design, and which discusses the design's strengths. You should also be prepared to defend any design weaknesses.

Make notes on the presentations given by the other groups. Using these notes, outline the criteria that you think are essential for the successful design of a new suburban community.

FIGURE 10–26 What will your plan for a new urban community look like?

Social Issues

In a world in which we all strive to adapt to change and new challenges, a fundamental global resource should not be overlooked — us! Human resources and social issues play a significant role in our ever-changing global community.

Gender inequality

Whether at an individual, national, or international level, a core issue that challenges our social progress is gender inequality, that is, the unequal power afforded males and females due to the different roles assigned to them by society. It most often negatively affects women.

People have begun to work toward solving this issue that impacts our political, social, and economic structures, regardless of time, or wealth, or where we live in the world. Even one of the United Nations' top-ranked places in the world to live — Norway — is experiencing significant gender differences in the workforce: only 5 percent of women working in offices hold managerial positions. This is not due to differing levels of education, since women in Norway make up the majority of university students, but to stereotypical views that men are the "breadwinners."

Gender inequality is a long-standing global issue, but over the past few decades, it has been receiving greater international attention. A session of the United Nations General Assembly called "Women 2000: Gender Equity, Development, and Peace in the Twenty-First Century" attempted to go beyond the conventional links between population, development, and women's equality, expanding them to also link the advancement of women with other global issues such as poverty, disease, illiteracy, violence, conflict, and political power.

By examining how these global challenges affect women, organizations are able to provide policy direction and action to assist governments and communities in combatting gender inequality.

- Poverty: The United Nations Development Fund for Women (UNIFEM) argues that 70 percent of people living in poverty are women. The World Bank reports that countries facing a crisis of gender inequality tend also to have more poverty, slower economic growth, and a lower quality of life than societies with less gender discrimination.

- Disease: The emergence of new diseases and the persistence of existing ones present a major challenge to many countries, particularly if access to adequate primary health care and medicine is limited. The United Nations AIDS Epidemic Update Report in 2000 estimated that 36 million people worldwide are infected with HIV/AIDS, of which over 16 million are women. Since its discovery in the early 1980s, 9 million women have died of the disease.

FIGURE 10–27 Do you see evidence of gender inequality in your daily life?

The United Nations Development Fund for Women suggests that as gender inequalities continue, more women are being affected by this epidemic as a result of limited access to education, health-care facilities, prevention programs, self-sustaining employment, and the influence of social norms on the role of women.

- Illiteracy: According to the United Nations High Commissioner for Human Rights, the literacy rate for women worldwide is 71 percent, while it is 84 percent for men. However, in developing countries, the literacy rate for women is only 39 percent, as opposed to almost 60 percent for men. Of the 130 million school-age children worldwide who do not receive an education, 56 percent are girls; of the 930 million illiterate adults worldwide, 67 percent are women.

- Violence: In a recent United Nations Children's Fund (UNICEF) Report on Violence Against Women, it is estimated that 20 to 25 percent of women around the world have experienced domestic violence. The International Centre for Migration Policy Development estimates that of the almost half million people smuggled into the European Union (EU) each year, the majority are females attracted by false promises of employment, and who often find themselves involved with the sex trade or forced labour.

- Conflict: The United Nations Development Fund for Women asks, "If women are half of every community, are they therefore not half of every solution?" A United Nations study on the role of women in the peacekeeping process found that women's participation in missions encouraged more women to become involved in the peace process, and that women living in conflict areas would feel more comfortable confiding in a female peacekeeper. Nevertheless, only five women had leadership positions in the large United Nations mission to Kosovo in 1999.

- Political power: Even though women constitute one-half of the world's population, no country has equal numbers of women and men in political decision-making roles. Women make up only 12 percent of all legislative bodies in the world. For democratic political systems in North America and Europe, the lack of women in politics is viewed as a deficit of democracy. According to the United Nations Development Fund for Women, only 8 nations — most of them Scandinavian — have reached the globally agreed target that women should occupy at least 30 percent of seats in national parliaments. The most dramatic increase in the number of women involved in politics occurred in South Africa in the mid-1990s, following the end of apartheid: the number grew from one individual to 30 percent of the governing body. With the exception of a few nations, why are the numbers so low? In some countries, women fear the hostility that might face them if they were to seek political power. Some women may be reluctant to add further commitments to their career and family responsibilities.

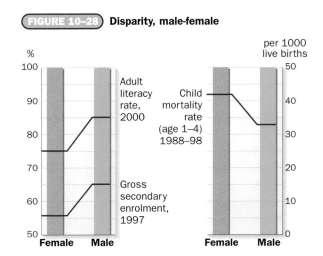

FIGURE 10-28 Disparity, male-female

Across the world, women lag behind men in literacy and secondary enrolment. They surpass men in one area — child mortality.

Narrowing the gender divide

Even though the challenges regarding gender equality are presented separately above, it is important to keep in mind that the contributing factors are interconnected. For example, if a woman is uneducated and illiterate, how will she find employment, let alone run in a local election? The World Bank suggests that countries work to ensure that men and women have the same rights and equal access to education, jobs, property, and credit. They believe that if women's involvement in politics increases, child mortality will decrease, population growth will be slowed, and overall economic development will improve.

The Grameen Bank in Bangladesh, for example, does not follow conventional banking processes — it provides credit to its poorest customers in rural Bangladesh, without any collateral, or additional assets (that is, property, stocks, or bonds) promised as security for repayment of the loan. Currently, the Grameen Bank is the largest rural finance institution in Bangladesh, with more than 2.3 million borrowers, 94 percent of whom are women. The Grameen Bank's founder argues that providing millions of poor people — including poor women — with needed credit, "… can add up to create the biggest development wonder."

Other possible solutions or actions to narrow, or even remove, the gender divide include:

- Gender mainstreaming: Proposed by a branch of the Organization for Economic Co-operation and Development, gender mainstreaming aims to increase opportunities for women (and for disadvantaged men) through training, information sharing, and education. For example, in the Philippines, Jamaica, and South Africa, gender-mainstreaming policies have taken into account the different needs and perspectives of men and women. This has resulted in increased female literacy rates and greater numbers of women working in civil service.

- Political involvement: Both India and Uganda have constitutional guarantees that one-third of seats in local politics are to be filled by women.

- International laws: The Convention on the Elimination of All Forms of Discrimination Against Women (CEDAW), adopted by the United Nations General Assembly in 1979, is often described as having created an international bill of rights for women. CEDAW created a standard definition of gender discrimination, and legally binding obligations for member states. This was done in order to end discrimination against women by incorporating equality into the legal system, establishing tribunals or public institutions to protect women against discrimination, and ensuring the elimination of all acts of discrimination against women. Today, 168 states have signed the CEDAW agreement.

- Education: In Brazil, illiterate women have 6.5 children on average, while those with high-school education have an average of 2.5 children. In Africa and south Asia, education has provided females with an opportunity to develop more efficient farming methods, improve crop output, and raise awareness of the ecology of the land.

- Women in peacekeeping: In 2000, the United Nations Security Council officially stated that they would include more women in international peacemaking negotiations and missions by sending women as special representatives to conflict regions as ceasefire negotiators and as policy advisors.

- Technology: The Association for the Development of Women and Health, formed by the United Nations Development Programme, set up an Internet service to provide women in rural Cameroon with an opportunity to exchange or research information about agricultural practices. In a country with only one telephone line for every 200 people, the program relied on its Web site, and the help of the organization's members in setting up computers in several towns and villages. According to the United Nations Development Programme, this service now assists over 10 000 people through its Internet help desk.

A female NATO peacekeeper writes home from abroad. The UN believes that more women should assume peacekeeping roles.

16. Outline and briefly describe the main challenges facing women in our global community.

17. Are these challenges only limited to women in developing nations? Why or why not?

18. Create five newspaper headlines that you think would describe the issue of gender inequality. Remember, your headlines need to grab the reader's attention, but should not mislead them.

19. Using one of your newspaper headlines, write a news article that would provide the reader with a more informed understanding about the gender inequality topic raised in the headline.

20. Review the possible solutions outlined in the text. Which do you think would be the most/least challenging to implement? Justify your selection.

21. In addition to those solutions given in this chapter, brainstorm a list of possible solutions to the issue of gender inequality. How many more can you think of?

22. As a co-ordinator for Women's Rights International, you need to devise a new awareness campaign about gender inequality. Your campaign needs to have a title, purpose statement, brief outline of why people should be concerned and what they should do, a catchy slogan, and a sketch or model of an item that people can use or wear to show their support for your campaign.

Case in point — Canada

Throughout history, women have had fewer rights and opportunities than males. In North America, the twentieth century witnessed the rise of women's movements that challenged the stereotypical roles that women played in society.

The issue of gender equality in Canada is deeply rooted. It was brought to the forefront in the early 1900s through the **suffragist movement** (that promoted giving women the vote). Today, as women and men continue to work for greater income equality in order to help reduce the **gender gap**, modern laws such as **affirmative action** have been passed. These laws seek to ensure equal social and economic opportunities through preferential hiring practices and pay equity (equal pay for work of equal value).

Despite these efforts, the gender gap still exists in Canada, especially in terms of income. According to a 2001 Status Report on Gender Inequality in Canada, women still lag behind men in terms of their earning power.

At a glance — *Gender inequality in Canada*

Occupation and gender in Canada

Occupation	% females
Skilled crafts and trades	5
• tailors and dressmakers	85.5
• carpenters and cabinetmakers	2
Clerical personnel	71
Senior managers	21
Middle managers	33.5
Professionals	53
• nurses	95
• teachers	69
• engineers	15
Skilled services	43
• hairstylists	82
• police and firefighters	10
Semi-professionals and technicians	48

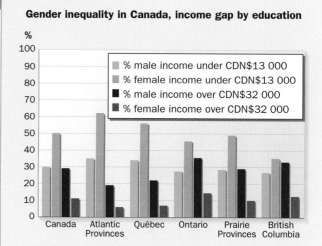

Gender inequality in Canada, income gap by education

- % male income under CDN$13 000
- % female income under CDN$13 000
- % male income over CDN$32 000
- % female income over CDN$32 000

Income and gender across Canada

Region	% male income under CDN$13 000	% female income under CDN$13 000	% male income over CDN$32 000	% female income over CDN$32 000
Canada	30	50	29	11
Atlantic Provinces	35	62	19	6
Québec	34	56	22	7
Ontario	27.5	45.5	35.5	14.5
Prairie Provinces	28.5	49	29	10
British Columbia	27	35	33	12.5

In terms of income levels, the 2001 Status Report on Gender Inequality in Canada found that:

- Women's incomes average only 61 percent of what men earn.
- Of people living in poverty, 20 percent are women (in particular, visible minorities, and/or those who are single mothers, have disabilities, or who live alone).
- Significantly fewer top income earners are women.

- There are very few women in certain professions or skilled trades such as fire or police services.
- Women hold only 21 percent of senior management jobs.

The Statistics Canada (StatsCan) report titled "Women in Canada 2000" mirrors some of the above findings:

- The majority of employed women continue to work in occupations in which women have traditionally been concentrated.

- Even though the number of women in managerial positions (as well as financial and professional fields) has increased their share in the total employment, women continue to account for only about one in five professionals employed in the natural sciences, mathematics, and engineering.

- Even when employed, women are still largely responsible for looking after their homes and families.

- The average earnings of employed women are still substantially lower than those of men.

- Women continue to make up the large majority of single parents.

Parts of the picture show a slight reduction in the gender gap:

- Women who work in unionized environments like the Canadian Union of Public Employees (CUPE) earn an average of 82 percent of men's income.

- Higher levels of female education help to reduce the income gap between men and women.

- According to Statistics Canada, over 50 percent of women aged 15 years and older are working today, compared to 42 percent, 25 years ago.

- Unemployment rates in 1999 were slightly lower among women (7.3%) than men (7.8%).

Nevertheless, Canadian society still has a long way to go. Women are still overwhelmingly relegated to part-time, temporary, and often low-paying jobs with little economic security. It may be that greater family responsibilities continue to be placed on women. As the structure of our society changes — under the influence of factors such as later marriages, higher divorce rates, double-income families, and single motherhood — women and their families are becoming more reliant on women's incomes. If many women continue to find themselves in low-paying jobs, and with limited access to education, then higher rates of poverty will result, and the overall health and productivity of our society will suffer.

What can we do about this? The 2001 Status Report on Gender Inequality in Canada outlines the following suggestions:

- A national child-care program should be implemented to provide women with greater employment flexibility.

- The rate of unionization should be increased to provide an avenue for organization and negotiation around wages, working conditions, and job security.

- Women should have greater access to colleges and universities via loans or reduced tuition fees, or free access to these institutions.

- Women should have more access to full-time employment and/or benefits, and there should be more job security for part-time workers.

- Pension plans for women should be improved, regardless of earnings and/or years in the workforce.

This report has outlined a few possible solutions to a complex issue facing Canadian society. It is the responsibility of every global citizen to recognize challenges and to work toward changes that aim to create greater equality for all members of our society.

23. Why does a gender gap between men and women continue to exist in Canada? Make a list of facts as supporting evidence.

24. a) Using your list of facts from the previous question, select three pieces of evidence that you think are most worrying about the gender divide in Canada.
    b) Briefly explain why you selected these three facts and outline possible solutions to the situation.

25. Write a letter in response to the 2001 Status Report on Gender Inequality in Canada, expressing your opinion about gender inequality in Canada and outlining what steps you think government, businesses, and society as a whole should take.

Conference planning

You and a team of fellow international consultants have been hired by the United Nations to plan a world conference that addresses one of the many social issues facing our global community in the twenty-first century. Your goal is to make a digital presentation to the United Nations Communications Panel (your classmates and teacher).

Your presentation must outline:

- the focus of your conference and your conference title
- the location of the conference
- a brief biography of the keynote speaker

To accomplish this goal, you will need to do the following:

- Complete preliminary research for a minimum of three global social issues such as (but not limited to) equity and racism, disease, urban sprawl, and technological advancements.
- Once your preliminary research is complete, select one social issue that your group considers most pressing to our global community. Gather more information about your selected issue.
- Using the gathered information, analyse the issue in terms of its political, environmental, social, and economic aspects.
- From your analysis and research, develop a focus for the conference. Give the conference a name, and provide a written paragraph explaining why the issue has been selected.
- Research several international conferences online. Examine the ways in which these conferences are (or were) organized and promoted. What do you like and dislike about these conferences? What sorts of individuals are invited to speak at these conferences? Which elements might be applied successfully in your own conference planning?

- Determine the location of the conference and explain how your site selection will contribute to the success of your conference.
- Select a keynote speaker for the conference. A strong keynote speaker will attract people to the conference and will enlighten and motivate the audience. Look for individuals who are viewed as "global contributors" — Nelson Mandela, Mary Robinson, Mother Teresa, or Kofi Annan. Your speaker should have some connection to the issue your conference will be discussing.
- Include a brief biography of your chosen keynote speaker, outlining her or his contributions and current role in society. For ideas, research biographies of keynote speakers at recent or upcoming conferences.

The United Nations Communications Panel will evaluate your presentations. The panel will use the information to determine which five conferences they will sponsor over the next five years, in their efforts to raise awareness, discussions, and possible solutions to global social issues.

FIGURE 10–30 Nelson Mandela, a much admired keynote speaker, addresses the House of Commons in Ottawa.

Course Culminating Activity

Reflecting back — Looking forward

You have completed a study of significant world issues that are facing the world today. These issues are in a continual process of change.

It is appropriate in a chapter titled "Change and Challenge" to reflect upon these two notions with regard to issues that are of particular interest to you. On page 3 in Chapter 1, you were asked to collect a portfolio of articles regarding one issue of your choice.

a) Review the articles and make point-form notes under the headings "Change" and "Challenge." What are the specific challenges this issue offers the global community? What about the local community? To what extent is your chosen issue in a process of change? Has the issue, or media coverage of it, changed since you first began your portfolio? How?

b) Reflect on how your feelings about this issue have changed or evolved over the duration of the course, and how you predict the issue will unfold or be resolved in the future.

c) Based on your portfolio, how do you think the media have influenced public opinion of your issue? Is a balance evident in the coverage, or does it seem one-sided?

d) Select one article or resource from your portfolio that facilitates a greater understanding of the issue than the others. This is an issue "cornerstone." Be prepared to justify its selection.

e) In groups of four, share your portfolios with one another. Explain your thoughts on parts b) and c) above.

f) If you could do this activity again, would you select the same issue? Why or why not?

Contents

The "issues approach" to solving problems

Step 1: Define the issue. World issues are complicated. For example, consider some of the issues related to the ocean: fisheries worldwide are catching fewer fish than 20 years ago; the growing world population demands greater amounts of fish for food; oceans are becoming increasingly polluted. The many different aspects to problems such as these can be overwhelming.

The first step in analysing an issue is to define the issue itself in clear terms. Which issue do you wish to analyse: Overfishing? Global population growth? Ocean pollution? Or would you like to consider all issues currently affecting the ocean? It is important to know your goal — which specific issue you wish to analyse — up front.

Step 2: Brainstorm. Brainstorming is writing down everything you already know about a topic so that you may refer to it as you analyse the issue. This can be done individually or in groups. While brainstorming, you may also think of questions about the topic. Questions are helpful because they can guide your research further on. The web diagram shown on page 5 of Chapter 1 (and again in each chapter) is an excellent way to get your thoughts on paper.

The order or organization of items is not important; what is important is writing down as many words or phrases as possible that relate to the issue. You may be surprised at the ideas that come to mind while you work through this process.

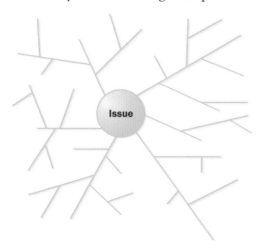

Step 3: Organize your thoughts. Brainstorming involves knowledge you already have about the issue. Depending on your level of knowledge, or the number of questions you come up with, your webbing diagram may be very complex. It is helpful to organize these individual items into the four categories introduced in Chapter 1 (page 5). These categories are: political, environmental, social, and economic.

Decide where each of the items on your web diagram fits best and add it to your organizer. For example, "ocean pollution" fits best under the *environmental* heading, while "loss of jobs for people in the fishing industry" fits best under *economic* implications.

It is important to note that many items could fit under more than one heading. This is because the many factors related to any individual issue are interrelated. The loss of jobs in a fishing town is not only an economic consequence of the issue, but it will also have social implications, as people must find new means of earning a living. If you find it helpful, you may wish to write items like this under both headings on your organizer.

This issue-organizer step can be completed again after you have fully researched the issue (Step 4) as a means of organizing the new information you have gathered.

Step 4: Research. Now that you have begun to clarify your thoughts on the issue, it is time to add to your knowledge of the topic. The best way to start your research is to read newspapers or magazines, to search for your topic on the Internet, and to visit the library for books on the topic. Consider breaking the issue down into subtopics and research each individually.

If possible, consult a variety of **primary and secondary sources**. Primary sources are original, first-hand sources of information. For example, a specialist who conducts research on your topic could provide information and would be a primary source. Surveys, experiments, and eyewitness reports are examples of primary sources of information. On the other hand, an article on your issue in a news-magazine, written by an author who researched the topic from other sources, would be a secondary source.

Step 5: Organize your research. Organize your research in each research session, and again once all your research is complete. You may choose to update or recreate the Issues organizer you created in Step 3. This is a good way to consider each implication independently, and to see the interrelation among the four categories.

Step 6: Formulate possible solutions. Now that you have researched the issue and have analysed its political, environmental, social, and economic aspects and implications, you are ready to formulate possible solutions to the issue. This can be done individually or in groups. You may wish to brainstorm some solutions on your own first and than gather with others to share ideas and decide as a group on the best solutions.

Step 7: Create a plan of action. Depending on the issue you have analysed and the solutions you have considered, you may create a plan of action. Consider the possible solutions to the issue — are they solutions you can take part in? Can you, for example, write a letter to a politician or government official explaining your ideas, or suggesting ways to improve the situation? Can you make a change in your life that would improve the situation? If so, you may create a detailed plan of action and begin making a positive difference!

Distinguishing between fact and opinion

It is important when analysing issues or doing research of any kind to distinguish between fact and opinion. This is similar to being aware of bias (see Chapter 1, page 5). While facts are things that can be shown to be true, opinions are conclusions an individual or group draws from the facts. These opinions are subject to interpretation, and therefore bias.

Examples of facts and opinions:

Fact	Opinion
According to Statistics Canada, over 50 percent of women aged 15 years and older are working today, compared to 42 percent, 25 years ago.	According to one prominent human rights organization, despite the fact that progress has been made in terms of gender equality, this progress has not come quickly enough.
In 2000, Tanzania spent nearly five times more money paying its external debt than it spent on the country's entire health-care costs.	Those governments to whom Tanzania is in debt should consider forgiving the debts so Tanzania is able to spend more on health care.

WHERE TO FIND INFORMATION

- library
- textbooks
- the Internet
- people in your school or community (teachers, principals, local politicians, experts in the subject area such as scientists, researchers, or academics)
- organizations and community groups
- corporations and businesses
- magazines and newspapers
- films

Researching on the Internet

The World Wide Web, or Internet, is a useful tool for conducting research. Information on the Internet is up to date, but it is important to note that it is not always accurate. Anyone who wishes to post information or opinions on the Internet can do so, making it important to analyse the source of a piece of information to determine whether it is credible or not. Even if you are confident a source is reliable, it is wise to check all facts against at least one other source.

Below are some popular search engines to help you locate information on your chosen topics. To use a search engine, simply enter a key word or phrase. For example, to locate information on the African country Sudan, you might enter "Sudan" or "Africa" to begin your search.

POPULAR SEARCH ENGINES

- AltaVista www.altavista.com
- Canada.com www.canada.com
- Excite www.excite.com
- HotBot www.hotbot.lycos.com
- LookSmart www.looksmart.com
- Lycos www.lycos.com
- Yahoo! www.yahoo.com
- Yahoo! Canada ca.yahoo.com

Writing essays or research papers

A research paper is a paper researched and written to support and explain an opinion. Use the research tips on page 304 to conduct useful research sessions.

Compose a thesis statement. Once you have completed your initial research, it is time to compose a thesis statement, that is, a statement of your position on a topic. Examples:

- *Global warming is a threat to local ecosystems.*
- *Drip irrigation methods will improve freshwater availability in the Middle East.*

Your thesis will guide the remainder of your research because it clarifies your goal.

Get support for your thesis. You have done enough research to develop your position statement, but you may not have gathered enough support to prove it in your research paper. Continue to research your topic until you are satisfied you can fully support and explain your position on the issue.

Assemble an outline. An outline helps you organize facts and arguments about your topic. Remember that an outline is not fixed; it is a guide for your rough draft and final copy. You may choose to alter the structure of the paper as you write.

TIPS FOR CREATING AN OUTLINE

- Write your thesis at the top of your outline.
- Include your introduction and your conclusion — point form is adequate at this stage.
- Organize your information in a logical sequence, ensuring every item relates back to your thesis statement.
- Eliminate any weaker sections, or research these areas more fully.

Write a draft. A draft is a rough version of the paper. Do not spend time polishing your sentences. This is the time to determine if the outline works or needs to be revised. Writing a draft version of your paper will highlight any problem areas so you can address them before beginning your final version.

Revise and edit. Once your draft is complete, make any additional revisions and edit it so you are ready to write the final version. It is a good idea to set your draft aside for a time (an hour, an afternoon, or a day, depending on the deadline) before revisiting it for a final check.

Prepare the final version. Just before creating your final paper, read the assignment again. Remind yourself of the due date, the required page count, and other specifics: whether a title page is expected, whether visual support (maps, diagrams) are needed, how your teacher would like the paper spaced (double-spaced is often the preference), and so on. Finally, use your edited draft to prepare your final version.

Oral presentations

A successful oral presentation is similar in some ways to a successful research paper. They both begin with an introduction that interests the reader and clearly states the thesis (goal of the presentation). Like a research paper, the content of a presentation should be clearly organized and come from valid, credible sources. The conclusion should sum up the key messages presented.

TIPS FOR ORAL PRESENTATIONS

- Show interest in your own topic! The audience will want to learn more about the topic if it is clear you find it interesting yourself.
- Make your presentation relevant to your audience — tell them how the issue at hand affects their lives or community.
- Do not read your presentation; instead speak to your audience, while glancing at notes you have prepared and familiarized yourself with beforehand.
- Speak clearly and explain any difficult terms or concepts.
- Use visual aids, if relevant, to highlight key ideas and concepts.

Role-playing

Role-playing is an excellent way to get "inside the issue." By playing the role of someone directly involved or affected by an issue, you get a better understanding of the issue. Also, by sharing this understanding with classmates who have taken on different roles, you all become more aware of the different viewpoints and perspectives on an issue.

TIPS FOR ROLE-PLAYING

A few things to think about when you are assigned a role:

- What do you know about the issue or situation?
- Where is the issue taking place — locally, regionally, globally, or all of these?
- Who is directly or indirectly involved in this issue?
- What are some of the suggested solutions to the issue, if any have been put forth yet?
- What is your role?
- How does your "character" feel about the issue, and about the other individuals involved?
- Do you share viewpoints with any of the others in the role play?
- Is your position in opposition to them?
- What outcome do you hope to achieve?
- How will this outcome affect the others?
- What might their opposing arguments be?

Creating and conducting surveys

Surveys are excellent tools to determine pubic opinion, to gather information, and to raise awareness about an issue.

To create a successful survey:

- You must have a clear goal in mind — what do you hope to achieve by creating and distributing a survey?

- Write a simple, direct questionnaire that states the goal up front. Choose the format for answers: short answer; check-off lists; *yes* or *no* questions; or statements requiring a degree of assent (that is, *strongly agree*, *agree*, *disagree*, *strongly disagree*). You may choose to have a variety of these types of questions. Specify clearly which type of response you seek for each section of the questionnaire.
- Be sure to leave space for answers.
- Limit the number of questions in the questionnaire — people will be more likely to complete your questionnaire if it is short.

To conduct your survey:

- Surveys can be done in person, by phone or by mail. The best way is face-to-face: you can either ask the questions and record the answers yourself, or hand out a questionnaire and let people know when and where they can return the completed questionnaire.
- Distribute your survey to as many people as possible, but keep your target audience in mind. Are you seeking responses from a specific age group, an interest group, or the general population?

To assess the results:

- Organize the information on completed surveys using charts or tables. Then summarize the findings in a report.
- As you interpret the data, be aware of the respondents. For example, did more women than men respond? Did more young people complete the questionnaire than adults? These sorts of factors may affect the results of your survey.

Sources and resources

It is very likely that some issues will interest you more than others. There may be some topics you wish to research further. You may want to find out how you can become involved in working toward solutions. For this reason, the following list of sources and resources has been compiled.

This list is not complete; it is to be used as a starting point for further research and involvement. Keep in mind that every organization has its own mandate and agenda, so check all information with at least one other source. Before becoming involved with any organization, make sure its methods and goals are acceptable to you.

Human rights and social issues

Amnesty International — Canada
214 Montreal Road, 4th Floor
Ottawa, Ontario K1L 1A4

Canadian Human Rights Commission
344 Slater Street, 8th Floor
Ottawa, Ontario K1A 1E1

The Centre for Social Justice
489 College Street, Suite 303
Toronto, Ontario M6G 1A5

Defence for Children International — Canada
1350 Sycamore Drive
Burlington, Ontario L7M IH2

Human Rights Watch
350 Fifth Avenue, 34th Floor
New York, NY 10118-3299 USA

Kids Can Free the Children
50 High Oak Trail
Richmond Hill, Ontario L4E 3L9

International Organization for Migration
17, Route des Morillons, C.P. 71
CH-1211, Geneva 19 Switzerland

Office of the United Nations
High Commissioner for Human Rights
Department of Public Information
Development and Human Rights Section
United Nations, Room S-1040
New York, NY 10017 USA

UNICEF Canada
Canada Square
2200 Yonge Street, Suite 1100
Toronto, Ontario M4S 2C6

Environmental issues

Canadian Wildlife Federation
350 Michael Cowpland Drive
Kanata, Ontario K2M 2W1

Defenders of Wildlife
National Headquarters
1101 14th Street, NW #1400
Washington, DC 20005 USA

Environmental Defense
257 Park Avenue South
New York, NY 10010 USA

Friends of the Earth
1025 Vermont Ave; NW,
Washington, DC 20005 USA

National Environmental Trust
1200 18th Street, NW, 5th Floor
Washington, DC 20036 USA

New Internationalist
55 Rectory Rd
Oxford OX4 1BW UK

Sierra Club of Canada
National Office
412-1 Nicholas Street
Ottawa, Ontario K1N 7B7

World Resources Institute
10 G Street, NE (Suite 800)
Washington, DC 20002 USA

World Wildlife Fund Canada
245 Eglinton Ave. East, Suite 410
Toronto, Ontario M4P 3J1

Hunger and health issues

Consultative Group on International Agriculture
CGIAR Secretariat
The World Bank
MSN G6-601
1818 H Street NW
Washington, DC 20433 USA

Food First/Institute for Food
and Development Policy
398 60th Street
Oakland, California 94608 USA

The Food and Agriculture Organization
of the United Nations
Viale delle Terme di Caracalla, 00100
Rome, Italy

Freedom From Hunger
1644 DaVinci Court
Davis, California 95616 USA

The Hunger Project — Canada
260 King Street East, 4th Floor
Toronto, Ontario M5A 1K3

World Hunger Education Service
P.O. Box 29056
Washington DC 20017 USA

The World Health Organization
525 23rd Street, NW
Washington, DC 20037 USA

World Hunger Year
505 Eighth Ave., Suite 2100
New York, NY 10018-6582 USA

Economic and poverty issues

Canadian International Development Agency
200 Promenade du Portage
Hull, Québec K1A 0G4

Campaign Against Child Poverty
c/o 355 Church Street
Toronto, Ontario M5B 1Z8

International Labour Organization
International Labour Office
4, route des Morillons
CH-1211 Geneva 22 Switzerland

International Monetary Fund
700 19th Street, NW
Washington, DC 20431 USA

The National Anti-Poverty Organization
#440–325 Dalhousie Street
Ottawa, Ontario K1N 7G2

National Council of Welfare
112 Kent Street, 9th Floor
Place de Ville, Tower B
Ottawa, Ontario K1A 0J9

Organisation for Economic Co-operation
and Development
2, rue André Pascal
F-75775 Paris Cedex 16, France

Organization of the Petroleum
Exporting Countries
Obere Donaustrasse 93, A-1020 Vienna, Austria

Oxfam Canada
#300-294 Albert Street
Ottawa, Ontario K1P 6E6

RESULTS Canada
#503-49th Avenue SW
Calgary, Alberta T2S 1G4

The United States Agency for
International Development
US Agency for
International Development Center
Ronald Reagan Building
Washington, DC 20523-1000 USA

The World Bank
Headquarters — General Inquiries
1818 H Street NW
Washington, DC 20433 USA

Peace

Canadian Peacebuilding
Co-ordinating Committee
1 Nicholas Street, #510
Ottawa, Ontario K1N 7B7

The Center for Defense Information
1779 Massachusetts Avenue, NW
Washington, DC 20036 USA

The World Institute for Non-Violence and
Reconciliation
P.O. Box 352 Kingston 7050
Tasmania, Australia

Canadian government

Environment Canada
Inquiry Centre
351 St. Joseph Boulevard
Hull, Québec K1A 0H3

Statistics Canada
Advisory Services
Arthur Meighen Building, 10th Floor
25 St. Clair Avenue East
Toronto, Ontario M4T 1M4

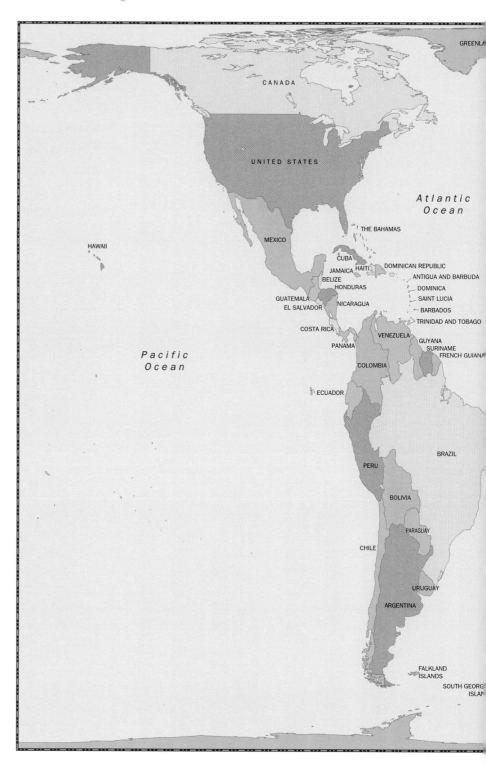

GREENLA[ND]

CANADA

UNITED STATES

*Atlantic
Ocean*

THE BAHAMAS

HAWAII

MEXICO

CUBA
DOMINICAN REPUBLIC
JAMAICA HAITI
BELIZE
HONDURAS
GUATEMALA
EL SALVADOR
NICARAGUA
ANTIGUA AND BARBUDA
DOMINICA
SAINT LUCIA
BARBADOS
TRINIDAD AND TOBAGO

COSTA RICA
VENEZUELA
GUYANA
SURINAME
FRENCH GUIANA
PANAMA
COLOMBIA

*Pacific
Ocean*

ECUADOR

BRAZIL

PERU

BOLIVIA

PARAGUAY

CHILE

URUGUAY

ARGENTINA

FALKLAND
ISLANDS

SOUTH GEORG[IA]
ISLAN[D]

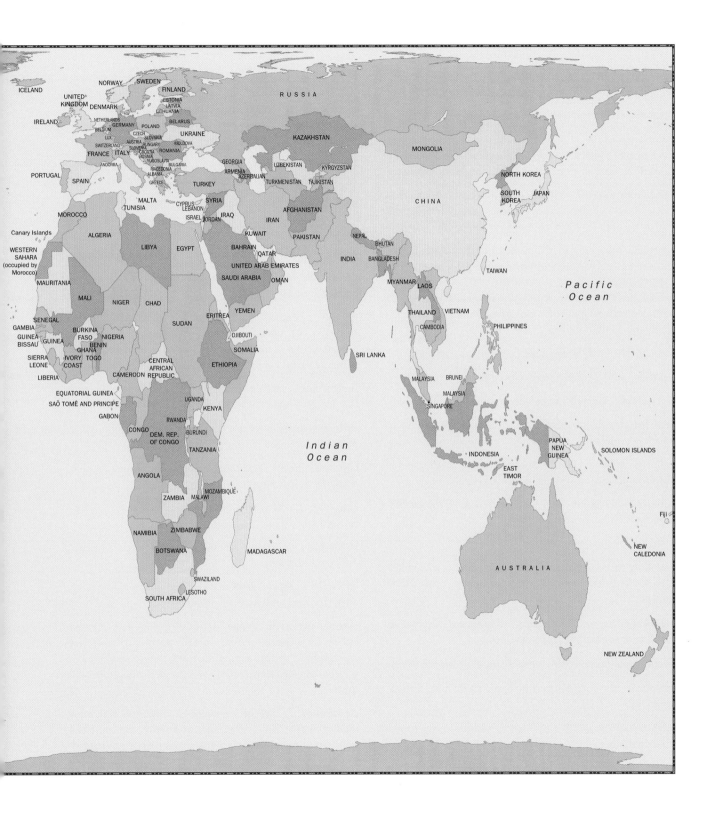

absolute poverty a condition in which people are unable to acquire life's basic necessities

aerosols a suspension of fine particles in a gas

affirmative action a policy that takes active measures to ensure equal opportunities in areas such as employment or education, in order to redress past acts of discrimination

agricultural run-off chemicals used in pesticides, herbicides, and fungicides that contaminate groundwater and follow natural drainage systems into the ocean

apartheid rule a system wherein racial discrimination and separation had been institutionalized by a series of "apartheid laws" that were put in place in 1948 (Examples of such laws were those prohibiting interracial marriages, outlining "white-only" jobs, and prescribing where blacks could and could not live.)

aquaculture fish farming for commercial purposes

aquifers underground reservoirs of freshwater

arable land land fit for growing crops

arid (or dry land) dry land with poor-quality soil, which is loosely called "desert"

autarky what a country practises when it adopts an absolute protectionism policy

autonomous regions self-governing regions, sometimes existing within one country

base flow the part of a river flow that enters the channel from underground water supplies, as opposed to surface run-off

big rollover where the demand for oil exceeds the rate at which new sources are being developed

biomes ecological communities sharing similar life forms

biosphere the environments on earth where living things are found

birth rates the number of births per 1000 of the country's population

brain drain when a country or region loses highly educated or skilled people to another country

brainstorm the process of understanding the complexities of an issue through the use of an issue-analysis web by placing the term/issue in the centre of the web and then surrounding it with as many words as come to mind when thinking of this issue

branch-plant economy a country with many foreign-owned companies is said to have a branch-plant economy

branch plants foreign-owned companies

capital money and investment available for spending

carbon budgets the balance between carbon sinks and carbon sources

carbon credits a country's promise to grow more forests or cut down fewer trees, in order to be allowed to exceed its 1990 limit or reduce its promised cuts (thus using its carbon sinks as carbon credits)

carbon sinks storage reservoirs such as oceans and plants that act as sponges, absorbing large amounts of carbon

carbon sources storage reservoirs such as oceans and plants that release more carbon than they can absorb

carrying capacity the maximum number of people that a habitat can support

cash crops crops grown not for local consumption, but for monetary gain

chauvinism excessive feelings of superiority over other peoples and states

choropleth maps maps that use a graded shading technique to represent varying amounts

chronic persistent hunger (CPH) a condition caused either by undernutrition, where people do not get enough food to eat, or malnutrition, where people have poorly balanced diets and do not receive enough specific nutrients

clearcutting a method of forest harvesting in which no trees are left to decompose and, as a result, the soil lacks nutrients and the forest often takes over 50 years to regrow

colonialism the process whereby colonial powers exploited people and resources in undeveloped regions in

Africa, Asia, and Central and South America, which made these colonial powers wealthy

commercially viable   when a profit can be made from extracting and consuming a resource

consumed   materials are consumed when industries turn raw materials into a manufactured product

consumerism   the level of consumption of goods and services

continental shelves   the submerged edges of the continents

critical resource   a renewable resource that is dependent on good sustainable techniques for it to remain unharmed or for its supply to remain undiminished

crop rotation   changing what is grown in the same fields from year to year so that the same nutrients within the soil are not exhausted

cultural mosaic   when a society comprises a number of culturally distinct groups

death rate   the number of deaths for every 1000 people in a country

decentralization   a plan of development that shifts development powers from the central government to local areas

deforestation   the rate of forests being cut down

demarcation   the actual marking of the ground limit of a country's control (a boundary on the physical landscape)

de-merging   the breaking up of bank conglomerates

demographers   scientists who study human population using statistical data of a population

demographic transition   a model of population change illustrating the stages that a society or country may pass through regarding birth and death rates

dependency load potential population   the percentage of the population under the age of 15 and over the age of 65

dependency loads   the ratio of people under 15 and over 65 to the working population between 15 and 65 (the population upon which the youngest and oldest individuals are dependent — sometimes referred to as an economic base)

Dependency Theory   a theory that explains how communities in poorer countries developed to help shift local

resources via a network of increasingly larger communities to a final port destination

depopulation   where the total population of a country is declining from one year to another

deregulation   reduction or elimination of regulations that control existing government requirements, for example, the length of time needed for a hunting licence

desertification   the deterioration of land quality, due to excessively dry conditions

developed countries   industrialized countries whose economies have created higher levels of consumerism, wealth, and development of infrastructure

developing countries   less-industrialized countries that are developing their economies toward higher levels of consumerism, wealth, and development of infrastructure

dilution theory   a theory based on a belief that the ocean was so vast and deep it could be used as a waste area

disparity   the degree of difference and inequality, for example, the difference in quality of life generated by relative wealth

dissemination   dispersal of knowledge and information either locally or globally

dominant culture   when a majority of a country's population identifies with a specific culture and language to the degree that it becomes the most widely accepted culture

double crop   the growth and harvest of two successive crops in one year

drip irrigation   whereby water is routed through small pipes directly to a plant's roots

drought   a temporary period without rain, which has always occurred as a result of the natural cycles of climate patterns

ecological footprint   a concept used to measure the total area needed by people to provide resources for consumption

ecological overshoot   when resource demands exceed nature's supply

economically recoverable   cost effective for companies to extract and process resources

economic cartel   a group that controls the price of food and local level of wages

economic colonialism when large financial organizations, such as the World Bank and the International Monetary Fund, are seen to finance and control the economy of a developing country

economic dependence when poorer economies — such as those found in cities — become dependent on the economic well-being of the developed world

economic integration when countries that were previously part of colonial empires become integrated into the new global economy, ruled by giant multinational corporations

economic migration migration for economic reasons such as better jobs or prospects of higher income

economies of scale refers to the economic benefits associated with mass production and purchasing; lower per unit production costs result when processing or purchasing occurs on a large scale

ecosystems systems formed by the interaction of living things

ecozones complete ecological units that contain living and non-living resources in an interactive system

El Niños changes in temperature of tropical Pacific ocean currents that affect weather patterns

embargoes economic and/or political restrictions or control placed upon a country by another country or group of countries, over such matters as the free movement of goods and services

entrepreneurs people who start their own businesses

environmental refugees people forced to move for their health and safety as a result of the deterioration of their environment

erosion the wearing away of soil by wind, water, or even human forces

ethnonationalist or separatists groups groups that are mobilized along common ethnic lines and seek to establish their own states

ethnopolitical movements those in which the political mobilization of minority groups is organized along ethnicity lines, or where groups align themselves with political parties or interest groups that promote their ethnicity

Exclusive Economic Zone (EEZ) an area extending not more than 370.4 kilometres (200 nautical miles) from a country's coastline over which it has economic control of its seabed and ocean resources

exponential growth the growth of a population when its increase is proportional to its base amount

famine a condition of rapid and severe undernutrition, where food shortages occur because of an inability to grow or collect food

fertility lag when medical advances and improved living environments produce a decline in death rates in some areas, but there is no immediate corresponding fall in birth rates

fertility rates the number of births per 1000 women of childbearing age

forced migration migration that takes place out of necessity of health and safety, and results in people becoming refugees

foreign aid money and other means of assistance, such as expert advice given to a country to help it develop

foreign direct investment the flow of money as an investment from one country to another

fossil fuels hydrocarbon deposit that originated from vegetable and animal remains and changed into a combustible fuel such as natural gas, oil, or coal

free trade agreement an agreement that spells out which goods and services are (or are not) exempt from tariffs

free trade when trade is open to anyone, and when products and services flow between countries without the restriction of tariffs or quotas

gender gap a disparity between the sexes in terms of social attitudes, politics, employment, and education

gender inequality an unequal power relationship between males and females

genetically modified organisms (GMOs) any organisms that are altered by the addition of foreign genetic material, or by genetic engineering

genetic engineering altering hereditary characteristics by linking DNA fragments from different organisms

genocide the systematic attempt to exterminate defined groups of people with different religious or ethnic backgounds

geocentric company a company that targets the world as its open market; the products it makes are designed for universal world consumption

geopolitics examining the political, environmental, social, and economic interactions of power and influence within and among countries

globalization the process of greater global interaction among peoples, such as the economic force of making the world one big marketplace

global warming the rising of temperatures above the natural level, thought to be caused by the addition of large amounts of carbon, methane, nitrous oxide, and other trace gases into the atmosphere through industrialization, transportation, and the burning of forests

green energy environmentally friendly energy such as solar power, wind power, nuclear power, geothermal energy, biomass energy, and hydro-electricity

greenhouse effect a term introduced when scientists compare the warming of the earth's atmosphere to the transfer of the sun's heat into and out of a greenhouse. The greenhouse effect describes the trapping of energy within the atmosphere after short-wave radiation has rebounded from the earth's surface as long-wave radiation. This energy is trapped by greenhouse gases such as carbon dioxide, methane, nitrous oxide, and other trace gases

greenhouse gases those gases within the atmosphere that absorb part of the infrared long-wave radiation and redirect it back to the earth's surface, such as carbon dioxide, methane, and nitrous oxide

Green Revolution science's contribution to increasing food yields through biotechnology applications

gross domestic product (GDP) the value of all goods and services produced and consumed domestically, that is, within a country

gross domestic product per capita (GDP per capita) a measure of the value of the total production and consumption of goods and services taking place within a country in one year, divided by the number of people living in that country

gross national product (GNP) per capita the total value of all goods and services produced by a country's economy — including those produced abroad — divided by the number of people living in that country, for each country. Note that this is a different calculation to that for gross domestic product (GDP).

groundwater water that seeps through the ground into springs and wells and lies in subterranean water supplies such as aquifers

halocarbons greenhouse gases mostly used in the production of refrigeration and air conditioning

humanitarian assistance help provided in order to protect civilians from harm, but usually done through non-government organizations (NGOs), rather than in conjunction with military tactics

humanitarian intervention help provided in order to protect civilians from harm or from human rights violations; often used in conjunction with military intervention in the internal affairs of a state

human resources human skills, abilities, and knowledge, for example, an architect or craftsperson who has the skills to design and build homes

hydrologic cycle the cycle of evaporation of moisture from the oceans and land, then of condensation and precipitation, back to the earth's surface (also known as the water cycle)

hyperinflation when the value of money falls at a very fast rate, making costs rise quickly

imperialism one country extending its rule and control over other countries

import quotas limits on the quantity of imports allowed

income-poor those who have a low level of financial income in relation to the cost of living

industrial powers countries in which large industry plays an important part in the economy of that country, and that dominate industrial economic activity with other countries

infant mortality when children do not survive beyond the first year of life

infilling sprawl development that occurs when developers take advantage of infrastructure and services that have already been provided, and build in spaces found in existing developed areas

infrared the part of the invisible spectrum consisting of electromagnetic radiation with long-wave wavelengths in the range from 750 nanometres to 1 millimetre

infrastructure the basic services provided for the functioning of a community, for example, roads, water pipes, telephone systems, airports, rail lines, and so on

in-migration people migrating into the country (referred to as immigrants)

integrated pest management (IPM) using knowledge about natural systems to protect against the enemies of plants

international capital flow the movement of money from one international investment market to another

internationalization bringing territory under the control of several nations

intervention the act of interfering or mediating, especially by one state in the affairs of another

ionosphere the outermost layer of the atmosphere, sometimes called the thermosphere

irredentism the desire to incorporate all areas within the state that were once part of the state, or to absorb those areas occupied by people who belong to the nation but do not reside within state boundaries

irrigation supplying dry land with water from elsewhere

isolationism when a country decides that it does not need to trade much with other countries, and introduces high tariffs and complex regulations to deter foreign producers and competitors from entering its economy

Kyoto Protocol an agreement stating that industrialized countries should reduce their greenhouse gas emissions by a given percentage of those levels emitted in 1990

land degradation the deterioration in quality of soil, which may lead to such things as erosion of the earth's foodlands

land reclamation waste and building materials dumped into coastal waters to extend the shoreline artificially

land subsidence the movement and resettlement of land caused by such things as heavy soaking of rainwater or underground rock movement

Law of the Sea an agreement stipulating that a set distance from a shoreline would form a boundary that all countries had to recognize

leapfrogging the development of land at some distance from the urban fringe

linear sprawl sprawl that stretches outward from a city along major highways and transportation corridors

Living Planet Index an index used to quantify changes in earth's ecosystems

megacity a city with a population in excess of 10 million

melting pot an analogy used to describe cultural assimilation (when a society assimilates different national groups and their culture into one dominant culture)

mesosphere the layer of the atmosphere between the stratosphere and ionosphere, characterized by decreasing temperature with altitude

microstates independent countries with a total area measuring less than 450 square kilometres

migration a permanent or semi-permanent change of residence. International migration involves the crossing of national borders.

military intervention the deliberate act of a nation or group of nations to threaten or use military force or coercion to alter an existing conflict where political and civil rights are being violated

monocropping growing one crop only; large-scale planting of a single variety of plant such as soya beans or wheat

monoculture planting and growth of only one major crop variety

mujahidin various groups of Islamic fighters, especially those who fought in Afghanistan during Societ occupation between 1979 and 1989

Multilateral Agreement on Investment (MIA) an agreement designed to allow capital and investment to flow more freely between countries by such means as restricting laws within a country that could prevent or hinder investments being made

multinational corporations corporations or companies based in more than one country

multinational a society made up of a number of equally empowered ethnic groups

national cultural integration an attempt to bind people together in a shared national identity by means of a common language, history, or customs

nationalism feelings of patriotism and a sense of belonging to a national group

nation a large group of people who are aware of, and share, one or more cultural features such as language, ethnicity, historical experience, identification with a "homeland," customs, values, and religion (derived from the Latin word *natio*, meaning "of birth")

nation-state a combination of the state and the nation (In order to achieve a sense of unity, nation-states use their government powers to try to create a common culture.)

natural change the difference between how many people are born and how many people die

natural resource a commodity that is harvested from a natural environment that is in economic demand, for example, the wood extracted from a forest, used to construct homes

natural stocks the earth's resources, some of which are renewable

New Green Revolution new breakthroughs in food production that will create larger yields, look at ways in which food production could be increased in non-grain groups, develop research centres to create a new generation of plants and animals, use the latest methods of genetic engineering to create genetically modified organisms (GMOs), and further isolate specific plant characteristics and manipulate their blending patterns to form new species

nitrous oxide laughing gas; also a greenhouse gas

non-critical resource one that can be used without being in any danger of becoming harmed

non-renewable resources resources that, once used, are gone forever

normal sprawl sprawl that usually takes place along the urban fringe of a town or city

North American Free Trade Agreement (NAFTA) a trade agreement that came into effect on January 1, 1994, which called for the gradual removal of tariffs and other trade barriers on goods produced and sold in North America

old-growth forests forested areas that have reached extreme ecological maturity and which contain trees that are extremely old and large

optimum (ideal) population a level of population that could thrive without harming the earth's resources while sustaining a standard of living that would be satisfactory

out-migration migrants leaving the country (referred to as emigrants)

patrilineal dominated by male influence, for example, inheritance through the male line

photosynthesis the process by which plant cells make sugar from carbon dioxide and water, in the presence of chlorophyll and light

polycentric company a company that focusses more on manufacturing products designed for local markets and needs

population-doubling time the time a country takes to double its population

population momentum when the rates of growth are expected to decelerate, but the actual population numbers continue to grow

population pyramid graphs showing the pattern of change in a country's population. These graphs compare the percentage of males and females in a given population and year by their age cohorts

post-cold war era the time period following the end of the cold war in the early 1990s

potable water water fit for drinking

poverty line the line dividing those able to afford life's basic necessities from those unable to do so

pronatalism a positive attitude toward having larger families

protectionism policies, such as the use of tariffs, that encourage the consumption of local goods rather than imported ones

pull factors the factors that draw people into an area, such as more job opportunities, higher wages, and better access to social services such as health care and education

purchasing power parity (PPP) measures the income of people against the relative local cost of something simple, such as a basket of food, taking into account the local cost of living when comparing one country with another

push factors the factors that drive people away from an area, such as deteriorating farmland or conflict

race to the bottom   the practice of creating a business (for example, in industry or farming) in developing countries where environmental and safety regulations are less stringent

rationalize   cutting back on those parts of a company's operations that are less profitable, making it a more streamlined operation

Red River Floodway Channel   a 47-kilometre flooding diversion ditch that was dug around the eastern edge of the city of Winnipeg, completed in 1968

reforestation   the rate of trees being replanted

refugees   migrants who flee a country or region for religious, political, social, or environmental reasons in order to protect themselves and their families, or in order to survive

religious terrorists   terrorists who are motivated by religious beliefs

renewable resources   resources that can be sustained by renewal, reuse, and regrowth, by sound sustainable management practices

replacement fertility rate   when couples begin having two children each

replacement levels   where the number of people being born equals the number that are dying

resource   a supply of something that is used to meet the needs of individuals, groups of people, or organizations

Rule of 70   a calculation estimating the number of years a country will take to double its population. The relative change is divided into the number 70. For example, if a country is growing at 2 percent per year, it will take 70 ÷ 2 = 35 years to double its population.

run-off   surface water that collects and then runs into other water sources such as streams and rivers, or drainage ditches and systems

salination   when the content of water becomes saltier

scenic resources or aesthetic resources   visually appealing resources that make our environment a better place to live in

secession   an attempt to withdraw from the power and control of a state's authority

sharecroppers   tenant farmers who pay a portion of each crop as rent

silviculture programs   the replanting and care of trees in areas where logging has occurred (this planting mechanism is also used for commercial purposes)

solar cells   photovoltaic cells that allow solar energy to be converted into energy

solar energy   energy created by radiation from the sun

solar radiation (insolation)   radiation travelling as short-wave radiation that passes through the earth's atmosphere and warms the earth's surface

sovereign   the ability of a country to make its own independent decisions and laws, free from external control or influences

sprawl   the expansion of urban areas, usually along their edges, that can either be planned or not planned

standpipes   vertical pipes that hold water and maintain water pressure

state   a political entity, institutional structure, or organization that is referred to as a country

state-sponsored   action that is funded or supported by the state

stock resources   non-renewable resources; a limited stock (supply) that can be depleted

Strategic Lawsuit Against Public Participation (SLAPP)   a lawsuit that enforces a company's legal right to access and use the property, for example, the enforcement of a trespass order

stratosphere   the upper atmosphere between the troposphere and the mesosphere, characterized by a slight increase in temperature with height

stream resources or flow resources   renewable resources; a constantly renewable supply is always "on-stream"

structural adjustment program (SAP)   an economic policy imposed on a country so that it can qualify to receive financial help from international agencies such as the World Bank or the International Monetary Fund

subsistence economies   when families work the land to feed themselves

suffragist movement   a political movement in Edwardian times demanding the right for women to vote

supranational capitalism   the situation where globalization may force states to alter their political and economic policies while placing additional pressure on them to produce wealth or face opposition

sustainability the earth's ability to support our needs and those of every other species on earth, on a continual basis

tariffs trade taxes placed on the import cost of a product or service in order to protect domestic products or services

temperate moderate climate, or climate without extremes of weather conditions

threshold the consumption limits of a resource beyond which supply cannot be sustained

time-space convergence when people temporarily decrease what geographers call the "friction of distance," as travel time and the frustration of commuting from the edges of cities become less

time-space divergence when these improved roads become popular and attract more traffic volume, and this contributes to increased traffic jams and travelling time

total fertility rate (TFR) refers to the average number of children each woman will have in her lifetime

trade blocs trade alliances formed among countries in a specific geographic region

tragedy of the commons, the the theory that societies have developed that act essentially in their own interest, and not for the good of society as a whole, for example, exploiting resources that are free to everyone

transboundaries boundaries outlining an area that may cross country boundaries

transhipment points cities that act as points through which local goods pass for shipment abroad

transnationalism allegiance to more than one country

trickle-down economics the theory that benefits for wealthy corporations and individuals are passed down through high levels of wages and benefits

troposphere the lowest layer of the atmosphere characterized by a gradual drop in temperature with altitude

two-stepped migration movement from poor rural areas into cities, followed by movement to another country

under-5 mortality the number of children dying under the age of 5

union republics independent nation-states that were once part of the former USSR

urban populations that live in towns and cities

urban fringe the edge of a city or town acting as a divide between urban and rural areas

urban inertia growth in an urban community as a result of consumer spending; as more local people consume products, more local businesses — and therefore more employees — are needed, and hence the population grows

urbanization the movement of people to urban environments

voluntary migration those who migrate voluntarily, including those who move for better jobs, for family unity, or for study purposes

water tables the level at which we find natural underground water

wealth-poverty polarization where the majority of the "have" states are in the northern hemisphere and the majority of the "have not" states are in the southern hemisphere

Every reasonable effort has been made to trace owner-ship of copyrighted material. Information that would enable the publisher to correct any reference or credit in future editions would be appreciated.

2 "Fishing for a Future" by Jamie Wilson, © *The Guardian*, August 14, 2000. / 4 "Temperature change between 1975–1985 and 2040–2060." Environment Canada. / 18 "The Club of Rome model." Reprinted from *Beyond the Limits* © 1992 by Meadows, Meadows, and Randers. With permission from Chelsea Green Publishing Co., White River Junction, Vermont. www.chelseagreen.com / 18 "How to catch a monkey" from *New Internationalist*, Issue #329, Nov. 2000, adapted from "Developing economies and the steady state" from *Steady-state economics* by Herman Daly (London: Earthscan, 1992). Reprinted with permission of the *New Internationalist*. / 29–30 "End of the population crisis?" an interview with Mark O'Connor with Robyn Williams on Australia's Broadcasting Corporation (ABC) Radio *Ockham's razor*, Sunday 07/03/1999. / 33 "Growth of population and food resources over time." Courtesy of John D. Grimes, Ph.D., Dept. of Geography and Anthropology, Louisiana State University / 44 Source: OAGEE Monograph V46. No. 3. / 62–63 "Case in point — Brazil" © 2001, *Newsweek*. Reprinted with permission. / 66 "Examples from the Human Development Index" from HUMAN DEVELOPMENT REPORT 2001 by United Nations Development Programme, © 2001 by the United Nations Development Programme. Used by permission of Oxford University Press, Inc. / 68 "Regions classified by the Human Development Index" from HUMAN DEVELOPMENT REPORT 2001 by United Nations Development Programme, © 2001 by the United Nations Development Programme. Used by permission of Oxford University Press, Inc. / 73 "Official aid received as % of GNP," *New Internationalist*, #332 (March 2001). / 75 "Total debt as a percentage of gross national product — Top 50 percentages." Reprinted with permission of the World Bank / "Foreign popula-tion as a percentage of total population," *New Internationalist*, #305 (September 1998). / 80 "Pattern of migration," *New Internationalist*, #305 (September 1998). / 83 "The ten largest groups of refugees, listed by country of origin, 2000" and "The most popular

countries of resettlement of refugees, 2000" reprinted with permission of the United Nations High Commissioner for Refugees (UNHCR). / 86 "Food sup-ply shortfalls" reprinted with permission of the Food and Agriculture Organization of the United Nations (FAO). www.fao.org / 90–91 "Twelve myths of hunger" adapted from material published by Food First Books (The Institute for Food and Development Policy) / 93 "Predicted land needs." Reprinted from Beyond the Limits © 1992 by Meadows, Meadows, and Randers. With permission from Chelsea Green Publishing Co., White River Junction, Vermont. www.chelseagreen.com / 94 "World fertilizer use, 1950–1999" reprinted with permission of Worldwatch Institute Press. www.worldwatch.org / 95 "Plant dam-age caused by insects in rice plants" reprinted with per-mission of Worldwatch Institute Press. www.worldwatch.org / 99 "Climate data for Khartoum, Sudan" and "Climate data for Juba, Sudan" reprinted with permission of Online Weather. www.onlineweather.com / 101 "Sorghum and wheat production in Sudan, 1961–2000" reprinted with per-mission of the Food and Agriculture Organization of the United Nations (FAO). http://apps.fao.org / 112 "Climagraph for Mekele" reprinted from Agriculture and Agri-Food Canada (AAFC) Prairie Farm Rehabilitation Administration (PFRA). / 135 "Construction of proposed gas pipeline" from *Maclean's Magazine*, June 11, 2001. Reprinted with permission. / 144 "The Future of Canada's Water: Gerry White's Story" and "The Future of Canada's Water: Maude Barlow's Story" from CBC News OnLine June 2001. Courtesy of Canadian Broadcasting Corporation. / 150 "Threat to coral reefs." From *Reefs at Risk* by World Resources Institute. / 151 "Areas in the Mediterranean threatened by pollution." From www.panda.org/resources/publications. Reproduced with permission from WWF. © 2000 WWF — World Wide Fund for Nature (formerly World Wildlife Fund) and Shoreline. All Rights Reserved. / 154 "Predicted vulnerability to water scarcity, 2025" reprinted with permission of the World Resources Institute. www.wri.org / 155 "Regional difference in water use" reprinted with permission of the World Resources Institute. www.wri.org / 158 "Populations without access to safe drinking water" from *The World's Water:*

The Biennial Report on Freshwater Resources by Peter H. Gleick (Covelo, CA: Island Press, 1998). / **161** "Aral Sea data" from German Remote Sensing Data Centre. / **176** "Global warming" based on information from "Tropical Cyclones and Global Climate Change: A Post-IPCC Assessment," *Bulletin of the American Meteorological Society*, January 1998. / **179** (**top**) "The earth's atmosphere" from WGBH Educational Foundation. www.pbs.org/wgbh/nova/balloon/science/atmosphere.html / **179** (**bottom**) "Contributions to global warming" reprinted with permission of the World Resources Institute. www.wri.org / **181** "Trends in carbon dioxide concentration" from Environment Canada and Meteorological Service of Canada. www.msc.ec.gc.ca/cd//climate/factsheets / **182** "Total world carbon emissions by region" reprinted by permission of US Department of Energy, Energy Information Administration. www.globalchange.org/dataall/97sep5f.htm#Table%20A35 / **184** "Variation in annual temperature compared to 1961–1990 average, northern hemisphere" from *The Toronto Star*, April 9, 2001. Reprinted with permission — The Toronto Star Syndicate. / **185** "Four predictions of global mean temperature." Information supplied by the Met Office © Crown Copyright. www.metoffice.gov.uk/research/hadleycentre/pubs/brochures/B1997/future.html / **186** (**top**) "Predicted change in annual temperature." Information supplied by the Met Office © Crown Copyright. www.met-office.gov.uk/research/hadleycentre/pubs/brochures/B1997/future.html / **186** (**bottom**) "Predictions made by the Centre for Climate Prediction and Research" from WGBH Educational Foundation. www.pbs.org/wgbh/nova/balloon/science/atmosphere.html / **187** "Predicted change in annual precipitation." Information supplied by the Met Office © Crown Copyright. www.met-office.gov.uk/research/hadleycentre/pubs/brochures/B1997/future.html / **189** "Change in global temperature" from the Canadian Centre for Climate Modelling and Analysis (CCCMA), Environment Canada. www.cccma.bc.ec.gc.ca/models//cgcm1.shtml / **190–191** "Criticisms of the global warming theory" based on "Criticisms of Global Warming Theory" by David Wright, *Geography Review*, September 1998. / **192** "Rate of ice level change, Greenland." From www.solcomhouse.com. Used by permission. / **194** (**top**) "Antarctic ice." From www.solcomhouse.com. Used by permission. / **194–195** "Effects of warming temperatures in a polar region" based on "Antarctica's Hints of Global Warming" by David Helvarg. David Helvarg is an investigative journalist and author of *Blue Frontier:*

Saving America's Living Seas. / **196** "Temperature change, 1950–1998," *Toronto Star*, April 10, 2001. Reprinted with permission — The Toronto Star Syndicate / **197** "Heat waves and pollution — a deadly duo." From Environment Canada. www.msc-smc.ec.gc.ca/cd/climate/newsbytes/story4_e.cfm / **201** "The carbon cycle," *Toronto Star*, April 8, 2001. Reprinted with permission — The Toronto Star Syndicate / **203** "Data for countries participating in the greenhouse emissions summit," from The World Resources Institute, World Factbook 2001, UN Food and Agriculture Organization. / **210** "Ethnic divisions in Sri Lanka." www.lib.utexas.edu/maps/islands_oceas_poles/sri_lanka_charts_76.jpg / **215** (**left**) "Total number of wars, 1946–1999." Centre for Systemic Peace, University of Maryland. / **215** (**right**) "Trends in violent conflict, 1946–1999." Centre for Systemic Peace, University of Maryland. / **220** "Areas of political instability in Africa," © Minister of Public Works and Government Services Canada, National Defense / **230** "Afghanistan and its neighbours" from BBC Written Archives Centre. http://news.bbc.co.uk/hi/english/static/in_depth/world/2001war_on_terror/key_maps/ethnic_groups.stm / **232** (**left**) "Areas occupied by Taliban and Northern Alliance prior to US-led intervention" from www.afghan-info.com/Maps/Northern_Alliance_Map.gif / **255–257** "A Canadian perspective" from *What Everyone Should Know About Economics and Prosperity* by James Gwartney and Richard Stroup (Vancouver: The Fraser Institute, 1993). www.fraserinstitute.ca / **258–259** "Globalization Mainly Benefits One-Fifth of the World" by Joe Lauria, Radio Free Europe/Radio Liberty. www.rferl.org/nca/features/1999/07/F.R.U.990713143430.html / **262** "Who Owns Canada? Foreign Ownership Is on the Rise" by Mark MacKinnon, *Globe and Mail*, February 1, 1999. / **264** "World Bank Mission Visited Ukraine for New Loan Discussions," The World Bank. / **268** "Water for the People — Ghanaians Protest Privatization" by Katharine Ainger, *New Internationalist*, Issue #337, August 2001. Reprinted with permission of *New Internationalist*. / **270** "Boom Towns Changing Farmers' Lifestyle," *People's Daily Online*, People's Republic of China. / **273** (**right**) "World urban and rural population," Johns Hopkins University Center for Communication Program. www.jhuccp.org / **274** "Illustration of the Dependency Theory and resource extraction" from *Advanced Geography Concepts and Cases* by Paul Guinness and Garrett Nagle (Oxon: Hodder &

Stoughton, a member of the Hodder Headline Group, 1999) / **275 (top)** "Population living in urban areas" and **(bottom)** "Average annual urban growth" from World Resources Institute. www.wri.org/wrl/wr-96-97/ud_f2.gif / **276** "Population growth in cities," Population Division of the Department of Economic and Social Affairs of the United Nations Secretariat, March 2000 (28), World Urbanization Prospects: The 1999 Revision / **277–279** "Case in point — Kenya" Information Services Section, Office of the Deputy Executive Director, UN-HABITAT, United Nations Human Settlements Programme. www.unchs.org/unchs/english/hdv6n4/ kenya_traged.htm / **280** "Types of urban sprawl" from *Urban Dynamics* by Fraser Cartwright (Toronto: Oxford University Press Canada, 1991) / **281** "Rush-hour commutes around Toronto" from City of Toronto / **282 (bottom)** "Prime farm land, 1967," and **(top)** "Population projections for the GTA (millions)" from City of Toronto. /

283 "Time-space convergence model" from *Urban Dynamics* by Fraser Cartwright (Toronto: Oxford University Press Canada, 1991) / **288** "Coping with/preventing sprawl — three models," from *The Toronto Star*, June 2000. Reprinted with permission — The Toronto Star Syndicate. / **293** "Disparity, male-female," United Nations educational, scientific, and cultural organization (UNESCO). Reproduced bypermission of UNESCO. / **296 (top, left)** "Occupation and Gender in Canada" from *1996 Employment Equity Data Report (Release #2)*, HRDC and Statistics Canada, Ottawa, 1999. / **296 (top, right)** "Gender inequality in Canada, income gap by education" from *2001 Status Report on Gender Inequality in Canada*. / **296 (middle)** "Income and gender across Canada" from *Special Run of Survey of Labour and Income Dynamics Statistics Canada for the CSJ Foundation 1999–2000*.

framing the issue, 6
and hurricanes, 176
GMOs (genetically modified organisms), 106, 109
GPS (global positioning system), 76–77
GNP (gross national product) per capita, 31
Grand Banks, 22
Great Lakes, 157
green energy, 140
greenhouse effect, 179–180
greenhouse gases, 180
Kyoto Protocol, 200
reducing emissions, 198–99
Green Party, 260
Greenpeace, 24
Green Revolution, 15, 101, 104–105
New Green Revolution, 106–109
gross domestic product (GDP), 18
GDP per capita, 66
gross national product (GNP) per capita, 31
groundwater, contamination, 158–59
overpumping, 156–57

halocarbons, 183
Hardin, Garrett, 14–15, 17, 19
HDI (Human Development Index), 65, 66, 67
"heat-island" effect, 190
heat waves and pollution, 197
HFCs (hydrofluorocarbons), 180
high-yielding variety seed program (HVP), 104
HPI (Human Poverty Index), 65, 66–67
Human Development Index (HDI), 65, 66, 67
Human Development Report, 61, 65
humanitarian assistance, 224
humanitarian intervention, 224, 226, 233
humanitarian organizations, 226
human poverty, 65, 67, 68, 69
Human Poverty Index (HPI), 65, 66–67
human resource, 114
hunger, 88, 90–91
hurricanes, and global warming, 176
HVP (high-yielding variety seed program), 104
hydrofluorocarbons (HFCs), 180
hydrogen energy, 140
hydrologic cycle, 117
hydroponic greenhouses, 122
hyperinflation, 62–63

ice levels, and global warming, 192–95
ice reduction on highways, 285
IGOs (international government organizations), 226
ILO (International Labour Organization), 79

image differencing, 103
IMF (International Monetary Fund), 74
immigration and emigration. *See* migration, global
imperialism, 210
import quotas, 244
income poverty, 65, 67, 68, 69
India, 104
Kashmir, 227
Kerala, 110–11
industrial powers, 11
infant mortality, 46
infilling sprawl, 280
informal urban settlements, 277–79
infrared radiation, 180
infrastructure, 57
in-migration, 82
integrated pest management (IPM), 95
international aid, 58, 72–75, 91
International Boundary Commission, 212
International Court of Justice (UN), 213
international government organizations (IGOs), 226
internationalization, 216
International Labour Organization (ILO), 79
International Monetary Fund (IMF), 74
International Organization for Migration (IOM), 78
Internet, 240, 252–53
intervention, 223–26
IOM (International Organization for Migration), 78
ionosphere, 178
IPM (integrated pest management), 95
irredentism, 210
irrigation, 10, 96–97
Aral Sea problem, 159–61
drip irrigation, 156, 161
Middle East, 170, 172–73
isolationism, 244
Israel, 171–73
issue-analysis web, 5
issues, framing, 4–7
four basic areas, 5

Japan, aging population, 41
Jordan, 171–73

Kashmir, 227
Kazakhstan, 160
Kenya, 277–79
Kerala, 110–11
Kurds, 211
Kyoto Protocol, 138, 200

Map Index